Richard H. Lee

AC 7378

To Richard Lee

as a proof of

my appreciation

Mark.

Milwaukee November 27-61

Ferrous
Production Metallurgy

JOHN L. BRAY

*Head, School of Chemical and Metallurgical
Engineering, Purdue University*

NEW YORK
JOHN WILEY & SONS, Inc.
London: CHAPMAN & HALL, Limited

ac 7378

To My Wife,
JEAN

PREFACE

Twenty years of teaching experience have convinced the author of the truth of Don Quixote's sage remark: "He that publishes a book runs a very great hazard, since nothing can be more impossible than to compose one that may secure the approbation of every reader." It appears that matters have not changed greatly in the more than three hundred years since these words were written, for technical books are no exception to this general rule. Some teachers of metallurgy wish a textbook to combine production metallurgy and metallography, others wish to include foundry practice, others shaping of metals and even pyrometry. It is the belief of the author that there is need in courses in metallurgical engineering for a textbook devoted solely to the production of iron and steel and that such a book:

1. Should fit fundamental theories into successful practice, every process being carefully explained from a physical-chemical standpoint.

2. Should contain condensed descriptions of equipment accompanied by simple line drawings (giving only principal parts and dimensions) rather than photographs, in an effort to avoid the confusion created by the multiplicity of detail involved in the use of working drawings.

3. Should avoid the use of photographs as unduly expensive and not as effective as lantern slides.

4. Should be accompanied, in class, with lantern slides. Cheap and rapid photographic processes now available permit the instructor to cover a wider range of subject matter and keep it up to date. These slides furnish detail that halftones lack.

5. Should keep to a minimum all statistical material, including in this only important countries and significant years.

6. Should confine the subject matter to a compass of less than 500 pages, in order to be able to publish the book at a moderate price.

With the above ends in view, this textbook has been written as a companion volume to *Non-Ferrous Production Metallurgy*, for use in a junior or senior course in the production of iron and steel meeting three or four times per week during a semester of sixteen weeks.

Throughout the book suggestions for the use of physical chemistry are made in the form of simple problems. These problems have been furnished by Dr. Herschel Hunt of Purdue University, who, with Dr. R. H. Ewell, has been very successful in a pioneer course, "Applied Physical Chemistry," required of students in metallurgical

vii

engineering. Thermochemical data were obtained from the International Critical Tables, *Thermochemistry of Chemical Substances* (Bichowsky and Rossini), McGraw-Hill Book Company, and Bureau of Mines *Bulletin* 324. In the treatment of these data this nomenclature has been followed:

$$c = \text{macrocrystalline state}$$
$$l = \text{liquid state}$$
$$g = \text{gaseous state}$$
$$gl = \text{glass state}$$
$$amorp = \text{amorphous state}$$
$$aq = \text{aqueous solution}$$
$$K = \text{equilibrium constant}$$
$$\triangle H = \text{change in heat content}$$
$$\triangle S = \text{entropy change of the reaction}$$
$$\triangle F = \text{the standard free energy change}$$
$$T = \text{the absolute temperature}$$
$$C_p = \text{specific heat at constant pressure}$$
$$R = \text{gas constant}$$
$$P = \text{vapor pressure}$$
$$graph = \text{graphite}$$

In the equations given in the text a negative sign for $\triangle H$ indicates that the system loses heat; no sign (or a positive one) that it gains heat according to the general relationship $\triangle F_t = \triangle H - T \triangle S$.

Many friends in industry have contributed freely of both criticism and material. The author is especially indebted to the A. M. Byers Company and Dr. J. Aston for reviewing the chapter on wrought iron; to J. Gould of Lorain, Ohio, and A. D. Beers of Gary for reviewing the chapter on the open hearth; to C. V. Lauer of Gary for many helpful suggestions for the chapter on the blast furnace; to B. P. Mulcahy of the Citizens Gas and Coke Utility for reviewing the chapter on fuel; to H. M. Banta of the Jones and Laughlin Steel Corporation for criticisms and suggestions for the chapter on the Bessemer process. For statistics, data, and descriptive material the writer is indebted also to A. D. Beers of Gary, to E. W. Davis of the United States Bureau of Mines, the American Iron and Steel Institute, to Bradley Booth of the Jackson Iron and Steel Company, to G. B. Waterhouse of the Office of Production Management, and to Thomas Chalmers of the Tennessee Coal, Iron, and Railroad Company.

JOHN L. BRAY

PURDUE UNIVERSITY
September, 1942

CONTENTS

CHAPTER I

HISTORY

"Gold is for the mistress—silver for the maid—
Copper for the craftsman, cunning at his trade."
"Good," said the Baron, sitting in his hall,
"But Iron—cold Iron—is master of them all."
                                              KIPLING

1. General. The history of mankind can be divided into an Age of Stone and an Age of Metals, but just when the Bronze Age merged into the Iron Age or even whether iron was not actually used before copper has not been definitely settled. Recent discoveries of the Fine Arts Expedition of Yale University on the Euphrates River has caused us to move back the date of the Iron Age at least seven hundred years. For the reason that few metals, least of all iron, occur naturally in the metallic form in amounts large enough to be of industrial importance, we are concerned not so much with the first use of metals as with the first production of the metal from its ores. The discovery that, with the aid of fire, metal could be reduced from, or melted out of, a rock was one of the most momentous steps in man's conquest of nature and marked the beginning of that complex state of living which we characterize as civilization. When one of our long-armed and beetle-browed ancestors first raked from the ashes of his campfire a piece of impure copper, he could not appreciate the importance of that event. He could have no idea of the tremendous sequence of events which would lead to our present civilization; but we, who can look back down the aisle of the ages, stand astonished at the consequences. As T. A. Rickard, in his classic work, *Man and Metals*,[5]* has written, ". . . But that was only the beginning. The red beads of copper that were sweated out of the stone on the hearth of the prehistoric savage were destined to be stretched into whispering wires across the earth; along them were to be brought the energy of the mountain torrent, to move the wheels of industry; to illumine the ways of man; and to light his dwelling."†

* Such superior numbers as these refer to certain of the numbered references at the ends of the chapters.

† By permission of T. A. Rickard.

1

The production of copper, however, was only the beginning, for actually it is easier to reduce iron oxide than the ores of copper; and man's natural curiosity soon led to the discovery and use of other metals, which in turn furnished the means for making instruments of greater precision for the scientific discovery of the secrets of the universe.

No other metal is capable of giving the wide range of physical properties that makes iron so attractive and valuable. It can be made stronger than any other common metal, although it resists corrosion remarkably well, and it possesses magnetism in a far greater degree than other metals. While it is true that no other metal has received more study, new uses for the present alloys, and even new alloys are being discovered almost daily.

The early history of iron is inextricably tied up with mythology, religion, and folk lore. Unquestionably, the first iron to be used by primitive man was meteoric iron, for, besides having potentialities as a tool or weapon, this material possessed two characteristics that impelled these primitive people to worship it. The first was the necessity of having as a fetish some object of supernatural origin so that the spirit which was supposed to dwell therein could be merged with the fetish until the two were indistinguishable. Secondly, this fetish must be readily transportable so that in time of stress or danger, and especially in those times of tribal conflict, early man could have a god that was close at hand and not one that was far away, in some ill-defined heaven. As a result meteoric iron was an ideal fetish because it undoubtedly came from the sky, and as a celestial visitor it was a suitable home for the spirit. It was usually not too large in size, could be conveniently transported, and, because of the attractive properties of the metal, it was relatively permanent.

Biblical references to iron are a measure of its antiquity. There are ninety references to this metal in the Old Testament, but only seven in the New, tending to indicate that after the birth of Christ iron had become so common that it no longer merited unusual consideration. The allusions to iron in the Old Testament fall naturally into two divisions. The first division, which contains only one reference, is the mention of Tubal-cain's birth in Genesis 4:22, where he is spoken of as "an instructor of every artificer of brass and iron." The other eighty-nine references trace the history of iron from the time that it carried an ancient taboo by primitive man, because they were afraid of it, up through the deification of iron by the Hebrews in the

Exodus from Egypt, and finally the adoption by the Hebrews of the idea of an anthropomorphic or manlike God.

The Chinese tradition has a distinct metallurgical flavor. According to this account, Pan Ku, a god, put the metals in the ground. His successor, Sin Jen, a god, and Fu Hsi, the first Emperor, did not know how to get them out. In 2700 B.C. Shen Nung discovered the process of smelting. It was then a holy occupation to be followed only by people whose character and morals were above reproach. Metals were both male and female; consequently, in making alloys, there was much ceremony and a strict ritual to follow. The bellows of the furnace were worked by an even number of virgin boys and girls; when the metal was poured, the girls sprinkled it with water. If it developed a blister, there was too much of the male metal in the mix; but if it developed a crack, there was too much of the female metal. It was then reworked with the proper correction for the deficient metal. If the master was sure of his proportions and results were still unsatisfactory, grave doubt was cast upon the moral purity of one or more of his youthful helpers. When these early metallurgists began to smelt iron, they soon became involved in difficulty, apparently because of the sex element. Iron was a male metal; the deity of the forge was also male; hence there could be no sexual union. They overcame this by having the wife of the smith work the bellows and, as the metal was poured, she would drop into the molten mass some of her hair or fingernail clippings. This was supposed to effect a spiritual union between the wife of the master and the god of the forge, and the iron would be of high quality and easily worked. This sort of ceremony went on for centuries. It is related that during the Han Dynasty a daughter of an iron master voluntarily threw herself into the molten mass in order that her father might have the honor of casting perfect metal—a human recarburizer. The outstanding fact is that the average Chinese of 500 B.C. was further advanced metallurgically, and perhaps mentally, than the average European of 1500 years later. Furthermore, these early Chinese put the metals to use for tools in peaceful vocations rather than for implements of war—a sad commentary on present conditions in World War II, when most of our iron and steel is being used for martial purposes.

The King of the Hittites seems to have originated our modern steel mill "Code of Fair Practice." Witness the fact that in a letter written about 1300 B.C. to his impatient customer Rameses II, he writes, "As to the good iron about which thou has written me: There is no good iron in my sealed house in Kissuwadna. It is a bad time to make iron, but I have written ordering them to make good iron. So far they have not finished it. When they finish it, I will send it to thee. Behold now I am sending thee an iron dagger blade." This is a translation of the hieroglyphics found on the clay tablet now preserved in the Berlin State Museum.

The Romans reduced iron in a furnace shown in Figure 1 and probably brought the iron-making art to Britain. They used it for both warlike and domestic purposes and knew how to make it. The Anglo

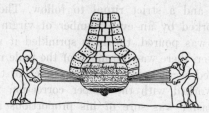

FIG. 1. An Early Furnace.

Saxons, who succeeded the Romans, treated a smith as an officer of the highest rank, and special mention is made of Saint Dunstan, who lived in the tenth century, as a skilled metallurgist. The first reference to steel in England occurred about 1267.

2. Oldest Iron. It is fairly well established that iron was known long before it came into general use. The oxidized remains of some iron beads found in a Predynastic (4000 B.C.) cemetery at El Gerzeh, forty miles south of Cairo, are the oldest evidences of the use of iron. Up to the present time, the oldest piece of iron yet discovered is a small sickle found between two of the inner blocks of stone, in the great pyramid of Khufu, which was constructed about 3000 B.C. Another fragment of iron, found along with some copper tools, belonged to the Sixth Dynasty (circa 2500 B.C.). These are apparently sporadic occurrences, for the metal did not come into general use until about 1700 B.C. or at the time of the Egyptian invasion of Asia. References to objects of iron are frequently found in the inscriptions of that period, and by the time of Rameses II (1324-1258 B.C.) the use of iron was, apparently, rather common in Egypt, for rings, spear heads, halberts, and tools of metal have been found in the buildings of that period. Analyses of ancient and meteoric irons are given in Table 1.

3. Meteoric Iron. The fact that some tools were made of iron as early as 2800 B.C. and yet that metal did not come into common use in Egypt until seven hundred years later is a puzzling discrepancy.

TABLE 1

ANCIENT AND METEORIC IRONS*

Location and Date	Per Cent								Brinell Hardness
	Fe	C	Si	S	P	Mn	Co	Ni	
Karnak A.D. 1250		0.110	0.100	0.024	0.015	tr			72
Delhi Pillar A.D. 300		0.08	0.046	0.006	0.114	nil			188
Roman bloom A.D. 100		0.097	0.046	0.025	0.044	0.04			
Roman nail A.D. 40		0.080	†	0.046	tr	nil			
Meteor Bates Co., Mo.	89.12				0.12		0.26	10.02	
Meteor New Mexico	87.93				0.36		0.33	11.15	

* G. N. Friend, *Iron in Antiquity*, Charles Griffin & Co., London, 1926.
† Not determined; too much slag.

Some hint of this is furnished in references in old religious texts (about 3500 B.C.) to baa-en-pet or "Metal of Heaven." Likewise in the primitive picture-writing of Babylonia, iron was denoted by two characters, one of which represented "heaven," the other "stone." Furthermore, according to Homer, one of the prizes awarded at the games in honor of the funeral of Patroclus was a "self-fused" mass of iron large enough "to suffice its possessor for all purposes during five years." In view of the fact that it must have been small enough for the winner to carry away, iron evidently was not in common use. It is interesting to compare the Greek word for iron, *sideros,* with the Greek word for star, *aster,* and the Latin, *sidus, sideris.*

Ross, on his trip to Greenland in 1818, reported that iron tools, made from meteoric iron, were common. One of three great masses observed by him had been nearly cut in half by the natives. This mass (weighing 6000 pounds) was known as "The Woman" by them because it was softer and more easily worked. The Aztecs when first known to the Europeans had very little iron, but what they did have was prized above gold, not only because of its superior properties but also because it had come from the heavens. In Arabia, in Africa, even in this country, we have further evidence of the wide use of meteoric iron in the manufacture of early tools and implements. They are easily identifiable because the iron of meteors averages about 7 per cent nickel and also exhibits the peculiar crystalline structure known as the Widmannstatten figures.

4. Ease of Reduction. The finding of "iron from heaven" helped man only indirectly to locate and smelt the metal from terrestrial ores. Having found a piece of meteoric iron, primitive man was naturally impelled to attempt to find it in the earth. It must be remembered that the ways of primitive man were pretty much those of a child, for his mental faculties were not fully developed as yet. Being attracted by what was pretty, he would pick up gold first, then native copper; and after he had melted the copper and found it to be useful, he would sooner or later be led, naturally, to the smelting or reduction of the ore in which the native metal was incased. On the other hand, native iron was not known to him, so a similar chain of events did not occur. However, once he had, through some accident, ascertained that the red or brown stone (hematite or limonite) would yield a new and useful metal, malleable like copper but harder and stronger, he would experience little difficulty in producing it. This reduction was relatively simple, owing to the fact that the smelting of an iron ore does not involve the complete fusion of the metal, it being obtained in the form of a spongy mass or "bloom" (from the Anglo Saxon *blooma*, meaning a lump).

Although iron becomes soft and agglomerates at about 700°C., complete fusion does not take place until a temperature of 1530°C. is reached. This simple fact was of the greatest importance to the early metallurgists because they could collect the malleable pieces or lumps that were reduced from the ores and weld them together by hammering or forging. This was the only method by which large pieces of iron could be produced by primitive races.

The famous Delhi pillar of India is a tribute to the early (A.D. 300) metallurgists, for this shaft (24 feet high, 12½ inches in diameter at its upper end, and 16½ inches at the lower, weighing about 6 tons) is not a casting but a huge forging. It was built up by welding together discs of iron (the marks of welding are still visible—thus has the wrought iron withstood the ravages of 1600 years). As a matter of fact, the natives of British East Africa still obtain their iron ore as a magnetite sand which they concentrate and then reduce on a clay-lined hearth. This hearth is filled with alternate layers of ore and charcoal into which air from a goat-skin bellows is introduced through an earthenware nozzle or tuyère. When the process is finished, the charcoal on top and along the sides is removed, the remaining contents of the hearth cooled with water, and from it extracted the mass of metal and slag. Further cooling and working remove the pieces of slag from this lump or bloom, and they subsequently are heated and hammered to shape on an anvil. The iron thus produced was, of course, soft and for a long time was used as such with all its limitations until it was discovered that certain grades of it could be hardened by heating and sudden quenching in water. The delay in making this discovery may have been brought about by the fact that primitive man had formerly worked only with copper, which is hardened by hammering (cold work) but softened by heating (annealing) and quenching in water. Such a furnace is shown in Figure 41.

5. Chinese Iron. It should be emphasized at this point that all iron made by these primitive peoples, and by processes similar to the ones already described, was wrought iron. The temperatures attained were not sufficient to liquefy it, and up to about 1935 it was commonly supposed that cast iron was first made in Germany in or around the year A.D. 1350. A recent excavation at Atlanta, Georgia, brought to light a cast-iron shield, believed to have been lost by one of the men accompanying De Soto on his expedition to the Mississippi Valley. This cast-iron calendar was further set back through the discovery of a cast-iron incense burner bearing a native date equivalent to A.D. 1000. Recent researches carried out by H. W. Chu, in translating early manuscripts, indicate that cast iron was first made in China between the dates of 300 B.C. and A.D. 100.* Ralph M. Shaw, Jr.,† has photographed and described Chinese temples with cast-iron roofs which were made sometime during the eleventh century—page the publicity agent of the Cast Iron Association.

6. Metallurgical Industry in the United States.[1] The American Indians did not know how to manufacture iron. It remained for the white man to introduce it in a useful form to this continent and for him to open up the vast resources of high-grade iron ore, coal, oil, and other raw materials which have been the chief factors (aside from men) in the swift rise of American industry.

The first attempt to manufacture iron in America was stimulated by economic necessity because in England charcoal was the only fuel then known to be satisfactory for blast furnace use, and the supply

---

* See also Article 86.

† "Cast Iron—It Dates Back to 3000 B.C.," *Iron Age*, Jan. 30, 1936.

of timber was being rapidly depleted. The shipbuilding industry was a part of the economic picture because so acute became the shortage of timber for this vital industry that English iron works were prohibited from using timber growing within fourteen miles of the sea or on the shores of any navigable river. The first permanent English colony in America was founded in 1607 at Jamestown, Virginia; and within a year it had shipped iron ore to the mother country. Finally, in 1619, the Society of Southampton Hundred was granted permission to build iron works in the New World. A furnace was erected in 1620, 66 miles above Jamestown; but the death of important workmen, lack of capital, and hostile savages brought about the failure of the project.

The first successful iron works in the United States was established at Lynn, Massachusetts, in 1645. This furnace was lined with slate or schist so that the widest part of the interior was not more than 10 feet in diameter. A bloomery, or forge, was also built to produce wrought iron. The records indicate that the furnace could produce 18 tons of cast iron per week and the forge 8 tons of wrought iron. Another furnace forge was built at Braintree, Massachusetts, in 1648, and one at New Haven, Connecticut, in 1658. New Jersey entered the field in 1674, and the Pennsylvania industry had its start with the first blast furnace built at Colebrookdale, about eight miles north of Puttdown, in 1720. In Ohio, the industry was started with the erection of a blast furnace known as the "Hopewell" at Colon on Yellow Creek not far from its junction with the Mahoning River.

The story of the great "iron plantations"[6] which flourished in Pennsylvania during the eighteenth century is one of the least known but most interesting chapters of colonial history. Although they produced iron rather than cotton, in many other respects they were very like the southern cotton and sugar plantations. They were extensive in area (up to 10,000 acres); their economic and social life centered about the large mansion house of the owner; and clustered around this mansion were the houses for the workers and their families. Instead of vast fields of cotton, however, the living areas were surrounded by forests of oak, hickory, ash, chestnut, and pine. The woodcutters and charcoal burners outnumbered any other group of craftsmen because a typical blast furnace required, each day, the wood from an acre of land.

A further, and still more significant and spectacular, development took place in the Calumet District of Illinois and Indiana. Mr. W. E. Hadley of the Carnegie-Illinois Steel Corporation has pointed out in an address that "the romance of the discovery of gold in America in the middle of the nineteenth century has been repeatedly related to every schoolboy from 1849 to the present time. While, no doubt, he could not in youth, and more than likely could not in later years, comprehend the full economic significance of that discovery, he nevertheless was thrilled by the romantic tales incident thereto, and where is the man that is not stirred by the magic word—'gold'? Although an equally significant discovery on the American continent occurred

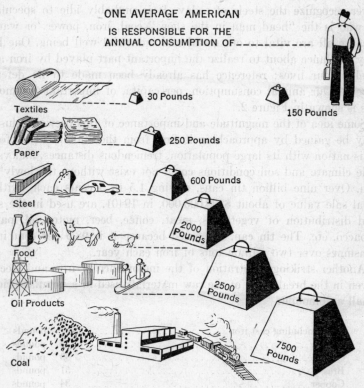

ONE AVERAGE AMERICAN
IS RESPONSIBLE FOR THE
ANNUAL CONSUMPTION OF

Textiles — 30 Pounds

150 Pounds

Paper — 250 Pounds

Steel — 600 Pounds

Food — 2000 Pounds

Oil Products — 2500 Pounds

Coal — 7500 Pounds

FIG. 2. American Consumption of Raw Materials.

nearly simultaneously with the discovery of gold, very little was it heralded, because no human being then realized its tremendous national importance. Iron ore was discovered on the Marquette range in the Lake Superior region in 1844." This discovery not only resulted in the erection of the first Lake Superior furnace by Stephen R. Gay at Marquette, Michigan, in 1858, but completely changed the metallurgical map as well as the industrial development of the United States. The discovery of this easily obtained and cheap ore made this

raw material available for the Eastern furnaces and also initiated the
remarkable metallurgical development of the Middle West, which development is still in progress. The reader is referred to Table 25,
which gives in brief form the chronological details of the development.

7. **Economics.** The age in which we live is frequently referred to as
the Steel Age. In the mind of the author a better designation might
be the Alloy Age, for the iron makers of the Civil War days would
never recognize the steels of today. It is probably idle to speculate
on who is the "head man in the show," coal, iron, power, or water,
because all are vital to our social and industrial well being. One has
only to glance about to realize the important part played by iron and
steel in our lives; reference has already been made to its defense
aspects. Our annual consumption, per capita, of important commodities is shown in Figure 2.

Some idea of the magnitude and importance of this prewar industry
may be gained by approaching it first from the standpoint of food.
This nation with its large population, tremendous distances, and variable climate and soil conditions could not exist without the lowly tin
can. Over nine billion tin cans, costing 1.5 to 5 cents each (with a
total sale value of about $200,000,000, in 1940), are used in the sale
and distribution of vegetables, meat, coffee, beer, motor oil, paint,
tobacco, etc. The tin can, ill named because it is 98.5 per cent iron,
consumes over two million tons of iron each year.

Another striking illustration of the importance of iron and steel is
given in the breakdown of the raw materials used in a popular-priced,
small automobile:

Steel, including cast iron	1919	pounds
Rubber	770	pounds
Cotton	89	pounds
Brass	51	pounds
Copper	34	pounds
Lead	31.5	pounds
Zinc	14.5	pounds
Manganese	14.5	pounds
Aluminum	10.6	pounds
Tin	4	pounds
Wool and mohair	3.5	pounds
Chromium	2.8	pounds
Antimony	1.5	pounds
Nickel	0.8	pounds
Cadmium	0.7	pounds

Less amounts of tungsten, vanadium, molybdenum,
platinum, columbium, and cobalt.

It is interesting to note that the selling price of this automobile was about 20 cents per pound. In this connection, it might be observed that the tonnage of steel involved and its cost are quite different things. Too much emphasis is placed on the cost of steel by the manufacturers of automobiles. As a matter of fact, the cost of steel in the above car is only 13 per cent of the f.o.b. price, or about 10 per cent of the delivered price. Consequently, a 10 per cent reduction in the price of steel should be accountable only for a 1 per cent reduction in the price of the car.

BIBLIOGRAPHY

1. Bishop, J. L., *History of American Manufactures*. Philadelphia: E. Young and Company, 1864. 2 vols.
2. Boyer, C. S., *Early Forges and Furnaces in New Jersey*. Philadelphia: University of Pennsylvania Press, 1931. 287 pp.
3. Boylston, H. M., *An Introduction to the Metallurgy of Iron and Steel*. New York: John Wiley and Sons, 1936. 563 pp.
4. Francis, C. B., *The Making, Shaping, and Treating of Steel*. Pittsburgh: Carnegie-Illinois Steel Company, 1940. 1440 pp.
5. Rickard, T. A., *Man and Metals*. New York: McGraw-Hill Book Company, 1940.
6. Swank, G. M., *Introduction to a History of Ironmaking and Coal Mining in Pennsylvania*. Philadelphia: Published by the author, 1878. 125 pp.

CHAPTER II

RAW MATERIALS

IRON ORES

8. General. Iron dominates the world; metallurgical minded peoples have always dominated agricultural ones. The more one contemplates the status of iron as a power in the modern world, a power probably greater than that of all other metals combined, the more one realizes why nations must secure control of iron ore resources. Perhaps that control and other national demands really spell the "Lebensraum" now being sought by certain nations. No war can be waged without considerable stocks of iron nor an industrial fabric woven without plentiful and easily available supplies of it. Countries that have achieved dominion over the principal sources of supplies have the best chance to win a conflict, provided, of course, that they have the furnaces and fuel to reduce and smelt the ore, and the technical knowledge, men, and spirit to achieve this economically and efficiently.

Coal is also essential to the reduction of the ore, but there are other sources of energy, some more convenient, like natural gas, some more costly, like electricity. In countries so fortunate as to have plentiful supplies of electricity, it is not unlikely that the new hydroelectric developments now being made by this government may be the means of changing radically the methods of reduction. Every country has air, most of them limestone (the other essential raw materials for smelting), but not every one has iron ore. Certain favored few like France (before the present conflict), Sweden, Brazil, and the United States have large and very valuable deposits, in some cases more than they can utilize themselves. Others like Japan and Italy have practically none, or ores of very low grade; Germany's greatest weakness in World War I was her dependence on Sweden for her iron ore requirements as well as on other nations for manganese, chromium, tungsten, and nickel. To meet this deficiency, Germany normally imports iron ore from France in exchange for coke and from Sweden in return for manufactured products; she also obtains manganese ore from South Africa, chromite from Turkey, tungsten from China, and nickel from Canada. Italy's deficiency, on the other hand, is taken care of, in peace times, largely by imports of scrap iron, principally from the United States, and by more extensive use of pyrite ash in the production of pig iron in electrical furnaces. Even Great Britain also imports part of her iron ore (her own is uniformly low grade) and scrap iron and all of her manganese, chrome, and nickel ores. A summary of the prewar coal and iron situation is shown in Table 2.

Science does not give the vaguest suggestion that anything will displace iron and steel as the most essential material tool of modern civilization, although aluminum, at 15 cents per pound, is an active competitor for certain special uses. Iron possesses hardness, strength, elasticity, resists atmospheric corrosion to some extent, is cheap—veritably a unique combination of properties; but, unfortunately, it does not occur, like copper, as the native metal, save in the form of

TABLE 2

SUMMARY OF COAL AND IRON SITUATION (1939)

Country	Coal Status	Iron Ore Status	Iron and Steel Status
Belgium-Luxemburg	Reserves and output small; imports necessary	Reserves small; low-grade ores, imports desirable	Production relatively large; mostly exported
France	Reserves small: imports up to one-third requirements necessary	Enormous reserves; heavy exports	Capacity moderate; small exports
Germany	Reserves and output largest in Europe; ample for export	Reserves small; heavy imports necessary	Capacity very large: second only to U.S.; heavy exports
Great Britain	Reserves and output very large; heavy exports	Large reserves low-grade ore; heavy imports	Capacity large; heavy exports
Soviet Union	Very large reserves	Large reserves	Small but rapidly growing industry. Coal and ore far distant from one another
Spain	Few reserves	Moderate reserves; practically all exported	Non-existent
Sweden	No reserves	Large reserves of high-grade ore; heavy exports	Small, high-grade output

meteoric iron. It must be reduced from its ores; and these ores, as well as the fuels used, contain deleterious impurities.

TABLE 3

BLAST FURNACE BURDENS

(Tons of raw material per ton pig iron produced)

	Ore	Sinter, Cinder, etc.	Scrap	Total	Lime-stone	Coke
All U. S. ores	1.718	0.138	0.041	1.897	0.361	0.903
Alabama	1.723	0.585	0.123	2.431	0.212	1.108
Lake ores	1.735	0.130	0.038	1.903	0.329	1.108
United Kingdom	2.333	0.165		2.498	0.296	1.123

9. Blast Furnace Burdens. Table 3 furnishes data on the blast furnace burdens in this country as well as abroad. For the moment we are concerned only with the first item in this table—iron ore. That item alone is a tremendous one when one considers the national requirements (in 1941 the consumption was over 87 million gross tons).*

Imagine an area of the earth one mile square and elevate it all over its surface 50 feet. This raised portion will represent the volume of iron ore shipped from the Lake Superior district in 1941. Put this iron ore in standard ore boats 600 feet long and let them travel past you end to end; it will take more than 72 hours for the parade to pass. Load the iron ore into railroad cars, and it will be necessary to make up a train of 1,320,000 cars, which will stretch out for 10,500 miles, or more than four times the distance between New York and San Francisco. Thus may we visualize the very large tonnage of iron ore moved for our annual requirements. This large tonnage of ore brought the total of all shipments from the Lake Superior district, between the discovery of the mines and December, 1940, to 1,851,779,065 tons.†
To pursue this comparison still further, elevate that original area of one square mile, 1120 feet, to a height about equivalent to that of a 98-story building, and again you obtain an idea of the majestic pro-

---

* All except about 2 million tons of this was consumed in blast furnaces. Total shipments of iron and manganiferous ores in 1941 were approximately 94 million gross tons, of which 81 million gross tons, or 86 per cent, came from mines in the Lake Superior district.

† In addition, Canadian mines shipped 3,935,000 tons between 1900 and 1935, and about 94,000 tons were produced in 1941.

portions of man's work—the immense tonnage of iron ore he has dug up and transported 1000 miles to the furnaces during the past fifty years. Incidentally, if you will slice off one-third of this huge block, you will have before you that portion mined and shipped by the United States Steel Corporation alone.

10. Minerals and Ores. An ore is a natural aggregation of elements or compounds whose chemical composition, physical form, location, and extent permit the extraction of a metal or metals at a profit. Although a vast number of minerals contain iron, there are comparatively few that are of any importance commercially, because in most cases the iron content may be too low to permit a profitable extraction of the metal, the deposits may not be of sufficient extent, they may occur in such a locality as to render them unavailable for use as ores, or they may contain harmful impurities. The value of an iron ore, therefore, will depend upon the following factors:

1. The deposit must be favorably located with respect to an adequate transportation system. The Lake Superior deposits furnish about 86 per cent of the United States' requirements, about 40 per cent of the world's. This is due, in part, to the very cheap lake transportation to the furnaces of Indiana, Illinois, Ohio, and Pennsylvania.

2. The percentage of iron in the ore must be of a high order of magnitude as compared to non-ferrous ores. A hematite ore containing 63 per cent of iron will contain 90 per cent of the pure mineral.

3. Undue amounts of water not only add to the cost of transportation but also consume energy in the smelting operation and dilute the top gases.

4. These impurities may be harmful to the iron or unduly burden the furnace: those which are never reduced, like alumina or magnesia; those which are partially reduced, like silica or compounds of manganese or chromium; and finally those which are always reduced, such as phosphorus, copper, or tin.

5. The physical condition must also be taken into account because the ores may range from soft, claylike, earthy varieties to hard, compact ones. Both extremes give trouble in the blast furnace by choking up voids in the burden, preventing the free circulation of gas and heat, and increasing the amount of flue dust formed. The hard, compact ones are difficult to reduce because they offer proportionately less surface on which the reducing gas may act.

Grouped according to their chemical composition, the iron-bearing minerals may be divided into four classes: namely, the iron oxides, carbonates, silicates, and sulfides. The principal ones are given in Table 4 together with their composition and the percentage of iron they contain theoretically. Of these, only the first class, the oxides, may be considered as major factors in the manufacture of iron and steel in the United States.

TABLE 4

IRON MINERALS

Name	Composition	Fe, per cent
Magnetite	Fe_3O_4	72.4
Hematite	Fe_2O_3	70.0
Limonite and		
hydrated oxides	$Fe_2O_3 \cdot xH_2O$	50–60
Siderite	$FeCO_3$	48.2
Pyrite	FeS_2	46.6

11. Magnetite. This important mineral is magnetic, varies in color from gray to black, has a specific gravity of about 5.0, and when pure contains 72.4 per cent iron. This magnetic property is taken advantage of, not only in locating ore bodies but also in concentrating the ores after they are mined. Unfortunately, only about 5 per cent of the world's supply of iron is obtained from magnetite. Another short-coming exists in the fact that magnetites are rather dense and, in presenting less surface to the action of the reducing gas in a blast furnace, materially reduce its capacity. The titaniferous magnetites are a peculiar class in themselves because the titanium is difficult to handle in the present refining methods, and it is often impossible to separate the titanite from the magnetite in ore concentration.

12. Hematite. This is unquestionably the world's most important iron mineral, and it occurs in a wide variety of physical forms and chemical compositions. Hematite is red to brownish red, steel gray, or even black, commonly fine-grained, but the specular varieties may be quite coarse. It ranges from massive to powdery and has a specific gravity of 5.2. The iron content ranges from 40 to 65 per cent.

13. Limonite and Hydrated Oxides. These minerals, of lower grade than the hematites or magnetites, are widely distributed throughout the world. In this country they are of little importance. They vary in water content from turgite, $2Fe_2O_3 \cdot H_2O$, up to limonite, $Fe_2O_3 \cdot 3H_2O$. On a theoretical basis the iron contents vary from about 52 per cent to 66 per cent, but the natural minerals are ordinarily much lower grade than this—ranging from 30 to 55 per cent.

14. Iron Carbonates. The most common member of this group is the mineral known as siderite ($FeCO_3$), which contains, in the pure state, 43.8 per cent iron. This percentage is frequently lowered by reason of the fact that a part of the iron may be replaced by other metals, giving rise to a series of minerals such as iron-calcium carbonate, iron-magnesium carbonate, etc. These ores are also known as spathic iron ore, kidney ore, black-band ore, etc., and frequently contain enough calcium to be self-fluxing. They are of little importance in this country.

15. Grades of Iron Ore. The presence or absence of certain impurities, which may or may not be reduced in the blast furnace, has given rise to another classification of iron ores on the basis of their metallurgical behavior. On the basis of the phosphorus content, or better, the relation of phosphorus to iron, the iron ores may be classified into the Bessemer and the non-Bessemer or basic grades. It has been found desirable to produce Bessemer steel that will contain not more than 0.1 per cent of phosphorus. A true Bessemer ore, therefore, would be one in which the phosphorus content of the ore plus the phosphorus content of the coke and limestone required to smelt and flux it would produce a pig iron with a phosphorus content not exceeding 0.10 per cent. If 10 per cent is allowed for conversion loss, the resulting pig iron would yield, on further treatment, steel containing less than 0.1 per cent of phosphorus. Conversely, a basic or non-Bessemer pig iron is one in which the phosphorus content exceeds this figure. Manganiferous iron ores are those which are used as a source of manganese for steel and ordinarily contain 2 to 10 per cent of manganese. Siliceous ores are those containing large amounts of silica, normally 18 to 40 per cent. High-phosphorus ores are those containing more phosphorus than normally present in a basic or non-Bessemer ore and will range from 0.18 to 1.0 per cent.

FOREIGN IRON ORES

16. General. The present great producers of the world's iron ore are:

1. The Lorraine deposit of "minette" ore in northern France.
2. The Lapland magnetite deposits in northern Sweden.
3. The sedimentary deposits in eastern England.
4. The high-grade hematites of the Ukraine and the magnetites of Siberia.
5. The Lake Superior deposits.

The magnitude of these deposits is shown in Table 5 and the world's production in Table 6. Germany has several scattered iron

TABLE 5

IRON ORES OF THE WORLD

Country	Reserves, millions metric tons		Fe, Per Cent (actual ore)
	Actual	Possible	
Germany	1,317	2,843	35
Great Britain	5,970	6,198	33
France and Lorraine	8,164	enormous	33
Soviet Union	2,000	enormous	49
Sweden	2,200	"	64
Spain	711	273	51
Italy	19	27	57
Poland	60	200	33
Japan	50		50
China	115	1,107	50
India	3,326	20,500	58
Newfoundland	4,000	8,000	55
Cuba	3,159	12,000	45
Brazil	7,000	enormous	60
Chile	440		60
United States	5,038	enormous	51

ore deposits that are being mined, and, although they are not important from the standpoint of domestic consumption, they cannot be compared in value to the ones listed above. Moreover, the magnetite deposits of the Soviet Union, situated as they are far from supplies of coal as well as centers of consumption, cannot be added to those of primary importance. Among the smaller countries, Spain, Norway, and Austria add a few million tons each year to the export trade in Europe, while in the Balkan States the iron deposits are small and relatively unimportant. It is very difficult to appraise or weigh accurately the reliability of iron ore estimates. For example, those for Sweden are known to be very conservative and to include only high-grade ore; those of the Soviet Union probably include deposits of low-grade ores requiring concentration and many of doubtful commercial value. However, Table 6 makes it evident that the known iron ore reserves are between 57 and 58 billion tons, enough to last about 1000 years, and that, although one-sixth of this lies within the United States, other countries are well supplied. Some of them are so

TABLE 6
WORLD PRODUCTION OF IRON ORE*
(Thousands of metric tons per year)

Country	1890	1900	1910	1918	1921	1929	1932	1938	....
Algeria	475	502	1,080	979	707	2,196	463	3,105	....
Chile		20		3	8	1,812	172	1,608	....
China			200		1,365	980	2,280		....
France	3,420	5,448	14,500	13,163	14,201	50,644	27,596	33,137	....
Germany	8,047	12,792	22,965	23,318	5,907	6,374	1,340	10,938	....
Great Britain	13,781	14,282	15,470	16,108	3,526	13,426	7,445	12,049	....
India		58	55		957	2,468	1,789	2,787	....
Luxemburg	3,359	6,172	6,263	3,397	3,032	7,571	3,213	5,140	....
Spain	6,065	8,676	8,667	5,092	4,768	6,547	1,760	2,513	....
Spanish Morocco					150	570	204	1,341	....
Sweden	941	2,628	5,184	7,191	6,464	11,468	3,299	13,928	....
United States	16,036	27,118	55,990	68,558	28,820	71,874	9,691	28,903	....
U. S. S. R.	1,796	6,107	5,758	30	153	7,265	12,200		....
World	57,000	88,300	145,000	106,007	74,000	199,000	77,198	162,000	....

* Compiled from *Mineral Industry* and *Mineral Yearbooks*.

well supplied, in fact, that strong competition has been felt for many years in this country, and they will be a greater factor in the post-war world.

17. **Germany.** It is a well known fact that one of the most serious problems confronting German industry as a whole is the deficiency of iron ore. Before the first World War, Germany obtained over 90 per cent of her requirements from the Lorraine deposits of minette iron ore. In preparation for the present conflict, Germany developed some of her own, although much less attractive, deposits.

Until recently the Siegerland district has been the largest producer. These deposits, veins of siderite 3 to 30 feet wide, yield ore containing about 35 per cent of iron, which when roasted yields a calcine containing 50 per cent iron and 10 per cent manganese. During the last few years, however, the output of the Peine-Salzgitter, Bavarian, and Lahn-Dill districts has been much greater, although the iron content of the high-phosphorus ore is only 30 per cent with 1.6 per cent manganese and 25 per cent silica. The Salzgitter district is the one now being developed in connection with the development of the gigantic Herman Goering Steel Works. The Lahn-Dill deposits yield hematite and limonite, containing 42 per cent of iron; and of course Austria's mines can also be included in Germany's reserves. These mines produce limonite-siderite ores averaging 33 to 38 per cent iron and 2.2 per cent manganese, which when roasted yield a calcine containing 45 per cent of iron. Because of its low phosphorus and sulfur content, this ore is comparable with those of Sweden. Germany also imports large quantities of burned pyrite containing up to 60 per cent iron.

18. **Italy.** The output of the Italian iron mines represents less than one quarter of the iron required by the nation. There are two important deposits of iron ore: the Elba mine, producing principally limonite, with a little hematite, and averaging 51 per cent iron, 10 per cent silica, 0.07 per cent phosphorus, and 0.09 per cent sulfur; and another deposit of limonite and siderite containing 46 to 52 per cent iron with 0.08 per cent phosphorus and 0.02 per cent sulfur.

19. **United Kingdom.** The principal sources of iron in England are the sedimentary deposits of Northamptonshire, Leicestershire, Grodingham, and Yorkshire, which districts supply about 80 per cent of the total production. The ore, when dried, contains 25 to 38 per cent iron (averaging 30 per cent) with 0.3 to 1 per cent manganese and 0.3 to 0.7 per cent phosphorus. They are mostly siderites and limonites, which must be supplemented by richer imported ores from Spain,

North Africa, and Sweden to maintain satisfactory furnace burdens. There are hematite deposits in Cumberland and South Wales, where hematite ore averaging up to 53 per cent iron is available. On the whole, England is favored with very large reserves of low-grade, self-fluxing ores, which can be mined cheaply; with extensive coking coal deposits adjacent to these iron ore mines; and with plenty of skilled labor for both the mining and steel industries. High-grade ores are imported, but the industry does not depend on these for its existence as do Germany, Italy, and Japan. Sweden, Spain, and North Africa are the principal sources of the imported ores, followed by Sierra Leone and Norway.

20. Poland. There are four important iron ore districts in Poland. Two of them, the Czestochowa and Kielce-Radom districts, produce siderite ores with about 29 per cent iron; the other two consist of limonite deposits containing 30 to 45 per cent. They are not of continental importance, only important to Poland because along with them she has large deposits of coking coal.

21. France. Before the present conflict, France possessed in the minette deposits of the Lorraine basin one of the most important iron ore deposits in the world, estimated at about 8 billion tons of actual ore, with a potential supply of 4 billion more. The ore is a hydrated hematite, usually not hard, often earthy, with a water content of 8 to 10 per cent. In general, it is comparatively high in phosphorus, low in iron (25 to 45 per cent), but basic and nearly self-fluxing. Two principal grades of ore are recognized: one the calcareous or basic ores, which are most prominent in the Briey and Thionville areas; and the other the siliceous ores produced in the region of Brittany and in the Nancy basin. These ores vary widely in composition, as indicated below:

COMPOSITION OF LORRAINE ORES

Constituent	Per Cent	
	Basic Ores	Siliceous Ores
Fe	26–37	30–39
CaO	12–20	4–10
SiO_2	5–10	12–25
Al_2O_3	2–10	5–10

The output of the basic ore is about four times that of the siliceous. The ore mined averages about 30 per cent iron, 0.3 per cent manganese, and 0.7 to 0.9 per cent phosphorus (its outstanding characteristic).

In Normandy the principal deposits are a series of hematites yielding ore containing 45 to 50 per cent iron, 12 to 18 per cent silica, and 0.6 to 0.7 per cent phosphorus.

Of future importance for France are very extensive surface deposits in French West Africa. The ore contains 48 per cent iron, 2 per cent chromium, and 1 per cent nickel, and occurs in beds 10 to 30 meters thick. It is near the sea and can be mined at a very low cost.

22. Sweden. Sweden occupies a unique position among the iron- and steel-producing countries in possessing ores with a very high iron content and a small amount of deleterious impurities, and in smelting these ores largely with charcoal. Sweden possesses one of the largest reserves of high-grade magnetite in the world (estimated at 2200 million of "actual" and 700 million of "possible" ore).

At Kiruna the ore mined is a mixture of magnetite and apatite, which is divided for shipment into six classes of ore, ranging from 0.03 to 1.8 per cent phosphorus and from 56 to 71 per cent iron. This ore runs not more than 0.05 per cent sulfur, 0.07 per cent manganese, and 0.03 per cent titanium. Kiruna is an open-pit operation, but at Gellizara there is another very large deposit of similar ore which is exploited by underground methods.

23. Soviet Union. The Soviet Union unquestionably has enormous deposits of iron ore (estimated at 2 billion tons), but some of these are low grade and others far removed from coal deposits. For the past decade or more, the Krizoi Rog iron mines have produced over 60 per cent of the total Russian output. The ore is essentially hematite and magnetite, averaging 57 per cent iron, 8 per cent silica, 0.25 per cent manganese, and 0.05 per cent phosphorus. In the Ural mountains there are several potentially important districts where the ore averages about 45 per cent iron.

24. Spain. Spain has always been an important producer of high-grade iron ore, exporting her product to England, Germany, and Holland. By far the most important deposits are at Bilbao and Santander. At Bilbao, the ore mined is hematite and limonite, ranging from 48 to 58 per cent iron, 1 per cent manganese, and 0.03 per cent phosphorus. In the Santander district there are the extensive deposits of argillaceous ores containing only 20 to 35 per cent iron; but these, on concentration in washing plants, yield a washed ore with 57 per cent iron. In addition to the iron ore, there are in Huelva very large deposits of pyrite, which material is first used for the manufacture of sulfuric acid, then processed to remove undesirable elements and agglomerated for blast furnace use. Unfortunately, the tonnage available is governed by the demand for sulfuric acid as well as the ability of the particular furnace to remove the small amount of residual sulfur they contain.

The iron mines in Spanish Morocco have come into prominence during the last few years, for they are very high grade, containing 62 per cent iron, and they are low in phosphorus.

25. Newfoundland. On Belle Isle, in this province, is one of the six great ore bodies in the world. The ore is an oölitic hematite ore known as the Wabana, containing about 51 per cent iron, 0.9 per cent phosphorus, 14 per cent silica, and 0.05 per cent sulfur. Authorities are in agreement that there are at least 3 billion tons in this deposit and some place it as high as 10 billion. Although the shipments up to date have been chiefly to Germany, Canada, and England, it is of great potential interest to the United States because of its location and its possibility as a future supply when the Lake Superior ores are exhausted and the proposed St. Lawrence waterway is completed.

26. Cuba. This island because of its proximity to the United States and its large ore reserves is of great interest to us. At the present time high-grade magnetites and hematites are being mined with an iron content of about 61 per cent, 0.03 per cent phosphorus, 9.28 per cent silica, 0.13 per cent manganese, and 0.035 per cent sulfur; but on the north coast of the island there are immense deposits of laterite said to contain at least one billion tons of ore (see Article 32). An unusual feature of these particular deposits is that they contain notable percentages of chromium, nickel, and cobalt, and thus yield, on conventional smelting, an alloy iron.

27. Chile. These deposits are important to us because they are close to the ocean, available for low-cost water transportation, and the Bethlehem Steel Corporation has developed large areas in Coquimbo province. The ores are of two varieties, the high grade containing up to 68 per cent iron, 0.01 per cent phosphorus, 0.08 per cent manganese, and 0.02 per cent sulfur; the lower grade containing about 58 per cent iron, 0.09 per cent phosphorus, 8.5 per cent silica, 0.01 per cent manganese, and 0.008 per cent sulfur. Incidentally, besides being very high grade, a number of these ores are virtually self-fluxing.

28. Brazil. This country without doubt holds another of the six

great deposits of iron ore (estimated at 7 billion tons) known to exist
at the present time. Nearly half of this deposit averages 63 to 70
per cent iron. As a matter of fact, the Brazilian deposits are probably
the greatest, although recent developments in India may tend to
change that situation. Certainly from an American standpoint the
Brazilian deposits are important in that they will probably be the
first foreign ones to which we shall turn to bolster our supplies when
depletion of Lake ores becomes an embarrassing fact. The most important ore is a bedded hematite containing about 57 per cent iron,
0.036 per cent phosphorus, 0.31 per cent silica, 0.29 per cent manganese, and 0.017 per cent sulfur. Others are almost equally high
grade in iron, seldom contain more than 0.04 per cent phosphorus,
and are low in sulfur. All together they are very important and attractive deposits, for not only do they lend themselves to low-cost metallurgical treatment but also reliable estimates indicate that this ore
could be landed at points on the Atlantic seaboard at a cost of
about 12 cents per unit of iron. It is also noteworthy that Brazil has
some of the most extensive manganese ore reserves in the world, most
of the 200 million tons being of excellent quality.

29. China. Actually only about 400 million tons of ore have been
developed in the Chinese deposits (a large part is in Manchuria),
and the average iron content of this is only about 40 per cent; but
authorities believe that this country does possess enormous, untapped
resources of iron ore. At the present time it is not a factor in the
world's market.

30. Japan. This nation is particularly deficient in iron ore, the nation supplying less than one-fourth of its domestic consumption.
Even if the known reserves of Manchuria are added, the total available is inadequate to supply even modest requirements for any great
length of time. The total actual reserves in Japan and Korea, ex-
clusive of low-grade ores and iron sands, is about 10 million tons.
The Manchurian reserves are given at 700 million tons of 35-40 per
cent iron ore. Much attention is being given to the development of
these low-grade ores and iron sands. One of the principal reasons for
Japan's aggression is the desire to obtain adequate deposits of iron,
chromium, manganese, and nickel to support an expanded ferrous
metallurgical industry.

31. British India. In recent years there have been some important,
even spectacular, discoveries of ore near Calcutta which have added
immense reserves to the world's supply. The United States recently
became conscious of the iron and steel industry there because at one

time India was leading the list of countries exporting pig iron to America. Although Indian ores are largely lateritic in character, they are of excellent quality. The Mayurbhanj ore may be considered typical and represents a very large tonnage, containing about 60 per cent iron, 0.08 per cent phosphorus, 4.17 per cent silica, and about 0.01 per cent sulfur. One authority on Indian matters, C. P. Perin, believes that Indian reserves exceed 20 billion tons (much of which can be mined by open pits), all within reasonable distance of India's best coal deposits.

32. The Laterite* Ores. At the present time, because of their physical character as well as high iron content, hematites, magnetites, and limonites have been almost universally used as the source of the world's iron. There are, however, particularly in many foreign countries, enormous deposits of low-grade, high-moisture, lateritic ores which may respond to concentration or new metallurgical processes and some day become a tremendous factor in the world's market. Vast tonnages of laterite are found in India, and it was this ore which brought about the development of the iron and steel industry in that country. The laterite ores of greatest interest to us, however, are those available for water transportation, notably the immense deposits in Cuba, lesser ones in Greece, Porto Rico, and the Philippine Islands.

The Cuban laterites would make an ideal ore supply for this country when our Eastern ores are exhausted were it not for the fact that they are high in alumina and moisture and are of a poor physical condition. Our industrialists are aware of this fact because practically all the available ore is owned in the United States. Before these ores can be widely used, however, some method of beneficiation must be evolved whereby the metallic iron can be removed from its association with chromium, nickel, and alumina, and the iron residue satisfactorily agglomerated.

33. Production of Iron Ore. Before the first World War, Europe, excluding Russia (or the Soviet Union), produced more than half the world's ore; but since then, Europe has been credited with less than half the world's total. Germany was the leading producer (1909 to 1918) but now produces only one-fourth as much as then. Other striking changes are the decline in Spain's production, the large increase in Sweden's (both countries export their ore), the rise of the Soviet Union to third place, and increases in India, Manchuria, and

---

* Laterite is a hydrated, claylike material, low in silica and containing considerable iron, resulting from the decomposition of complex silicates.

South Africa. These changes are shown in Table 6; but in considering them one should bear in mind that the iron content of much of the ore produced in France, the United Kingdom, Germany, and Luxemburg is relatively low grade and, if measured in terms of iron content, the output of these countries would assume less importance. This is more strikingly shown in Table 67, for while the United States produced only 18.9 per cent of the world's ore in 1938, she produced 22.8 per cent of the pig iron, steel, and ferro alloys (and at 39.6 per cent of capacity that was not an active year in this country).

TABLE 7

PRODUCTION OF ORE, LAKE SUPERIOR RANGES[30]

Range	Analysis, Per Cent						Year of Discovery	Production to Jan. 1, 1941
	Fe	P	SiO$_2$	Mn	S	H$_2$O		
Marquette	55.8	0.11	12.8	0.32	0.01	10.0	1854	206,937,733
Menominee	55.0	0.43	7.3	0.91	0.11	14.1	1877	189,247,825
Gogebic	60.0	0.07	6.8	1.14	0.11	14.9	1884	68,680,987
Vermilion	61.5	0.04	7.4	0.08		7.2	1884	221,557,124
Mesabi	58.1	0.06	8.1	0.6	0.01	16.1	1892	1,120,489,970
Mayville	44.9	1.19	5.2	0.1		23.2	1892	41,483,330
Baraboo	53.8	0.07	13.6	0.35		13.7	1904	2,379,865
Cuyuna	52.2	0.23	7.4	3.9	0.01	19.1	1911	643,033
Grand Total								1,851,419,867

DOMESTIC IRON ORES

34. Lake Superior. September 19, 1844, may be regarded as a notable date in the iron and steel industry in this country, as a matter of fact, in its industrial development as well; for on that day the compass needle of a government surveyor, W. A. Burt, brought about the discovery of the iron ore near Marquette, Michigan. A rush to the district resulted; and in the boom that followed, the Menominee and Gogebic ranges indicated on the map in Figure 3 were discovered. The really great discovery was not made until sometime later when, in the course of a gold rush to Vermilion Lake in 1865, Lewis Merritt brought back with him some red iron ore. He died in 1880 without developing the discovery, but his sons persisted in the search for large deposits of the ore. Finally a test pit, put down on November 16,

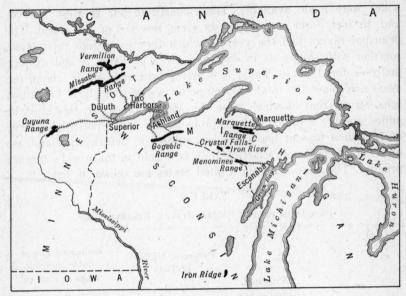

FIG. 3. Lake Superior Iron Ranges.

1890, encountered ore running 64 per cent iron, and the enormous deposits of the Mesabi* (an area about 100 miles long by 3 miles

TABLE 8

LAKE SUPERIOR IRON ORES[30]

(Average Analyses, 1940)

Ore	Tonnage	Per Cent Total	Per Cent				
			Fe (Nat)	P	SiO₂	Mn	H₂O
Bessemer	12,908,978	20.4	55.03	0.039	7.82	0.34	9.10
Low Phos. Non-Bess.	45,223,847	71.4	51.85	0.072	7.58	0.68	11.70
High Phos. Non-Bess.	2,747,378	4.3	51.84	0.403	6.50	0.28	8.59
Manganiferous	1,802,189	2.9	42.47	0.271	10.30	7.05	11.23
Siliceous	626,021	1.0	37.28	0.042	41.77	0.11	2.77
Grand Total	63,308,413	100.0	52.09	0.085	8.00	0.77	10.93

*Sometimes spelled Mis-sa-bay, Missabe, or Mesaba; means giant in the Chippewa Indian language.

wide) were made available. These constitute our greatest reserves and, in fact, form one of the six great reserves of the world. The principal ranges and the year in which they came into production, together with shipments to date, are given in Table 7, and average analyses for 1940 in Table 8. Careful estimates, made about ten years ago, place the total Lake Superior reserves at about 1.5 billion tons, 80 per cent of which is on the Mesabi range. To this must be added another 3 billion tons of probable ore and a potential reserve of 72 billion tons of low-grade ore, subject to beneficiation and use under conditions more exacting than now hold in the world's furnace practice. The reserves of the United States are shown in Table 9.

TABLE 9
IRON ORES OF THE UNITED STATES, RESERVES 1938

Area	Principal, Kind of Ore	Reserves, Millions of Tons		Estimated Life of Available Reserves in Years at Rate of	
		Available	Sub-marginal	1922–1930	1937
Lake Superior, total	Hematite	1,421	67,660	26	21
Marquette	"	49	16,000	13	9
Menominee	"	58	7,360	12	25
Gogebic	"	46	4,000	7	9
Vermilion	"	14	1,000	10	10
Mesabi	"	1,191	39,000	31	23
Cuyuna	"	62	300	48	85
New York	Mag. and Hem.	927	n. a.*	978	536
New Jersey	Magnetite	603	"	1,833	622
Pennsylvania	Mag. and Carb.	126	"	130	75
Birmingham	Hematite	1,003	"	128	156
Texas	Brown Ore	139	"	†	†
Wyoming	Hematite	15	"	†	†
Utah	Mag. and Hem.	77	"	†	†
United States, total		5,038	72,947	71	62

* Not available.
† Not computed, results of little value

More than half the 2 billion tons of high-grade ore is owned by the United States Steel Corporation. The remainder is mostly held by independent steel companies such as Bethlehem, Youngstown, Republic, Jones and Laughlin, Inland, and large ore companies such as Pickands, Mather and Company, M. A. Hanna Company, and Cleveland-Cliffs Iron Company. The vast Mahoning Pit* is operated by the Oliver Iron Mining Company, a subsidiary of the United States Steel Corporation and by Pickands, Mather and Company.

35. Alabama District. There is another major ore body in the United States which, like the Lake Superior, is highly concentrated, its rich and available veins stretching for 20 miles under the crest of Red Mountain and to depths of 2500 feet, for it is exploited by underground methods. The local chamber of commerce states that one can stand in a certain spot in Birmingham and throw a stone in one direction and hit iron ore, in a second and hit coal, and in a third and hit limestone. While this is an obvious exaggeration, proximity of raw materials and cheap labor place it second only to the Lake Superior district, and it is becoming increasingly important each year. Although some bodies contain 44 per cent iron, the largest tonnage is represented by the so-called red ore containing about 37 per cent iron, 12.5 per cent silica, 0.35 per cent phosphorus, 0.3 per cent manganese, and 0.02 per cent sulfur; and much of it is virtually "self-fluxing."

36. Other Domestic Deposits. The domestic iron and steel industry made its start with the hematite and magnetite deposits of Pennsylvania, New York, and New Jersey. There have since been added other deposits in the southern, the southwestern, and the northwestern parts of the country; but as yet these resources have not been utilized because of the obvious advantages of the Lake Superior district. In the eastern part of the country there is now available a reserve tonnage of probably 300 million tons of magnetite, 40 per cent of which is titaniferous. The brown and red ores centering in Tennessee amount to more than 600 million tons. Reliable estimates give the territory west of the Mississippi a total of over 1000 million tons, one-third of which is now available. Most of it lies in Texas, although Utah lays claim to about 40 million tons. The siderites of Ohio and eastern Pennsylvania are of interest because they are similar to England's great reserve, but they are not now in production. America's black-band ores exceed 300 million tons but like the English deposits are very low grade.

* This mine embraces not only the Mahoning mine itself but also Hull-Rust, Sellers, and Burt-Pool-Day. The total shipments to date from this pit are 281,084,599 gross tons.

37. The Great Lakes. The Great Lakes, besides being the largest body of fresh water in the world, occupy a peculiar position in the economy and politics of this country. Not only is Ontario a very rich province, frequently called "the Canadian Ruhr," but the war has also changed the status of the 4000-mile unfortified boundary between the two countries; it may still further change it, for, in the event of a defeat of England, Canada might (1) be the seat of a new British Empire; (2) apply for annexation to this country; or (3) be seized by Hitler. Whatever may happen, the industries of both countries depend to a very great extent upon the last of the world's free seas which has not floated a battleship for one hundred years; and, except for police and coast guards, not a fighting craft exists in the 1200 miles from Duluth to the end of Lake Ontario. As a matter of fact, a battleship could not now enter the Lakes.

Commerce, however, has been a binding link between the United States and Canada, and the bigness of this commerce may be gaged by these facts. There are 792 United States-Canadian carriers, only 28 of which are passenger boats. The remaining 764 are freighters, and of these 333 (293 of United States registry and 40 of Canadian) are bulk freight vessels. With an average trip capacity of 9055 tons, these ore vessels can make about thirty trips per navigation season of eight months, assuming return cargo about half the total number of trips.* During the 1941 season more than 169 million tons of iron ore, coal, limestone, and grain were transported. In contrast to this, in 1939 only 95 million tons of water-borne commerce were shipped from or received at all the Atlantic, Gulf, and Pacific coast ports. In 1942 the St. Marys Falls Canal will handle nearly 120 million tons, more than double that of the combined traffic of the Suez and Panama canals. It is significant that the average cargo entering and leaving Boston Harbor in 1937 was 1160 tons as against 9760 tons for Duluth, and equally so that the Soo Canal handles 100 per cent more tonnage in eight months than the Panama and Suez canals combined in a calendar year. Twenty-three ports on the Atlantic seaboard handle more than one million tons, but thirty-three (1940) lake ports do this.

* The 1941 season established a new record with the movement of 80,116,360 gross tons to the lower Lake ports. This record was made possible by unusually favorable weather conditions with a season of 259 days extending from April 1 to December 15; it would have been still higher had not an accident to a railroad bridge at Sault Ste. Marie closed the locks for two days. This is 26 per cent above the 1940 shipments of 63,712,982 tons and 23 per cent higher than the previous high mark of 65,204,600 in 1929. Stocks on hand at docks and furnaces as of December 1 were 45,534,633 tons.

TABLE 10

FREIGHT RATES ON IRON ORE[22]

Upper Rail Freight

   From Eastern Marquette..$0.65

        ” Mesabi.. 0.92

Water Rates

   Escanaba to Chicago.. 0.56

       ”   ” Lake Erie... 0.665

   Head of Lake to Lake Erie.. 0.94

Handling charge, rail of vessel to car..................................... 0.09

Rail freight from Lake Erie ports to

   Mahoning Valley.. 0.88

   Weirton.. 1.05

   Pittsburgh.. 1.21

   Johnstown.. 1.36

   Lehigh.. 2.00

Rail of vessel to stockpile.. 0.22

Stockpile to car (usually included in vessel freight)...................... 0.14

Storage charge per ton per month.. 0.01

Lake commerce, however, is a bit one sided in that little steel is transported by water, and ore boats must frequently return empty to Duluth. This is due to the fact that ore carriers in considerable numbers go from the lower lakes to Duluth in ballast. These vessels are constructed exclusively for the carriage of bulk freight commodities such as iron ore, coal, grain, and limestone. They have no facilities for the stowing, loading, and unloading of finished steel products, and their hatches are usually so spaced that this would be impracticable. There is a considerable movement of finished steel between such ports as Cleveland and Buffalo and the Detroit steel-consuming district. However, the cargoes are carried in relatively small vessels which are not adapted to the bulk freight trade. Quite naturally, also, the consumption of steel in the territory adjacent to Duluth is relatively limited, owing to the rural character of the country and the lack of large industries. In seasons of good operation it is generally assumed that about one-half the upbound vessel capacity is used for the transportation of coal to Lake Michigan and Lake Superior points.

The existence of this lake commerce and its importance in our metallurgical industry can be explained pragmatically by the fact that shipping by Lake freighter is the cheapest transportation known to man (see Table 10). Ore cargoes are carried an average distance of 800 miles for 77 cents per gross ton, or less than one mill per ton per mile. To move a ton of freight the same distance by rail costs about five dollars. As a matter of fact, it is more expensive to transport the ore from the mines to the docks (90 miles) than it is to transport it the rest of the way by ship (845 miles to Gary). On a return cargo of coal, the comparison is about the same; that is, it costs 45 cents for the average 500-mile haul as against three dollars by rail.

The necessity of rapid loading, because of the short season of less than 8 months,* has brought about a very elaborate system of docks and loading facilities at such ports as Duluth, Superior, and Two Harbors. In these docks, there are 24-foot pockets, each holding 250 to 400 tons, the spacing corresponding to the 12- or 24-foot spacing of the hatches of the boats. Much care must be exercised in handling the different shipments of ore in order to maintain a constant grade. At these docks there are as many as fifty different grades of ore handled from seventy-five different owners. These ores must be carefully blended on the basis of both physical and chemical properties. The seven docks at Duluth, Superior, and Two Harbors have 3030 pockets with a storage capacity of 819,100 tons. Normally, a 10,000-ton boat† is loaded in about 2 hours, but a record was established of loading 12,508 tons in 16½ minutes or at the rate of 758 tons per minute. The record cargo transported up to date is 16,498 gross tons in the *Harry Coulby* on July 12, 1941.

When the ore ships reach the Lake ports in Illinois, Indiana, or Ohio, they are unloaded by means of Hulett unloaders, shown in Figure 16. Each bucket of one of these unloaders holds about 17 tons, and by placing a battery of these unloaders in service at once a ship can be unloaded in 3 to 5 hours. The record was made on the steamer *J. P. Morgan* when 11,369 gross tons were unloaded in 2 hours and 15 minutes or at the rate of 4953 tons per hour.

Navigation on the Great Lakes is limited because of bad ice conditions, but the freezing of ore in the cars and the pockets at the docks is an important source of difficulty. Usually, navigation opens about April 15 and closes between December 8 and 15. By reason of this fact, the steel companies dependent on lake transportation must store large quantities of ore over the winter months.‡ For example, a twelve-stack blast furnace plant will require about 20,000 tons of ore per

* In 1902 the Soo Canal was open 264 days; the low mark was 158 days in 1905; in 1941 it was open 259 days.

† On February 28, 1942, the "Leon Fraser," the first of five new ore carriers, was launched. These will all be 639 feet long, 67 feet wide, 35 feet deep, and carry a cargo of 18,600 long tons of ore per trip at 24-foot draft.

‡ The monthly record was broken in October, 1941, when 6,612,186 tons were transported. On November 1, 1941, the stocks on hand were 43,945,751 tons, sufficient for about six months' operation at the October rate of consumption.

day and a stock pile of about 2.5 million tons to take it over the winter months.

38. St. Lawrence Waterway. When the Panama Canal was opened in 1915, Chicago and the Middle West moved away, economically, from the Pacific coast because of the enormous difference in water and rail transportation. During 1941 much appeared in the press concerning the likelihood of the construction of the St. Lawrence waterway as a defense project. Although the opening of this waterway to deep-draft ocean-going vessels might provide a rapid and cheap outlet for our manufactured goods, it would also have a tremendous effect on the iron and steel industry. It would bring into the domestic market the cheap, and in some cases, high-grade iron ores, such as those from Newfoundland, Brazil, and Chile. It would, however, disrupt our iron-mining industry (the value of whose facilities and properties used in delivering the ore has been estimated at nearly $800,000,000) and the well being of 40,000 men who earn, yearly, in the neighborhood of $50,000,000 in wages. What is still worse than this dislocation of our domestic economy is the fact that one more item would be added to the imposing list of vital raw materials* for which we are dependent on other countries. Many economists and industrialists believe its construction would be a serious detriment not only because of the dislocation of existing facilities but also because it would saddle the taxpayers with another burden (the cost would be enormous). The fallacy of promoting the importation of foreign iron ore with the concurrent deterioriation of the Lake bulk cargo fleet is now (April, 1942) vividly brought out by conditions existing on the Atlantic seaboard. Perhaps 50 per cent of the ore carriers have been torpedoed, thus cutting down shipments from Chile and Cuba. Fortunately the Lake fleet is at peak operating efficiency and may be able to increase production to take care of this deficiency. Most geologists agree that we have at least thirty years of high-grade ores ahead of us in the Lake Superior deposits and more than 70 billion tons of low-grade ores which can be beneficiated. It would seem better, therefore, from a metallurgical standpoint, not to build this waterway.

MARKETING OF IRON ORE

39. General. The mysterious Lake Erie price for iron ore, established each spring, determines the maximum price which will be paid during the following season for ore of Mesabi, non-Bessemer, base

---

* In 1941 the list included aluminum, antimony, chromium, coconut-shell charcoal, manganese, manila fiber, mercury, mica, nickel, optical glass, quartz crystals, quinine, rubber, silk, tin, tungsten and wool.

grade. The distinction between Bessemer and non-Bessemer ore lies in the phosphorus content (see Article 15). Theoretically, the ore should not contain more than 0.01 per cent, as much phosphorus as iron. Practically, however phosphorus is adjusted separately in fixing the final price according to a standard phosphorus table, which provides no adjustment at 0.045 per cent phosphorus with the scale of premiums for lower and penalties for higher phosphorus contents, as indicated in Table 12.

TABLE 11

Mesabi Non-Bessemer Ore (1940)[22]

(Base Price $4.45 at Lake Erie Port. Guarantee 51.50% Iron Natural)

		Lake Erie Unit Value	Lake Erie per Ton Value
For 61.00% Iron Natural	Unit Value	60–61%, $0.08641	$5.27
For 60.00% Iron Natural	Unit Value	59–60%, 0.08641	5.18
For 59.00% Iron Natural	Unit Value	58–59%, 0.08641	5.10
For 58.00% Iron Natural	Unit Value	57–58%, 0.08641	5.01
For 57.00% Iron Natural	Unit Value	56–57%, 0.08641	4.93
For 56.00% Iron Natural	Unit Value	55–56%, 0.08641	4.84
For 55.00% Iron Natural	Unit Value	54–55%, 0.08641	4.75
For 54.00% Iron Natural	Unit Value	53–54%, 0.08641	4.67
For 53.00% Iron Natural	Unit Value	52–53%, 0.08641	4.58
For 52.00% Iron Natural	Unit Value	51.50–52%, 0.08641	4.49
For 51.50% Iron Natural	BASE ORE	0.08641	4.45
For 51.00% Iron Natural	Unit Value	51–51.50%, 0.08641	4.41
For 50.00% Iron Natural	Unit Value	50–51%, 0.08641	4.32
For 49.00% Iron Natural	Unit Value	49–50%, 0.12961	4.19
For 48.00% Iron Natural	Below	49 %, 0.17282 per unit	4.02

Old Range Bessemer Ore (1940)[22]

(Base Price $4.75 at Lake Erie Port. Guarantee 51.50% Iron Natural; 0.045% Phosphorus Dry)

		Lake Erie Unit Value	Lake Erie per Ton Value
For 61.00% Iron Natural	Unit Value	60–61%, $0.09223	$5.63
For 60.00% Iron Natural	Unit Value	59–60%, 0.09223	5.53
For 59.00% Iron Natural	Unit Value	58–59%, 0.09223	5.44
For 58.00% Iron Natural	Unit Value	57–58%, 0.09223	5.35
For 57.00% Iron Natural	Unit Value	56–57%, 0.09223	5.26
For 56.00% Iron Natural	Unit Value	55–56%, 0.09223	5.17
For 55.00% Iron Natural	Unit Value	54–55%, 0.09223	5.07
For 54.00% Iron Natural	Unit Value	53–54%, 0.09223	4.98
For 53.00% Iron Natural	Unit Value	52–53%, 0.09223	4.89
For 52.00% Iron Natural	Unit Value	51.50–52%, 0.09223	4.80
For 51.50% Iron Natural	BASE ORE	0.09223	4.75
For 51.00% Iron Natural	Unit Value	51–51.50%, 0.09223	4.70
For 50.00% Iron Natural	Unit Value	50–51%, 0.09223	4.61
For 49.00% Iron Natural	Unit Value	49–50%, 0.13835	4.47
For 48.00% Iron Natural	Below	49 %, 0.18446 per unit	4.29

From 1907 to 1924, base-ore standards were 55 per cent iron for Bessemer ore and 51.5 per cent for non-Bessemer ores. Variations immediately above and below are settled on a straight unit basis except that there are concessions or penalties on ore much below base. Since 1924 the base grade for Bessemer and non-Bessemer has been the same, 51.5 per cent iron natural.

The Lake deliveries are chiefly at Lake Erie ports, from Toledo to Buffalo; consequently, it has been the practice to quote prices on Lake Superior iron ore f.o.b. Lake Erie docks. Normally, a single base price applies indiscriminately to all the Old Ranges and another to the Mesabi range, but a distinction is made between Bessemer and non-Bessemer grades. Thus, there are four prices making up the Lake Superior iron market, these being at the opening of the 1940 season.

Bessemer Old Range	$4.75
Bessemer Mesabi Range	4.60
Non-Bessemer Old Range	4.60
Non-Bessemer Mesabi Range	4.45
High Phosphorus	4.35

F.o.b. Lake Erie docks means, strictly speaking, at the rail of the vessel. Unit prices were figured by adding to the regular price, which is f.o.b. Lake Erie dock, an arbitrary charge of 60 cents, but this was discontinued in 1925 when the base grade of iron ore was changed to 51.50 per cent (see Table 11). Such a relationship arose in the old days when the freight to the Valley furnaces in Pennsylvania was approximately 60 cents per ton, the object being to equalize freight on material that was not iron. To carry out the principle correctly, the arbitrary amount should now be much higher, as freights are now higher (see Table 10). Even originally, the arbitrary figure was not high enough to equalize for Pittsburgh delivery, while for Lake front delivery it was really unnecessary.

40. Present System. Another diversion from the straight unit price occurs when ores contain less than 50 per cent iron, for the buyer is given more iron than on a straight unit price basis (see Table 11). Thus, one unit below 50 per cent is counted as 1.5 units, and two units are deducted for iron below 49 per cent. A 49 per cent ore is charged for as a 48.5 per cent ore, a 48 per cent ore as a 46.5 per cent ore, and a 47 per cent ore as a 44.5 per cent ore. These relationships are shown graphically in Figure 4.

To illustrate, if a Mesabi non-Bessemer ore is priced at $4.75, that is the base price f.o.b. Lake Erie dock for 51.5 per cent ore. The unit price, which is the basis for addition to or subtraction from the base price, is figured as

$$\$4.75 + \$0.60 = \$5.35$$
$$\$5.35 \div 51\tfrac{1}{2} \ = \$0.103883$$

For a 52.5 per cent ore this amount would be added, making \$4.853883, the price of that individual ore f.o.b. Lake Erie dock. For a 53 per cent

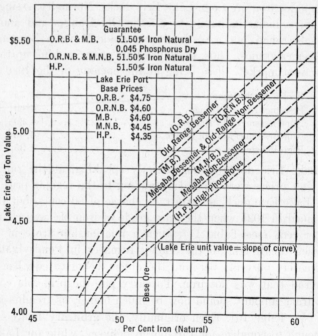

Fig. 4. Graph of Iron Ore Premiums and Penalties. (*Courtesy of M. I. Beard.*)

ore, 1.5 times the amount would be added. For a 50 per cent ore, 1.5 times the unit figure would be deducted; for a 49 per cent ore there would be an additional deduction of 1.5 times the unit figure; and for a 48 per cent ore there would be a further deduction of twice the unit figure.

For Mesabi Bessemer, Old Range Bessemer, and Old Range Non-Bessemer, the procedure is precisely the same, there being an addition to the dock price of 60 cents and this being divided by 51.5 to obtain the unit price. For Bessemer ores there is an adjustment for phosphorus to be applied after the computation is made as above. The

TABLE 12
PHOSPHORUS VALUES[22]

Phosphorus, Per Cent	Rate of Progression	Phosphorus Value
0.050	0.0100	−0.0450
0.049	0.0095	−0.0350
0.048	0.0090	−0.0255
0.047	0.0085	−0.0165
0.046	0.0080	−0.0080
0.045 base	0.0000	no adjustment
0.044	0.0080	+0.0080
0.043	0.0085	+0.0165
0.042	0.0090	+0.0255

standard content of phosphorus is taken as 0.045 per cent, ore being analyzed in its natural state, undried. Standard phosphorus values, ranging up to 0.050 per cent and down to 0.042 per cent, are shown in Table 12. Thus for a Bessemer ore containing 0.042 per cent phosphorus, 2.55 cents would be added to the per ton price.

Still another factor to be considered is the moisture content because it adds to the weight of ore to be handled and transported. Many soft ores of the Lake Superior region contain as much as 15 per cent moisture (bog ores as much as 25 per cent), as contrasted to as little as 0.40 per cent for the hard, red hematites. Incidentally, the marketing of the ores, and all burdening involving them, are based on analyses of samples dried at 100 to 105°C.

BENEFICIATION OF IRON ORES

41. General. In the early days of the iron and steel industry in this country there were many rich and easily exploited deposits whose ores could be smelted directly in the blast furnaces of that period without any preliminary treatment. At the present time, for the reasons outlined below, it has become necessary to beneficiate or concentrate a large and increasing proportion of our iron ores. Usually, the concentration of non-ferrous ores is carried out with the object of saving as much of the mineral as possible, thus reducing tailing losses to a minimum; the grade of the concentrate is of secondary consideration. In the treatment of iron ores, the situation is quite different because we are dealing with a material having a relatively low unit value.

The crude ore consists mainly of iron and silica. The silica is expensive to transport and still more expensive to flux and melt in a blast furnace. The concentration of iron ores is, therefore, a compromise or balance between (1) a grade of product that can be readily marketed, (2) a maximum weight recovery, and (3) a physical structure suitable for blast furnace treatment. Furthermore, an iron blast furnace requires, for most efficient operation, a uniform feed, as a consequence of which iron ores are mixed or blended so as to give uniform shipments throughout, not any lower and not any higher than the guaranteed analysis. It has already been pointed out that ores are sold before the shipping season starts. With this certain guarantee as to analysis not only of iron but also of silica, phosphorus, manganese, moisture, and sometimes alumina, the concentrate should not be any richer than the guaranteed grade because, if it were, the weight recovery would necessarily decrease; and under present market conditions the loss of iron in the tailings is not nearly balanced by the increase in price offered by reason of the additional iron content of the concentrate.

Weight recovery is the second important consideration in concentrating an iron ore, an average figure for a good grade of wash ore being 65 per cent weight recovery. This, of course, means that 3 tons of material will yield only about 2 tons of marketable concentrate; therefore, all mining or other costs incurred must be multiplied by about 1.5 when applied to the tons of ore actually shipped.

A third important consideration lies in the silica content. The average silica content of all ores being shipped from the Lake Superior region is approximately 8.50 per cent (dried at 212°F.). The silica analysis, dealt with in more detail in Article 47, is really more critical than the iron analysis. In general, a concentrate containing less than 12 per cent silica is desired, because if it contains more than this amount it is distinctly less desirable and sold at a discount. Furthermore, the lower the silica the better, because the ore can then be blended with more siliceous materials, and usually cheaper ones, to meet the desired shipping grade.

Not much can be done, in beneficiating iron ores, about the content of phosphorus or manganese because they are intimately bound up with the iron compounds of the ore; as a matter of fact, they both will increase somewhat in the concentrating process. However, if by any means the phosphorus analysis can be kept below 0.045 per cent, the elimination is well worth while because the ore commands a price premium.

With these factors in mind, particularly the guaranteed grade of "natural" iron assay, the required silica analysis, the economic necessity for high recovery, and the loss of iron in the tailings, it is obvious that the resulting iron unit recovery becomes of secondary importance. Unless the desired grade can be obtained, the ore is subject to a slight penalty or is not saleable at all; therefore, it is often economically sound to throw away a tailing fairly high in iron in order to obtain the maximum weight recovery of concentrate of the desired grade. These tailings are by no means lost, for they are now being impounded for future treatment.

Still another factor entering into the beneficiation of iron ores is the physical nature of the product as it affects its shipment and treatment in the blast furnaces. Very large lumps cannot be readily handled in cars, docks, boats, nor in the furnace itself, with the result that even in direct shipping of ores, if large lumps occur, they are simply screened out and the oversize crushed without any attempt at concentration. Excessively fine material in an ore will result in a greater flue dust loss at the blast furnace. At the present time, a weighted average of all ores shipped from the ranges indicates 15 to 20 per cent minus 100 mesh. Concentrates usually contain considerably less fines than the average, with the result that they are desirable for mixing with direct shipping ores.

The tailings from the concentrating plants contain varying amounts of fine free iron oxide, and greater attention is now being given to the saving of this fine material. Some companies now ship a portion of this fine concentrate to the blast furnace, where it is mixed with flue dust, sintered, and then made a part of the blast furnace charge.

42. Methods of Treatment. The following methods of iron ore concentration have been used, or suggested:

1. Cobbing or hand picking.
2. Calcination.
3. Drying.
4. Log washing.
5. Jigging.
6. Magnetic concentration.
7. Agglomeration or sintering.
8. Heavy-solution treatment.

Of the above methods, those involving crushing, screening, and washing are by far the most important in this country, for approximately 85 per cent of the ores being beneficiated in this country are so treated. The next method in order of importance involves magnetic treatment and subsequent sintering. Unfortunately, there are only meager reserves of magnetite in the Lake Superior district. If this method is to be more widely used, some process of heat treatment to convert the Fe_2O_3 into Fe_3O_4 must be devised, and usually such treatment is rather expensive. Table 13 gives data for the important Minnesota deposits.

TABLE 13*

SHIPMENTS OF CONCENTRATED ORE FROM MINNESOTA
1940

	Gross Tons	Per Cent Total
Washed	7,233,651	78.6
Jigged	1,114,904	12.0
Hi-Density	380,872	4.1
Sintered	222,710	2.5
Dried	255,544	2.8
Total	9,207,681	
Total Iron Ore Shipments	48,949,322	

* *Mining Directory of Minnesota*, 1941, Mines Experiment Station.

43. Classes of Ore. In view of the fact that more than half of the beneficiated ore produced in the United States is produced in Minnesota (most of that on the Mesabi range) and that the great bulk of our probable ore reserves is in that district, the general question of beneficiation is approached from the standpoint of the Mesabi ores. This range contains three classes of iron ore.

First is the unaltered taconite or banded iron-bearing chert. It is estimated that there are about 50 billion tons of this material, which contains 25 to 30 per cent iron. The second class consists of the merchantable or direct-shipping ores. The third class of ore lies between the first two; that is, the silica has been loosened from the iron in varying degrees by alteration but has been removed only partially by leaching. These are the so-called sandy or wash ores of the western Mesabi, and it is on these ores that concentration is now being practiced. This third class of ore may be subdivided into several other classes. There is first the easily washed ore, which consists of coarse and fine lumps of high-grade iron oxide mixed with fine free silica which can be removed by simply exposing the ore to a stream of water or by sizing it at about 60 mesh. In other classes of this wash ore, not only do the silica particles become coarser but the lumps of iron oxide also become more siliceous and approach closer and closer to the unaltered taconite. Consequently, on the poorer grade of ores, jigging or some other form of treatment becomes necessary.

TABLE 14

MAGNETIC ROASTING AND CONCENTRATION[11]

(Pilot Plant Results)

	Per Cent
Feed to plant, per cent Fe	46.07
" " " " " SiO_2	28.02
Discharge of reducing furnace, per cent Fe	51.54
" " " " " " SiO_2	25.54
Concentrate, per cent Fe	61.79
" " " SiO_2	12.02
Tailing, per cent Fe	21.73
Weight recovery	63.75
Iron unit recovery	89.3

44. Magnetic Roasting and Concentration. One of the proposed methods of treating the unaltered taconite is to subject it to roasting conditions which would promote the formation of Fe_3O_4, and then grind and concentrate with magnets.[13] Much experimental work has been done at the Mines Experiment Station at the University of Minnesota, where a new shaft-type roasting furnace has been developed to carry this out. With these laboratory tests as a basis, a ten-ton-per-hour pilot plant was built along the lines indicated in Figure 5. This plant was operated for five seasons, long enough to work out the

TABLE 15

WASHING PLANT, RESULTS OF OPERATIONS[11]

	Per Cent
Crude ore, per cent Fe	45.42
" " " " SiO_2	28.61
Concentrate, per cent Fe	59.38
" " " SiO_2	7.18
" " " P	0.047
" " " H_2O	7.97
Tailing, per cent Fe	15.0
Weight recovery	69.38
Iron unit recovery	90.73

necessary factors for commercial plant design and cost estimate. The
results of the 1937 operations are given in Table 14.

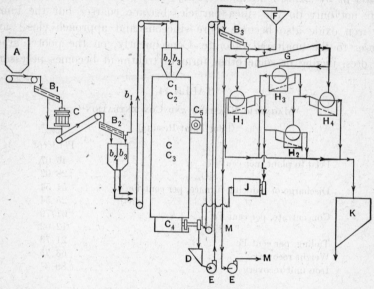

Fig. 5. Magnetic Roasting of Iron Ores.

A. Jig tailing bin
B₁. Vibrating screen—¾ in.
B₂.   "   "   —¾ in. and 3-mesh
B₃.   "   "   —3-mesh
b₁. Retained on ¾ in. to waste
b₂. −3M
b₃. +3M
C. Crusher
c₁. Drying zone
c₂. Heating zone
c₃. Reduction zone

c₄. Quenching zone
c₅. Combustion chamber and oil burners
D. Sump
E. Pumps
F. Surge tank
G. Dorr classifier
H₁,₂,₃,₄. Magnets
J. Ball mill
K. Concentrate bin
L. Middlings
M. Tails

45. Washing Plants.

A generalized flow sheet for the washing of the
Mesabi ores with bowl classifiers and secondary crushing is given
in Figure 6.[11] Compared to the earlier operations on such ores, the
flow sheet has been simplified and finer crushing has been put in,
with corresponding improvements in recovery and cost of operation.
Such operating results are given in Table 15, data taken from a plant
having a capacity of 375 tons per hour.

46. Other Processes.

Considerable work has been done since 1937
on sink-and-float separations using heavy fluids. In the case of iron
ores, it is necessary for the fluid to have a specific gravity of approximately 3.2; and, of course, since no true solution of commercial
practicability is available, such fluids are obtained by using thick concentrations of fine solids suspended in water. In the case of iron ore,

in order to obtain the desired gravity, ferrosilicon of the order of 55 mesh has been found to be satisfactory. To date it has been found preferable to treat plus–¼-inch material by this method, the under-size of the ¼-inch screens being treated on suitable jigs. In a pilot plant the results obtained are not quite so good as with magnetic roasting and straight washing, for the iron unit recovery is only 66.5 per cent, the weight recovery 53.8 per cent, yielding a concentrate containing 57.08 per cent iron and 12.14 per cent silica from a jig tailing containing 46.28 per cent iron and 27.62 per cent silica.

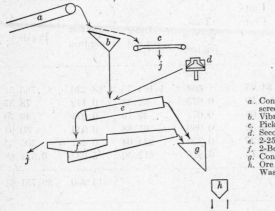

a. Conveyer from primary crushing or screening plant
b. Vibrating screen
c. Picking belt
d. Secondary crusher
e. 2-25 ft. Log washers
f. 2-Bowl classifiers
g. Concentrate bin
h. Ore cars
  Waste

Fig. 6. Washing Mesabi Ores.

Because of the success it has enjoyed in non-ferrous metal concentration, flotation has been suggested as a means of treating these low-grade ores. Actually, it is entirely possible to float the iron away from the silica or to float the silica away from the iron at will; however, there are two basic reasons why this has not been done commercially. The first reason is the high cost, for, if the ore is amenable to washing or jigging, then grinding and flotation could not compare in cost to these operations. The second reason is connected with the physical characteristics of the product, for fine flotation concentrates cannot be charged into the furnace in that condition; they must be sintered or agglomerated, and that additional operation would increase the cost of treatment. One important application of flotation to concentrating iron ores has been under consideration for a number of years. Much fine free iron oxide is lost in the washing plant tailing, not being recoverable by present water-gravity methods. Laboratory

tests have indicated that this fine material can be recovered by
flotation, and, since no grinding is necessary, such treatment might,
under certain circumstances, become economically attractive.

TABLE 16

DISTRIBUTION OF SMELTING COSTS*

(Producing 700 tons pig iron per day at Cleveland, Ohio, in 1938)

Item	Unit Cost	Quantity		Cost	
		Tons per ton pig iron	Tons per day	Per ton pig iron	Per day
Iron ore	$4.95	1.664	1,164.75	$8.236	$5,765.51
Sintering flue dust	1.50	0.075	52.38	0.112	78.57
Cinder and scale	1.00	0.071	49.70	0.071	49.70
Basic slag	0.50	0.089	61.88	0.044	30.94
Limestone	1.25	0.350	244.04	0.437	305.05
Coke	5.75	0.875	612.50	5.03	3,521.88
Total Raw Materials				$13.930	$9,751.65

Total departmental labor............................... $ 0.50
Steam, blowing.. 0.35
Miscellaneous steam, water, electricity..................... 0.19
Repair and maintenance materials........................ 0.18
Expense exhibits...................................... 0.19
Relining fund... 0.25
Works general expense................................. 0.10
Pigging and handling.................................. 0.25

Total operating cost above raw materials................ $ 2.01
Credit surplus gas.................................... 1.46

Total net operating cost above raw materials............ $ 0.55
Depreciation and fixed charges.......................... 2.35
Administration and selling.............................. 0.96

Total cost above raw materials......................... $ 3.86
Raw materials.. 13.93

Total cost... $17.79

* "Iron Ore Concentration and Lake Erie Price," *Transactions A. I. M. E.*, 1941.

47. Iron Ore Concentration and the Lake Erie Price. There is a rising tide of opposition to the mysterious Lake Erie price for iron ore because this price is entirely arbitrary and for many iron ore producers a very unfair one. T. L. Joseph, E. W. Davis, and G. W. Hewitt have written much in the last five years on this important subject and have shown conclusively that a new pricing system would be much more equitable to all concerned. The first authority demonstrated, as early as 1924, that the cost of smelting each unit of silica in an iron ore was a considerable one and probably of the order of magnitude indicated below:

COST OF SMELTING ADDITIONAL SILICA

Additional coke..................................	$0.08
Additional limestone.............................	0.075
Additional transportation........................	0.055
Decreased tonnage smelted.......................	-0.04
	$0.228
Distributed over 1.83 tons ore....................	$0.112

On the basis of these data and using a smelting cost of $17.79 (see Table 16), which was obtained in Cleveland in 1938, E. W. Davis[*] has devised the following simple formula as expressing a new and fairer price for Mesabi non-Bessemer ore:

$$V = 0.11944U - 0.12774(A - \tfrac{1}{4}B)$$

in which

V = Mesabi non-Bessemer lower Lake value of the ore when the price of base grade ore is $4.95 per ton.
U = number of units of iron in the ore.
A = number of units of acids ($SiO_2 + Al_2O_3$) in the ore.
B = number of units of bases ($CaO + MgO$) in the ore.

ANALYSIS OF BASE GRADE ORE

	Per Cent
Fe.....................................	51.50
SiO_2...................................	7.60
Al_2O_3..................................	2.00
CaO....................................	0.40
MgO....................................	0.40

Using this formula to determine the value of an ore of the follow-

[*] "Iron Ore Concentration and Lake Erie Price," *Transactions A. I. M. E.*, Vol. 145 (1941).

ing natural analysis: Fe, 52.55 per cent; SiO_2, 4.28 per cent; Al_2O_3, 2.28 per cent; CaO, 0.25 per cent; and MgO, 0.18 per cent—we have

$$V = 0.11944 \times 52.55 - 0.12774[(4.28 + 2.28) - \tfrac{1}{4}(0.25 + 0.18)] = \$5.453$$

Comparisons are shown in Table 17, from which it is obvious that, if ores were sold on the basis of computed values, which take into

TABLE 17
COMPARISON OF LAKE ERIE PRICE AND ORE VALUES*

Fe (Nat.), Per Cent	Lake Erie Mesabi Non-Bessemer, Price	Lake Erie Mesabi Non-Bessemer, Value	Percentage of Value to Price	Ore Factor
57.54	$5.531	$6.293	113.78	0.0789
48.70	4.602	4.932	107.17	0.1581
52.68	5.064	5.123	101.17	0.1737
51.50	4.950	4.950	100.00	0.1825 base ore
51.95	4.993	4.937	98.88	0.1911
53.27	5.120	4.982	97.30	0.2031
47.72	4.414	4.188	94.88	0.2479

* "Iron Ore Concentration and Lake Erie Price," *Transactions A. I. M. E.*, 1941.

account blast furnace operation rather than on the basis of Lake Erie prices, the blast furnace operator would not be affected because the formula adjusts the value so that pig iron can be made from all ores at the same smelting cost; only a change in the cost of the base ore would affect blast furnace cost. However, the change from price to value would have a very considerable effect on the ore producer, especially on operators engaged in making concentrates from low-grade ores. For example, consider an operator who has 10,000 tons of Mesabi ore to sell, containing 51 per cent Fe and 13 per cent SiO_2, neglecting for the moment the other constituents. Using the conventional Lake Erie price, this ore would be worth $49,021. Let us now assume that the operator removes five units or 112 pounds of silica from each ton of ore by some process of beneficiation. He would have left 9500 tons of ore containing 53.68 per cent iron and 8.42 per cent silica, the Lake Erie price of which would be $49,021, exactly the same as though the silica had not been removed. The ore producer would have saved the freight on 500 tons of ore, or $955, but probably this would not be sufficient to pay him for the expense of operating the plant to remove this silica. If this same ore were sold at its *value* at lower Lake ports, the 10,000 tons of 51 per cent iron ore would be worth only $44,309; but the 9,500 tons of 53.68 per cent iron ore would be worth $50,692, or an increase of $6383, to which the saving in freight of $955 may be added, making a total difference of $7338. This probably would be considerably more than the expense of operating the plant to remove the silica, since it would amount to as much as $0.73 per ton of original ore. This ore, of course, would be far more attractive to the blast furnace operator, and he would be willing to pay this increase in price or at least a part of it.

The future of the Lake Superior mining district, and to a large extent the iron and steel industry of this country, depends upon the development of methods for producing concentrates of at least a base grade from the enormous quantity of low-grade ore that is available. Unless the ore producers are credited with the full value of the product they ship, concentration operations will become less profitable in the future when it becomes necessary to produce concentrates of higher grade; such operations also would have a considerable effect on the influx of cheap, foreign iron ores of high grade. Any discussion of this matter invariably brings up the question of taxes, particularly in Minnesota, where a large part of the revenue of the state is derived from this source.

SINTERING OF IRON ORES

48. General. The sintering of iron ores, as distinct from the nodulizing and briquetting of very fine ores or concentrates, may be defined as the mixing of such fine materials with fuel and the burning of this mixture under induced draft. The first development of sintering was the Huntington-Heberlein process, in which fine sulfide ores mixed with fuel were charged into a pot and burned under the action of an upcast current of air introduced at the bottom of the pot.

The most commonly used today is the Dwight-Lloyd continuous sintering machine, shown in Figure 7. It consists of a strong frame of structural steel, supporting two heavy sprockets, and a steel track or guide. Traveling on these sprockets, and driven by them, is an endless system of pallets or pans with perforated bottoms. The pallets hold the charge (4 to 5 inches in depth) of ore, flux, and fuel during the sintering process. Underneath the train of pallets is a suction box which is connected with a fan to induce a downdraft through the perforated bottom and the ore charge (this box also acts as a dust catcher). Mounted above and near the fuel end is an ignition box fired with gas or fuel oil which serves to start the sintering process. The material sintered may range from the finest dust to particles ¼ inch in diameter; water (3 to 15 per cent by weight) is added to give the proper consistency. As the ore, once ignited, passes over the suction box, oxidation proceeds down through the mass and the cake is finally discharged at the other end of the machine.

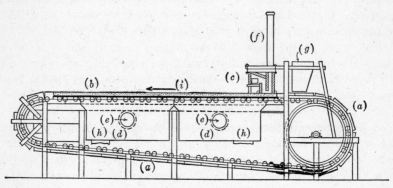

FIG. 7. Dwight-Lloyd Roaster.

(a) Pallets
(b) Ore
(c) Ignition furnace
(d) Wind box
(e) Suction pipe

(f) Stack
(g) Feed hopper
(h) Clean-out doors
(i) Direction of travel

The recent rapid increase in the use of sintering has been the cause of two great advances in metallurgical processes: flotation and the treatment of flue dust. It has become standard practice to treat iron blast furnace flue dust so that it can be recharged into the furnace. Low-grade magnetite iron deposits can be beneficiated by grinding and magnetic separation, and, when sintered, made into ideal material for blast furnace use.

49. The Sintering Process. Usually a thin layer of fine ore together with a small percentage of coal or other fuel, moistened with water, is spread on the sintering machine. The fuel in the surface layer of the charge is ignited, and the air is drawn down through the bed so that combustion, started at the surface, is carried progressively downward through the bed in a narrow high-temperature zone until this zone has progressed to the bottom of the bed, at which time the cinder cake is automatically discharged. The burning of the fuel develops sufficient heat to effect fusion of most of the mineral particles and cause partial reduction and recombination of the iron oxide so that the mass crystallizes into new forms. The period of intense heat for any part of the charge is extremely brief on account of the cold-air current. The air is also responsible for the development of the porosity so characteristic of sintered products. Only a few minutes are required to sinter a 4-inch bed, and any given particle in that bed is subjected to the maximum heat for a comparatively short time. The sintered product is ideal material for charging into a blast furnace because it is cellular and porous, but strong.

The continuous sintering process is very flexible by reason of instant control of the complete cycle of operation, such as:

1. Proportioning the constituents of the charge.
2. Regulation of proper moisture.
3. Proper depth of bedding on the grates.
4. Current intensity and distribution of ignition.
5. Constant observation and means of adjustment.
6. Control of the time element of sintering zones.
7. Automatic synchronism of proportions and volume of feed to the demands of the sintering machine.

50. Results of Sintering. A few years ago blast furnace operators maintained that only a limited amount of sintered iron ore could be used to advantage in blast furnaces and that when the furnace burden was increased much above 30 per cent trouble developed. Recent blast furnace operations have been reported in which sinter made up the entire ore charged, under which conditions the results have been exceedingly favorable; and with a sinter it was possible practically to double the rated capacity of the furnace and materially reduce the coke consumption. It is noteworthy, however, that results recently obtained by screening crude ore to a definite size for blast furnace charging have also shown radical improvements in capacity and coke consumption, indicating that it is the porosity of the charge that is of most importance in blast furnace operation rather than the chemical state in which the iron exists.

It has been proved that the percentage of iron existing as a silicate in sinter is notably greater than that in raw ore; and, since these silicates are difficult to reduce, it appears that the increased porosity of the charge, when using sinter, is of such value to the blast furnace that the increase in the percentage of the iron silicate minerals in the sinter is far overshadowed by this increase in porosity. Efforts are being made in sintering to cut down the amount of iron combined as silicates, and, although no good method has been determined by which this regulation can be carried on, the results give promise.

FUEL

51. General. It takes steel to keep the wheels of industry turning and to make the sinews of defense, but it takes fuel to make steel.* In certain favored districts, natural gas is beginning to be used in some metallurgical industries, but not in the production of iron and steel. The fuel used by the steel industry is coal. Some of this coal will be burned directly, as for example under boilers or in gas producers, but by far the greatest proportion of it will be converted into coke, which is required as a fuel and reducing agent for blast furnaces. Tar and fuel oil are used in open-hearth furnaces. This chapter is confined to a consideration of coke, which may be defined as the porous residue that remains after selected bituminous coals have been subjected to heat, out of contact with the air, a process now known as carbonization. As the coal is heated, it becomes plastic, at 350 to 475°C., forming a fused mass from which volatile matter is given off, slowly at first, more rapidly up to 950°C.

Low-temperature carbonization (750-800°C.), although not used for producing metallurgical fuel, is assuming an important place in the preparation of other grades of coke. This method gives (1) a weaker coke; (2) more condensables owing to absence of cracking; (3) a smaller yield of gas; and (4) a gas with higher heating value.

The physical properties of the coke produced, which are so important in blast furnace operation, as well as its composition, depend upon the size and type of oven, the time and temperature at which carbonization is carried out, and the type of coal used.

52. Coking Coals. Unfortunately, not all coals respond equally well to the coking process, nor has any method been developed by which

* Bituminous coal consumption in the United States in 1941 was distributed as follows:

	Thousands of Net Tons	Per Cent Total
Electric power utilities	61,943	12.6
By-product coke ovens	83,072	16.9
Beehive coke ovens	10,013	2.0
Steel and rolling mills	10,902	2.1
Coal-gas retorts	1,659	0.3
Cement mills	6,787	1.4
Other industries	120,720	24.4
Railroads (Class I)	97,384	19.9
Total industrial	392,480	
Retail dealer deliveries	96,160	19.5
Other known consumption:		
At mines	3,598	0.7
Bunker fuel	1,099	0.2
All consumption	493,337	100.0

the coking properties of a coal can be determined from its analysis. In a general way, the following properties should be taken into account when selecting coals which are to be used in the manufacture of metallurgical coke:

1. Rank.
2. Analysis.
   A. Moisture.
   B. Volatile matter.
   C. Ash and its fusion temperature.
   D. Sulfur.
   E. Phosphorus.
3. Carbonizing properties.
4. Storage and weathering.
5. Availability.

Coke plants, as a general rule, can use coal of almost any size from the smallest slack (preferred, to eliminate crushing) to lump. Of course this benefits both the coke plant and the coal producer, since the plant can take the sizes with the best analysis and the producer thus has an outlet for coal that may be difficult to move for other uses because of its unsuitability as a solid fuel.

Plants receiving Lake coal are obliged to store coal for five or six months at least; some may be in storage for nine months or more. In unusual cases, for emergencies, coal is stored in a permanent pile that may not be disturbed for ten to twenty years. The ability of the coal to withstand this sort of exposure must be considered.

The amount of volatile matter in a coal is of great importance. On the whole, high-volatile coals, when stored for normal periods, do not suffer greatly so far as the coking properties are concerned, whereas low-volatile coals frequently do give trouble through heating and deterioration during storage. Obviously, high-volatile coals with volatile matter running up to 38 per cent are preferred at gas plants because of their high gas yields. The lower-volatile coals in the high-volatile classification are preferred for producing furnace coke because they yield a coke with small cells, uniform texture, and high gravity. The low-volatile coals expand under normal operating conditions; the high-volatile coals contract; consequently the two are usually blended to neutralize these effects.

A minimum moisture in the coal is generally desired for a number of reasons. First, moisture in the coal is weighed and paid for as coal;

second, increased moisture* has the advantage of increasing shrinkage in the oven but decreasing the loss by dust and wind in handling.

Ash in coking coals is extremely important because it acts as a diluent for the coke plant operator; he pays for it at the delivered price of coal, and of course it decreases the yields of gas and by-products as well as the value of the coke. Some believe that ash up to 10 per cent or more, when present in finely divided form, may have favorable effects on the coking characteristics of certain coals. Ash in the form of free impurities such as slate, about 10 mesh in size, may cause fractures in the coke and thus decrease both size and strength. Ash content as well as ash fusion temperature has an important bearing on clinkering tendencies when coke is to be used as a domestic fuel and makes consequent trouble in operation.

High sulfur content in coal for coking is undesirable because the sulfur displaces coal, makes coke less desirable or even unsuitable for certain uses (particularly blast furnace and cupola operation), and increases gas purification costs. If sufficiently high, it may even produce objectionable amounts of organic sulfur in the gas, not removed by ordinary gas purification equipment.

At present, coals are selected for their coking properties by actual plant trial, for no entirely suitable laboratory tests have been developed. The physical characteristics of coke that influence the selection of a coal include apparent gravity, porosity, size, shatter, tumbler test, hardness, cell structure, and shape of coke pieces.

53. Methods of Manufacturing Metallurgical Coke. There are two methods for the manufacture of metallurgical coke, known as the beehive and the by-product, or retort process. In the former, air is admitted to a coking chamber, shown in Figure 8, for the purpose of burning therein all the volatile products of the coal in order to regenerate heat for the distillation process. Incidentally, this is a waste because all the gas is lost and some of the fixed carbon of the coal is also consumed. In the second method the coking chambers are airtight, and the necessary heat for distillation is supplied from external combustion of a part (usually about one-half) of the volatile products of the coal. In some cases excess blast furnace gas has been utilized. The beehive process was the leading method for the manufacture of coke up to 1918, but it has since been almost completely replaced by the by-product process. As a matter of fact, practically none of the old ovens were in operation up to the beginning of 1941.

* Increased moisture may also seriously affect coke structure and also damage the oven walls.

TABLE 18
Growth of By-product Coke Industry*

Year	By-product Production, Tons	Beehive Production, Tons	Total Production, Tons	Per Cent Total from By-product	Number of Ovens	
					By-product	Beehive
1892		12,010,829	12,010,829			42,002
1895	18,521	13,315,193	13,333,714	0.1	72	45,493
1910	7,138,734	34,570,076	41,708,810	17.1	4,078	100,362
1920	30,833,951	20,511,092	51,345,043	60.0	10,881	75,298
1925	39,912,159	11,354,784	51,266,943	77.9	11,290	57,587
1929	53,411,826	6,472,019	59,883,845	89.2	12,649	30,082
1932	21,136,800	651,900	21,788,700	97.0	13,053	19,440
1940	53,859,585	2,888,000	56,747,585	95.1	†	†
...	....	....	....	....	....	....

* *Minerals Yearbook.*
† Not available. In 1939, 12,724 by-product, 10,816 beehive.

On January 1, 1940, there were 15,150 beehive ovens in existence, 9148 operating, with 800 more to be added by February 15. These had a capacity of about 9 million tons of coke, as contrasted to a production of 6,472,000 in 1929. In 1920, the last year of great beehive production, the output was 20,511,000 tons. To take care of the great war emergency of 1942, new by-product ovens, to add about 1.5 million tons, are being built so that by the end of 1942 it is hoped by-product production will be 56 million tons and beehive 9 million. The growth of the by-product industry is shown in Table 18.

Beehive coke is generally brittle and degrades more easily on handling, which latter property is particularly undesirable in blast furnace operation. The by-product process obviously has better control. There is also a difference in the appearance of the coke, due mainly to the difference in coking temperature of the two processes, that of the by-product being considerably lower than the beehive. In general, beehive coke is silvery gray, whereas by-product coke is of a much darker color.

54. Operation of a Beehive Oven. The ovens are charged as soon as practicable after drawing the finished coke so that the stored-up heat from the previous charge will be sufficient to start the coking process. With the oven in readiness for charging, the door is partially bricked up and the charge (6 tons for a 48-hour cycle) dropped through the opening in the roof of the oven, forming a cone-shaped pile on the bottom. This is then leveled off by means of a scraper operated through the door, in order that the coal may lie in a bed of uniform depth and thus secure uniformity in the coking operation. The actual coking process begins very soon after leveling is completed because the ovens retain enough heat to start the distillation of the volatile matter. As more and more heat is conducted through the walls from the surrounding earth and brick, the temperature of the interior of the oven reaches the kindling point for these volatile gases. These ignite and in burning quietly, in the crown of the oven,

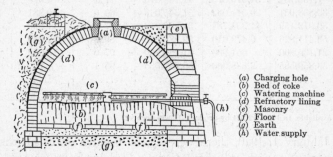

(a) Charging hole
(b) Bed of coke
(c) Watering machine
(d) Refractory lining
(e) Masonry
(f) Floor
(g) Earth
(h) Water supply

FIG. 8. Beehive Coke Oven. (*Courtesy of Carnegie-Illinois Steel Corp.*)

supply heat to continue the process. Coking proceeds from the top of the coal downwards so that the coking time depends mainly on the depth of coal. The coking time for blast furnace coke is usually 48 hours. At the end of the coking period, the brickwork of the door is torn down, the coke is cooled with water, as indicated in Figure 8, and drawn out either by hand or machine; a six-ton charge will yield about four tons of screened coke.

55. Construction of By-product Ovens. The Koppers type of oven, shown in Figures 9 and 10, has a coking chamber 37 feet long, 9 feet 10 inches high, and a width varying from 17 inches at the pusher end to 19½ inches at the discharge end (to facilitate discharging of the coke), with a total volume of about 500 cubic feet. Four charging holes are provided in the top for admitting the charge, and another opening at one end of the oven serves as an outlet for the gases. All parts of the ovens are constructed of the best grade of silica brick. The oven is of the vertical flue type with individual regenerative chambers. It is heated by means of thirty vertical flues which rise from the bottom of the chamber, where they are connected to the regenerative chambers and to the gas mains, to a large horizontal cross-

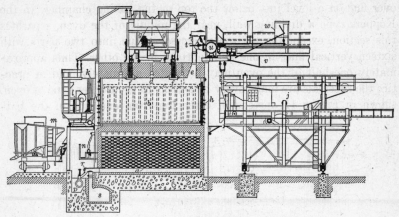

FIG. 9. Koppers Coke Oven (cross section).

a.	Checker chamber	l.	Door lifter
b.	Combustion chamber	m.	Coke watering car
c.	Horizontal flue	n.	Coke oven gas main
d.	Crossover flue	p.	Producer gas main
e.	Gas duct for coke oven gas	r.	Air valve
f.	Coal inlet	s.	Stack flue
g.	Hoppers of larry car	t.	Offtake
h.	Oven doors	u.	Collecting main
j.	Door lifting and pushing machine	v.	Crossover main
k.	Coke guide	w.	Gas pressure regulator

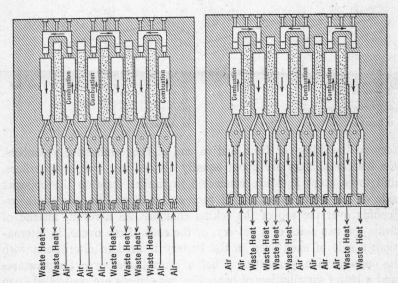

FIG. 10. Flow of Gas and Air. (*Courtesy of Carnegie-Illinois Steel Corp.*)

over flue on a level just below the top of the coking chamber. In the
Koppers type a dividing wall, near the middle of the oven, separates
this section, except the horizontal crossover flue, into two parts with
sixteen vertical flues in one and fourteen in the other. Thus approximately one-half of the oven may be heated alternately, and in practice the reversals are made every half hour. In the Becker type of oven,
shown in Figure 11, instead of extending from one side of the bat-

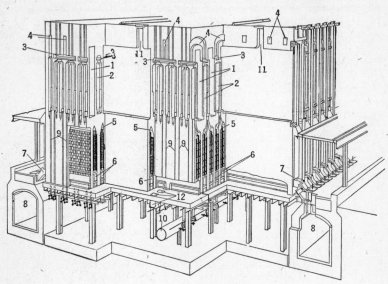

FIG. 11. Becker Coke Oven (perspective view).

1. Oven chamber	7. Gas and air connections to waste gas flue
2. Vertical flue	8. Waste gas flue
3. Horizontal flues	9. Ducts for coke oven gas
4. Crossover flues	10. Oven gas main
5. Regenerators	11. Charging holes
6. Sole flues	12. Air ports

tery to the other, or from end to end of the combustion chambers,
the horizontal flues are about equally divided into two or four flues,
and these short flues are connected to similar flues on the opposite
side of the oven by means of four or six short crossover flues extending over the top of the coking chamber. As a result, instead of
firing the two sides of a battery, or the ends of the ovens, in alternation, a side of each oven in the battery is fired in alternation with
its opposite side, permitting a better control over oven temperatures
and a better distribution of heat. The gas orifices are controlled from
below the oven, permitting easier adjustment than on the old-style
oven where they were controlled through holes in the top of the oven.

Two large underground flues, one on each side, extending along, in front of, and parallel to the battery, and connected to the checker chambers by means of cast-iron goosenecks, furnish means for the escape of the products of combustion through the battery chimney or stack. Air for combustion is admitted to the checker chamber through individual openings into each of the fourteen or sixteen vertical flues on the side of the oven where combustion is to occur. Likewise the gas for combustion, which is conducted from the gas main into a fire-brick gas duct, located below the vertical flues, is admitted through individual firebrick nozzles to each of the vertical flues at a point about ten inches below the air opening. Thus the gas and air meet in the flue, burn, and the hot waste gases are carried over to the opposite side of the battery by the horizontal flues, then down the vertical flues through the checker work, out through the gooseneck and into the large flues that lead to the stack. Control of the gas to each flue is effected by means of removable gas nozzles, or orifices, in each gas port which may be changed when desired.

56. Operation of the Becker Oven. The crushed and sized coal, taken from the storage bunkers, is charged into the ovens by means of larry cars that travel lengthwise of the batteries on top of the oven. Each car (usually divided into five bins) holds a single oven charge and is so constructed that the volume of the coal can be accurately measured. From the car, through large funnels, the charge (up to 21 net tons of coal) is dropped into the oven through the charging doors. Previously, the doors of the oven have been set in place and sealed with a mixture of loam, clay, and coke dust; but recently a new "self-sealing" door, not requiring luting, has been developed. A reciprocating leveling bar, carried on the pushing machine, is then inserted through a small opening at the top of the oven, on the narrower end (called the pusher side of the oven), and the coal leveled to a uniform depth, usually to within about twelve inches of the top. Finally all openings to the oven are closed, sealed, the standpipe valve opened to the collector main, and the coking process, which lasts for a period of 19 hours, begins.

The heat for coking is supplied from the heating chambers by conduction through the walls of the oven, coking proceeding from both sides of the oven toward the middle. Coking can be likened to a fusion process in which, as fusion progresses inward from the wall, gases are evolved and in their evolution leave the freezing mass in a porous state. Naturally there is some shrinkage, as the volatile matter is given off, so that finally, when these fusion zones meet in the center of the furnace, there is a marked line of cleavage, vertically, down the center of the whole charge. This gives the coke a sharp blocklike structure that distinguishes it from beehive coke, which has a long columnar one. At the end of the coking period the connection between the offtake and the collecting main is closed, the doors of the oven are removed by mechanical devices, and the coke is pushed out of the oven, from the narrower end, by means of a ram mounted upon the pusher car. The coke falls into a side-dump quenching car, is carried therein to a quenching or watering house, where it is cooled by a measured amount of water, and then discharged onto an inclined wharf or bin, where it is allowed to become dry and sufficiently cooled for subsequent conveying, crushing, and sizing into various marketable grades.* From a 21-ton charge of coal, with a 19-hour coking period, 14.5 tons of blast furnace coke will usually be obtained. The amounts of other constituents obtained are shown in Table 19.

TABLE 19

YIELDS FROM ONE NET TON OF COAL (2000 POUNDS)*

Gas	11,000 cubic feet
Coke (total)	1,400 pounds
Ammonium sulfate	25 pounds
Tar	10 gallons
Light oil	3.5 gallons
Calorific value of gas	550 B.t.u.

* Private communication.

57. Dry Quenching. One plant has been built in this country using the Sulzer or dry-quenching process,† but on the whole this system has not proved popular because of its initial high cost, higher maintenance cost, increased breakage of coke, and tendency to excessive dustiness. Coke, when discharged from the oven at a temperature of 1000°C., contains about 480 B.t.u. per pound of coke. This would be equivalent to 1000 pounds of low-pressure steam per ton of coke, or at 25 cents per thousand, if utilized, a saving of $11,000,000 for

* Foundry—over 2½ inches.
Furnace—over ¾ inch.
Domestic—½ to ¾ inch.
Breeze—under ½ inch.

Furnace and foundry grades are not made simultaneously. A 19-hour cycle is too short and flue temperatures too high to produce firm structure required in foundry coke. The same coals also may not be used to produce both grades.

† "Dry Quenched Coke for Blast Furnace," J. F. Miller, *The Iron Age,* August 24, 1933.

the country as a whole. In this system the red-hot coke is transferred to a sealed storage compartment through which is circulated an inert gas (air, the original oxygen being consumed). This gas as it leaves the oven at a temperature of about 900°C. passes over superheater tubes and then through a waste heat boiler, used for raising steam for the plant. The advantages of this system are said to be:

1. The generation of about 1000 pounds of steam per ton of coke quenched.
2. An improvement in the physical properties of the coke, particularly size and strength.
3. Production of a coke practically devoid of moisture, in contrast to a common content of 5 per cent.
4. Elimination of water handling and cooling.
5. A reduction in labor costs and conveyor operation.

The disadvantages are, first, the greater cost as compared to the conventional water-quenching system; and, second, the many troubles which have developed in the plants already erected. The fact that comparatively few of these have been built leads one to believe that further development work is necessary.

58. Separation of the By-products. Coal is a very complex substance and, when heated, may be made to yield a very large number of substances. These may be roughly divided into three classes, based on their state at ordinary temperatures:[19]

1. The fixed gases—principally hydrogen; methane, CH_4; carbon monoxide, CO; ethylene, C_2H_4; carbon dioxide, CO_2; ethane, C_2H_6; nitrogen, N_2; hydrogen sulfide, H_2S; propylene, C_3H_6; butylene, C_4H_8; acetylene, C_2H_2; butane, C_4H_{10}; oxygen, O_2; and ammonia, NH_3.
2. The substances which are liquid at ordinary temperatures—benzene, C_6H_6; toluene, $C_6H_5CH_3$; xylene, $C_6H_4(CH_3)_2$; carbon disulfide, CS_2; conglomerate tars and aqueous vapors.
3. The solids—naphthalene, $C_{10}H_8$; phenol or carbolic acid, C_6H_5OH; anthracene, C_4H_{10}; and heavy pitch.

These substances are treated in the coke oven by-product plant.

59. Advantages of the By-product Process. Except for a much greater initial cost, the by-product installation has many advantages over the beehive method of producing coke. These advantages are:

1. Many coals not suitable for coking in beehive ovens are made available for by-product ovens by blending with other coals.
2. Coking in a by-product oven permits the full recovery and use of the by-products and gases (see Table 19).

3. At the present time, the cost* of making by-product coke at the iron and steel works compares favorably with the cost of making beehive coke at the mines and transporting the coke to the blast furnace.

4. The by-product process gives better control over the conditions of carbonization with effects listed below:

    a. Rapid heating of the coal decreases the coke yield and increases the tar yield.

    b. The rate of heating through the preplastic range affects the yield as well as the composition of the gas.

    c. Slow heating through the plastic range increases the hardness of the coke, decreases the amount of liquid, has no effect on the weight of the gases, but increases the percentage of hydrogen and decreases the percentage of methane and ethane in the gas.

    d. This control is limited to 3 to 5 per cent variation in the coke and to 3 per cent in the liquids.

60. Value. Coke is a metallurgical fuel; consequently, the properties which determine its value are:

    1. Size.
    2. Hardness.
    3. Strength.
    4. Porosity.
    5. Absence of volatile or smoke-producing properties.
    6. Presence of a minimum of fusing and coking properties.
    7. High percentage of fixed carbon.
    8. Low content of sulfur.
    9. Cleanliness.

Coke for the modern blast furnace must be sufficiently firm and strong to resist shattering in handling, crushing through the pressure exerted by the heavy burdens, and attrition of the particles on one another. It should be free from dust and fines and not so large that it unduly retards combustion. It should be as porous† as possible in order that sufficient surface may be presented to the oxygen of the blast for rapid combustion. It should contain not over 2 per cent volatile matter and 85 to 90 per cent fixed carbon. The phosphorus may vary from 0.018 to 0.040 per cent for making Bessemer iron and slightly higher for basic iron. Sulfur varies from 0.6 to 1.5 per cent

---

* By-product is appreciably lower in cost than beehive because of flexibility and ease of adjustment to various market conditions. Beehive, in recent years, operates *only* in a strong coke market, even in areas close to mines and mills. One big factor in by-product coke production is the better size characteristics of the coke.

† This is disputed by certain operators who believe that a coke's combustibility can easily be increased by leaving a little volatile matter in the coke

but should be as low as possible (it usually is about 1 per cent) because the coke is the chief source of sulfur in the pig iron produced by the furnace. Moisture should not exceed 3 per cent and ash 10 per cent.

Roy P. Hudson,* as shown in Table 20, has graphically demonstrated the cost of an increase in the amount of ash in metallurgical

TABLE 20

COMPARISON OF PIG IRON COSTS*

Ash in Coal, Per Cent	Ash in Coke, Per Cent	Fixed Carbon in Coke, Per Cent	Coke per Ton of Pig Iron, Lb.	Tons of Pig Iron in 24 Hr.
6.00	8.70	89.80	1800	365.0
7.00	10.15	88.35	1860	353.2

COKE WITH 8.70 PER CENT ASH

Ore mixture, 4144 lb. or 1.85 tons at $5.50	$10.17
Coke, 1800 lb. or 0.90 ton at $6.50	5.85
Limestone, 1000 lb. or 0.50 ton at $1.50	0.75
Labor, $365 a day on 365 tons	1.00
Supplies and service, $250 a day	0.68
Overhead, $200 a day	0.55
Reserve for relining and depreciation	1.00
Total	$20.00

COKE WITH 10.15 PER CENT ASH

Ore mixture, 4144 lb. or 1.85 tons at $5.50	$10.17
Coke, 1860 lb. or 0.93 ton at $6.50	6.05
Limestone, 1034 lb. or 0.517 ton at $1.50	0.77
Labor, $365 a day for 353.2 tons	1.03
Supplies and service, $250 a day	0.71
Overhead, $200 a day	0.57
Reserve for relining and depreciation	1.00
Total cost with 10.15 per cent ash	$20.30
Total cost with 8.70 per cent ash	20.00

* R. P. Hudson, "Ash Is Best Measure of Blast Furnace Coke," *The Iron Age*, Feb. 11, 1932.

coke, as far as blast furnace operation is concerned. Ash in coke is composed of the ash inherent in the coal as well as the extraneous ash contaminating it. Evidently an increase of 1 per cent ash in the coal mixture causes an increase in the unit cost of coke, limestone,

* R. P. Hudson, "Ash Is Best Measure of Blast Furnace Coke," *The Iron Age*, Feb. 11, 1932.

labor, supplies, services, and overhead of 30 cents per ton. In other words, to achieve the same pig iron cost when using the higher ash coke its cost would have to be 30 cents less, or $5.75 per ton. The amount of fuel required per ton of iron varies with the available carbon of the fuel, and this in turn depends upon the ash content. Although the fuel required per ton of iron increases, the fuel burned per unit of time in a furnace remains constant; consequently there must be a corresponding reduction in output. In the case cited this amounts to 11.8 tons of pig iron per day, brought about solely by the increased ash. Each addition of fuel requires more limestone to flux its ash. Each pound of slag thus formed requires approximately 0.25 pound of carbon to melt it, or about 30 pounds of coke.

61. Problem 1. Calculate the equilibrium constant for the reaction $CO_2 + C \rightarrow 2CO$ at $1800°K$.*

(a) $2C \ (graph) + O_2(g) \rightarrow 2CO(g)$; $\Delta F° = -47,280 - 44.18T$
(b) $C \ (graph) + O_2(g) \rightarrow CO_2(g)$; $\Delta F° = -90,140 - 1.93T$

Combining (a) and (b), we have

$$C \ (graph) + CO_2(g) \rightarrow 2CO(g); \quad \Delta F° = +42,860 - 42.25T$$
$$\Delta F_{1800}° = 42,860 - (42.25 \times 1800)$$
$$= -33,240$$
$$= -RT \ln K_p$$

At $1800°K$. $K_p = \dfrac{(P_{CO})^2}{P_{CO_2}}$

$$= 1 \times 10^4$$

* In the treatment of these data this nomenclature has been followed:

c = macrocrystalline state.
l = liquid state.
g = gaseous state.
gl = glass state.
$amorp$ = amorphous state.
aq = aqueous solution.
K = equilibrium constant.
ΔH = change in heat content.
ΔS = entropy change of the reaction.
ΔF = the standard free energy change.
T = absolute temperature.
C_p = specific heat at constant pressure.
R = gas constant.
P = vapor pressure.
$graph$ = graphite

In the equations given in the text a negative sign for ΔH indicates that the system loses heat and no sign (or a positive one) that it gains heat according to the general relationship $\Delta F_t = \Delta H - T\Delta S$.

FLUXES

62. General. On the whole, the iron ores of the world are distinctly acid, although Germany, France, and Africa yield ores where the percentage of CaO may rise as high as 15 or 20. The ores of our country, and particularly those of Lake Superior, are no exception to the general rule, for the lowest silica content ordinarily encountered is 4 per cent, the highest 40, with an average for the year 1940 of 8.0 per cent. As contrasted to that, the lime-magnesia content of Mesabi ores shows a minimum of 0.2 per cent, a maximum of 1.5, and an average for the year 1940 of about 0.4 per cent. Blast-furnace slags being of the order of sesquisilicates,* require 1.34 parts of lime for one part of silica. As a result, the production of one ton of pig iron under present Lake practice requires the use of about 1.7 tons of iron ore and 0.4 ton of limestone. Limestone being the universal flux used in this country, it will be the only one discussed in this textbook. It is also commonly used for basic open-hearth and electric furnaces.

63. Smelting and the Functions of the Flux. Smelting is any metallurgical operation in which metal is separated, in a state of fusion, from the impurities with which it may be chemically or physically combined or mixed in the ore, the worthless constituents of the ore being combined in a product known as a "slag." Originally, the term slag was derived from a word meaning the "dross from metal," and Webster defines it as "the earthy material separated, in a more or less completely fused or vitrified condition, during the reduction of a metal from its ore." Slags produced in the iron blast furnace frequently are referred to as "cinder." Many of the impurities may be of a very refractory nature, and if they were to remain unfused would certainly retard the separation of the metal, perhaps completely block the furnace, and interfere in various other ways with the smelting. In order to render such substances more easily fusible, other constituents are added, and these are known as fluxes. A second function of a flux is to absorb certain impurities, notably sulfur.

* The average blast-furnace slag may be taken as:

	Per Cent	
CaO	40.2	} 45.7
MgO	5.5	
SiO_2	35.3	} 48.3
Al_2O_3	13.0	
CaS	3.9	
Misc.	2.1	

LIMESTONE

64. General. Limestone in a narrow sense is applied to rocks consisting essentially of calcite ($CaCO_3$). Commercially, however, it includes rocks in which magnesium carbonate is present in varying amounts. The term "dolomite" is applied to rocks consisting essentially of the double carbonate of lime and magnesia ($CaCO_3 \cdot MgCO_3$). Whenever smaller percentages of magnesium are present, the rocks may be termed "dolomitic limestone" or "magnesium limestone."

Special names are applied to limestones that differ in origin, texture, or composition from the ordinary type. Marl is a term applied to a loose, earthy form of calcium carbonate usually formed in lake basins. Calcareous tufa and travertine are more or less compact limestones, deposited from solutions. Oölitic limestone is made up of small, rounded grains of calcium carbonate, having a concentrically laminated structure. A siliceous or cherty limestone is one containing considerable silica; an argillaceous limestone, one containing clay or shale; and a ferruginous limestone, one containing small percentages of iron oxide.

Limestones also vary greatly in such physical properties as hardness, color, weight, porosity, and texture, all of which affect their desirability as a metallurgical flux. Porous limestone may weigh as little as 110 pounds per cubic foot, whereas the more compact varieties, which are preferred for furnace use, may weigh 150 to 185 pounds.

It is fortunate that limestone deposits are widely distributed in the United States, for we normally use 30 million tons of limestone per year as a metallurgical flux, most of this in the iron and steel industry. Naturally, the deposits of metallurgical limestone have been developed most widely near the centers of the great smelting industry; thus, the Ohio and Pennsylvania quarries supply enormous quantities of limestone for the smelting districts lying in and about Ashtabula, Youngstown, and Pittsburgh; Alabama quarries supply the Birmingham district; and Chicago, Cleveland, and Buffalo draw theirs from the quarries near Calcite and Rogers City, Michigan.

65. Effects of Impurities in Limestone. The amount of flux required will vary with the amount and nature of the impurities in the ore as well as in the stone itself. The foreign elements in fluxing limestone are usually the same as those in the ore, namely, silica and alumina. It should be emphasized that impurities in the limestone are doubly detrimental because (1) their presence reduces the percentage of lime and magnesia in the stone and (2) they require a certain share of the lime and magnesia for fluxing purposes (the flux must neutralize its own impurities as well as those of the ore).

"Available" carbonate is a term applied to the percentage of calcium and magnesium carbonates available for fluxing the ore after a sufficient percentage has been deducted to neutralize the impurities in the stone itself. In the average blast furnace slag, the ratio of silica plus alumina to lime plus magnesia is about one to one. Consequently, for every pound of silica and alumina present, one pound of lime is required. A pound of lime is derived from 1.785 pounds of limestone; hence, if there are 4 pounds of silica plus alumina in each 100 pounds of stone, not only does the stone lose this 4 pounds of impurities but also 4 x 1.785 of pure limestone which is required to flux the impurities. That is, a total of 11.14 pounds is lost; and the available carbonate in each 100 pounds of stone is only 88.86 pounds.

Another disadvantage in using impure stone is the formation of additional slag which serves to increase the fuel consumption. Extra slag requires extra coke. There is, however, a difference of opinion as to how much extra coke is needed, because other conditions may affect the amount of coke required for each additional pound of slag formed (see Articles 47 and 60).

A third source of loss due to the impurities in the limestone is reduced furnace output. This for a given ore is, in general, inversely proportional to coke consumption per unit of slag; and, as the extra slag requires extra coke, furnace production may be cut down, although the exact amount is governed somewhat by the amount of air blown into the furnace. If a furnace were blown a little faster to compensate for an increase in fuel consumption due to the use of low-grade stone, the furnace output might not suffer any reduction, but there would be a material increase in the flue dust produced and probably in furnace upkeep.

Other impurities in the limestone are sulfur and phosphorus, but usually they are present in such small amounts as to be virtually negligible. A sulfur content of less than 0.1 per cent does no harm, and it is unusual to find more than this amount in commercial limestone. Phosphorus is usually harmful only where the flux is used in the manufacture of Bessemer iron. For this purpose the phosphorus content should be as low as possible and not exceed 0.01 per cent, but for other grades of iron the phosphorus content may reach 0.1 per cent without harmful results. However, a content as high as this is exceedingly rare.

66. Effect of Magnesia. The effect of magnesia in limestone has not been definitely settled. Although some blast-furnace men are opposed to its use, others use it successfully; as a matter of fact, dolomite is widely used as a blast furnace flux in England. If it is assumed that all the magnesia unites with silica to form $MgSiO_3$ and all the lime unites with silica to form $CaSiO_3$, it would appear that magnesia is a better fluxing agent because 1 pound of magnesia will flux 1.51 pounds of silica as against 1.08 pounds for lime. This is not an entirely safe assumption, however, for undoubtedly other compounds are formed, such as dicalcium and tricalcium silicates as well as calcium aluminates.

There also seems to be some difference of opinion as to the effect of magnesia on the viscosity of slags. It has been assumed that magnesia tends to make slags ropy and viscous, but some recent work tends to indicate that over narrow ranges, in the lower brackets, magnesia actually decreases the viscosity of these slags.

Until recently magnesia has been generally regarded as less efficient than lime as a sulfur remover, but here again recent research tends to indicate otherwise (see Article 149).

67. Factors Governing the Use of Impure Limestone. The cost of the stone delivered at the blast furnace commonly has a very direct bearing on the quality of the stone used, because an inferior stone may be used if the price is low enough. As a result, the question of quality is so intimately related to cost that the problem of purity of blast furnace flux becomes quite a complex one. To clarify this point, it may be timely to make a distinction between the impurities, because in general they fall into two classes. Some, like sulfur and phosphorus, are detrimental to the quality of the pig iron produced; hence, the use of stone containing excessive quantities of these impurities could not be justified no matter how low the price might be. Other, and more common, impurities, like silica and alumina, are not regarded as detrimental to the iron, their chief disadvantage being the requirement of additional limestone and coke to convert them into slag. Let us suppose that both a pure stone and an impure stone are available and that the impurities are of the silica-alumina type. If the price of the impure stone is low enough to overcome these disadvantages, the impure one may be used in preference to the pure. For example, at one furnace which has come under the observation of the author, limestone running as high as 5 per cent silica is used extensively in preference to low-silica stone which must be transported a considerable distance by rail.

It should be evident from the above considerations that no definite rules can be laid down regarding the purity of a stone that may be used for flux. Every fluxing condition is a problem in itself and must be solved as such. A stone that might be condemned in one locality might be quite acceptable in another where conditions are different. Usually the use of an impure stone can be justified only because it has the advantage of close proximity to the furnace, thus eliminating the heavy expense of transportation.

68. Size of Limestone. Fluxing stone is used in a great variety of sizes with a common range in size from 4.5 inches down to 0.5 inch, although larger sizes are often employed. At some furnaces, the crusher run of limestone is used without screening, but usually the fines below 0.5 inch are screened out because they tend to obstruct the passages in the furnace and frequently contain more impurities than the raw stone (the sand and clay segregate in the fines). However, it is probable that the finer sizes are less detrimental than the practice seems to indicate. In general it may be said that uniform sizing improves the working of the furnace.

69. Rate of Liquefaction. Limestones vary greatly in the rate at which the lumps are assimilated by, and become liquefied in, the slag. Fragments of most well-consolidated limestones retain their original shape and are more or less solid after complete calcination.

It is a peculiarity of limestone, not yet adequately explained, that they vary greatly in the rate at which they dissolve or melt in the slag. Just as there is no complete correlation between the chemical composition of a coal and its coking properties, there is none between the behavior of a limestone in a blast furnace or open hearth and its chemical composition. For example, operators have learned that some limestones are readily absorbed by an open-hearth slag whereas others appear to be coated over with some refractory substance (see Article 320) and retain their original shape for a long time, even in the liquid slag. It would appear that a loosely consolidated limestone which would completely disintegrate during the process of calcination in the furnace would have the advantage of very rapid assimilation in the slag because of the larger surface exposed, but such a stone would be likely to produce excessive fines during the process of quarrying, crushing, and handling.

70. Problem 2. Calculate the equilibrium constant for the reaction $CaCO_3(c)$ $\rightarrow CaO(c) + CO_2(g)$ at 1800°K.

$$\Delta H_{291°K.} = [-151,700 + (-94,000)] - (-289,500) = +43,400 \text{ cal.}$$

At the higher temperature:

$$\Delta H_T = \Delta H_{291K} + \int_{291}^{T} (C_p dT)_{\text{products}} - \int_{291}^{T} (C_p dT)_{\text{reactants}}$$

$$C_p \text{ of } CaCO_3(c) = 19.68 + 11.89 \times 10^{-3}T - 3.076 \times 10^5 T^{-2}$$
$$C_p \text{ of } CaO(c) \quad = 10.00 + 4.84 \times 10^{-3}T - 1.080 \times 10^5 T^{-2}$$
$$C_p \text{ of } CO_2(g) \quad = 7.70 + 5.30 \times 10^{-3}T - 0.83 \times 10^{-6}T^2$$

or

$$\Delta H_{1800} = 43,400 + \int_{291}^{1800} (-1.98 - 1.75 \times 10^{-3}T + 1.996 \times 10^5 T^{-2}$$
$$- 0.83 \times 10^{-6}T^2)dT = 33,850 \text{ cal.}$$

The entropies for this reaction are:

$$S \text{ of } CaCO_3(c) \text{ at } 298°K. = 22.2 \text{ cal./mole-deg.}$$
$$S \text{ of } CaO(c) \text{ at } 298°K. = 9.5 \text{ cal./mole-deg.}$$
$$S \text{ of } CO_2(g) \text{ at } 298°K. = 51.00 \text{ cal./mole-deg.}$$

Therefore

$$\Delta S \text{ at } 298°K. = S_{\text{products}} - S_{\text{reactants}}$$
$$= 38.4 \text{ cal.}$$

$$\Delta S \text{ from } 298° K. \text{ to } 1800°K. = \int_{298}^{1800} \frac{C_p dT}{T}$$

$$\Delta S \text{ for } CaCO_3(c) \text{ from } 298 \text{ to } 1800°K. = \int_{298}^{1800} \left(\frac{19.68}{T} + 11.89 \times 10^{-3} \right.$$
$$\left. - \frac{3.076 \times 10^5}{T^3} \right) dT = 53.2 \text{ cal.}$$

$$\text{for } CaO(c) = \int_{298}^{1800} \left(\frac{10.00}{T} + 4.84 \times 10^{-3} - \frac{1.080 \times 10^5}{T^3} \right) dT = 24.7 \text{ cal.}$$

$$\text{for } CO_2(g) = \int_{298}^{1800} \left(\frac{7.70}{T} + 5.30 \times 10^{-3} - 0.83 \times 10^{-6}T \right) dT = 20.5 \text{ cal.}$$

$$\Delta S \text{ for the reaction at } 1800°K. = 30.4 \text{ cal.}$$
$$\Delta F = \Delta H - T\Delta S$$
$$\Delta F_{1800°K.} = 33,850 - (1800 \times 30.4) = -20,950 \text{ cal.}$$
$$\Delta F° = -RT \ln K_p$$
$$K_p = 34.4$$

BIBLIOGRAPHY

1. BACON, R. F., and W. A. HAMOR, *American Petroleum Industry*. New York: McGraw-Hill Book Company, 1916. 2 vols.
2. BATEMAN, W. H., "Liquefied Petroleum Gas," Symposium on Industrial Fuels. American Society for Testing Materials, and Engineers Club of Philadelphia, 1936.
3. BERGIUS, FRIEDERICH, *The Transformation of Coal Into Oil by Means of Hydrogenation,* First International Conference on Bituminous Coal, Washington, D. C., Carnegie Institute of Technology, November, 1926.
4. Billingham Hydrogenation Plant, *Iron and Coal Trades Review, Vol. 131* (October, 1935); *Colliery Guardian, 151* (October, 1935).
5. BOWLES, O., "Utilization Problems of Metallurgical Limestone." American Institute of Mining and Metallurgical Engineers, Vol. 80, 1928.
6. BOWLES, O., and D. M. BANKS, "Lime," *Information Circular* 6884R, Bureau of Mines, 1941.
7. BOYLSTON, H. M., *An Introduction to the Metallurgy of Iron and Steel*. New York: John Wiley and Sons, 1936. 563 pp.
8. CAMPBELL, M. R., "Our Coal Supply; Its Quantity, Quality, and Distribution," First International Conference on Bituminous Coal. Washington, D. C.: Carnegie Institute of Technology, November, 1926.
9. CHANCE, T. M., "The Sand Flotation Process," Second International Conference on Bituminous Coal. Washington, D. C.: Carnegie Institute of Technology, 1928.
10. CLERF, F., "Iron Ores of France," *Mining and Metals,* December, 1936.
11. COUNSELMAN, T. B., "Developments in the Concentrating of Minnesota Iron Ores," American Institute of Mining and Metallurgical Engineers, *Technical Paper* 1395, 1941.
12. DASHIELL, P. T., and F. H. TREMBLY, JR., "Manufactured Gas," Symposium on Industrial Fuels. American Society for Testing Materials, and Engineers Club of Philadelphia, 1936.
13. DAVIS, E. W., "First Magnetic Roasting Plant in Lake Superior Region," American Institute of Mining and Metallurgical Engineers, *Technical Paper* 731, 1937.
14. EVANS, F. C., "Empirical Relations for Coals in the United States," Engineering Experiment Station, Cornell University, *Bulletin* 3, 1925.
15. FEISS, J. W., "Iron Ores of United States and Foreign Fields," *Blast Furnace and Steel Plant,* January, 1931.
16. FIELDNER, A. C., "The Classification of North American Coals," Second International Conference on Bituminous Coal. Washington, D. C.: Carnegie Institute of Technology, Vol. 1, 1928.
17. FIELDNER, A. C., and W. A. SELVIG, "Coal and Coke, Occurrence, Testing, and Utilization," Symposium on Industrial Fuels. American Society for Testing Materials, and Engineers Club of Philadelphia, 1936.
18. FORBES, W. A., "Technological Problems of the Steel Industry," American Iron and Steel Institute, *Transactions,* October, 1927.
19. FRANCIS, C. B., *The Making, Shaping, and Treating of Steel*. Pittsburgh: Carnegie-Illinois Steel Corporation, 1940. 1440 pp.

20. FURNAS, C. C., "Rate of Calcination of Limestone," *Industrial and Engineering Chemistry,* Vol. 23, No. 5, 1931.

21. GORDEN, K., "Development of Coal Hydrogenation by Imperial Chemical Industries," *Institute of Fuel,* November, 1935.

22. Hanna, M. A., and Company, *Analyses of Iron Ores.* Published annually.

23. HARPER, R. B., "American Gas Association, Proceedings," Symposium on Industrial Fuels. American Society for Testing Materials, and Engineers Club of Philadelphia, 1936.

24. HAYWARD, C. R., *An Outline of Metallurgical Practice.* New York: D. Van Nostrand Company, 1940. 612 pp.

25. HODGE, W. W., and R. NEWTON, "Composition and By-Product Values of Some West Virginia Coals," Engineering Experiment Station, West Virginia University, *Research Bulletin* 9, 1933.

26. HOLBROOK, W. F., and T. L. JOSEPH, "Relative Desulfurizing Powers of Blast Furnace Slags," American Institute of Mining and Metallurgical Engineers, Iron and Steel Division, *Transactions,* Vol. 120, 1936.

27. HUME, H. V., "Industrial Fuel Oils," Symposium on Industrial Fuels. American Society for Testing Materials, and Engineers Club of Philadelphia, 1936.

28. JANITZKY, E. J., "A Study of Basic Open Hearth Slag by Solidification Tests," American Iron and Steel Institute, *Transactions,* October, 1929.

29. JOSEPH, T. L., and E. P. BARRETT, "Resistance of Iron Ores to Decrepitation and Mechanical Work," American Institute of Mining and Metallurgical Engineers, *Technical Paper* 372, 1930.

30. Lake Superior Iron Ore Association, *Lake Superior Iron Ores.* Cleveland, Ohio, 1938. 364 pp.

31. LOWRY, H. H., "The Chemical Coal," Coal Research Laboratory, *Contribution* 10. Washington, D. C.: Carnegie Institute of Technology.

32. LOWRY, H. H., "Need for Coal Research," American Institute of Mining and Metallurgical Engineers, *Technical Paper* 682, 1936.

33. SELVIG, W. A., W. H. ODE, and A. C. FIELDNER, "Classification of Coals of the United States According to Fixed Carbon and B.t.u.," American Institute of Mining and Metallurgical Engineers, *Transactions,* Vol. 108, 1934.

34. STOUGHTON, B., *Metallurgy of Iron and Steel.* New York: McGraw-Hill Book Company, 1934. 519 pp.

35. STOUGHTON, B., and A. BUTTS, *Engineering Metallurgy.* New York: McGraw-Hill Book Company, 1930. 441 pp.

36. TAIT, G. M. S., "The Choice of a Coal Cleaning Plant," Second International Conference on Bituminous Coal. Washington, D. C.: Carnegie Institute of Technology, 1928.

37. THIESSEN, R., "Some Recent Developments on the Constitution of Coal," Second International Conference on Bituminous Coal, Vol. 1, 1928, Washington, D. C.: Carnegie Institute of Technology.

38. WARREN, W. B., "Coal Carbonization," *Industrial and Engineering Chemistry,* Vol. 27, 1935.

39. WINDETT, V., "Observations on Gas Producer Operation," Engineers Society of Western Pennsylvania, October, 1927.

40. WOODHOUSE, T. G., "Elimination of Sulphur during Carbonization of Coal," *Fuel,* Vol. 14, September and October, 1935.

CHAPTER III

THE METAL IRON

71. Physical and Mechanical Properties. The physical and mechanical properties of pure iron are given below:

Atomic number	26
Atomic weight	55.84
Density at 100°C	7.85
" at 1535°C	7.45
Specific heat at 20°C	0.1075 cal./g./°C.
" " at 1500°C	0.171
Heat of fusion	64.9 cal./g.
Thermal conductivity at 20°C	0.135 cal./sec./cm./°C./cm.
Coefficient of expansion (linear) at 100°C	12.6 x 10⁻⁶
Melting point	1535°C.
Vapor pressure at 1590°C	1.0 mm. Hg
Boiling point	3000°C.
Electrical resistance	9.43 microhms/cm.
Tensile strength (ingot iron)	38,500 lb./sq. in.
Yield strength (ingot iron)	19,000 lb./sq. in.
Elongation, per cent in 2 in	43–48
Brinell hardness	67
Reduction of area	80 Per cent

CLASSIFICATION OF FERROUS PRODUCTS

72. Pig Iron. Pig iron is the alloy obtained directly from the blast furnace in smelting an iron ore, and termed pig iron whether it is used in the solid or molten condition. The name had its origin in the early method used in casting the molten metal in the form of small bars in sand. There was a main runner at the tap hole from which branched, at regular intervals, smaller runners with a still smaller depression the size of an individual ingot on one or both sides. There is a fancied resemblance to a sow with a litter of suckling pigs— hence the name pig iron. Because the use of the metal in the liquid state, particularly in certain special open-hearth processes, is common, it is frequently referred to as hot metal, in contrast to these small shapes or pigs, cast thus for convenience in handling. In the true sense of the word, therefore, there is very little pig iron now made because it is generally cast on a machine called a pig or pig-casting machine; nevertheless, the name pig iron is retained. Note that there is a qualifying phrase "smelting iron ore" in the definition in order to distinguish pig iron from other products of the blast furnace such as ferromanganese, spiegeleisen, silicospiegel, ferrophosphorus, shown in Table 21. Pig iron is further differentiated in the above statement from cast iron in that it is the direct product of the blast furnace whereas cast iron, which may be made solely of pig iron, may also represent rather complex mixtures of pig iron with steel, other alloys, or metals such as copper, nickel, and chromium. In this same table other common grades of pig iron are also listed, for it may be classified:

1. According to the raw materials from which it is made, as charcoal pig, anthracite pig (very little of either is now made in this country), coke pig, hematite pig, titanium pig, and alloy pig.

2. According to the use to which it may be put, as acid pig for the acid Bessemer open-hearth process, basic open-hearth or basic pig for the basic open-hearth or basic Bessemer process, forge iron or puddling iron pig for the manufacture of wrought iron, malleable pig for the manufacture of malleable cast iron, and foundry pig of numerous grades (chiefly on the basis of the silicon content) for use in the iron foundry for making castings.

3. According to its peculiar chemical composition, as high-silicon pig or silicon pig, low-phosphorus pig, high-phosphorus pig and alloy pig.

Formerly, the commercial grades were determined by the appearance of a fresh fractured surface of a broken pig, the color of which varied from white to silvery gray into the true gray of high-silicon pig. Although this method is still a convenient one for rapid sorting or analysis about the plant, at the present time the marketing and sale of these products are usually on the basis of a chemical analysis.

73. Steel. It is rather difficult to define rigorously the word steel, for it is loosely used in industry; witness the fact that a common variety of ferrous product is termed "semi-steel." C. B. Francis, in *The Making, Shaping, and Treating of Steel*, distinguishes steel from pig iron, cast iron, malleable iron, wrought iron, and sponge iron by defining it as "a malleable, essentially slag-free, relatively pure iron or iron alloy produced in the solid state by carburizing bars of low carbon content or by a purification process involving complete fusion in which the purification or adjustment of the composition of the charge is carried to an extent to give a metal initially malleable as cast." The chemical relationships between these various products are shown in Table 21 and the modern processes for making ferrous products are outlined in Table 22

TABLE 21
Chemical Relations of Ferrous Alloys

	Per Cent				
	Si	S	P	Mn	C
Pig Irons					
No. 1 Foundry	2.5 –3.0	0.035m	0.5 –1.0	1.0m	3.0 –4.5
No. 2 "	2.0 –2.5	0.045m	"	"	"
No. 3 "	1.5 –2.0	0.055m	"	"	"
Malleable	0.85–1.2	0.12m	0.2m	0.4m	1.75–2.3
Gray Forge	1.2 –1.75	0.05m	0.1 –0.35	0.5 –1.0	4.15–4.4
Acid Bessemer	1.0 –2.25	0.045m	0.04 –0.1	0.5 –1.0	"
Basic open-hearth	1.5m	0.05m	0.11 –0.9	0.4 –2.0	"
Low-phosphorus	2.0m	0.035m	0.035m	2.0m	
Alloys					
Spiegel (3 grades)	1.25m	0.03–0.05	0.14 –0.25	16–30	
Silicospiegel	8.0 –15.0	0.02m	0.15m	15–20	
Ferromanganese	0.5 –1.0	0.05m	0.2 –0.35	78–82	6.5 –7.5
Silvery iron	6.0 –17.0	0.05m	0.1 –0.4	0.3 –2.0	0.75–1.0
Ferrophosphorus	1.5 –1.75	0.05m	15–24	0.07–0.50	1.10–2.0
Wrought iron	0.03–0.32	0.01–0.04	0.08 –0.50	0.02–0.10	0.02–0.05
Carbon steel	tr–0.5	0.02–0.26	0.002–1.2	0.3 –1.0	0.07–1.5
Ingot iron	0.01m	0.035m	0.02m	0.02–0.10	0.02–0.07

m = maximum.

Examination of these shows that so far as processes and materials are concerned, steel is produced by purifying and refining liquid pig iron alone or as mixtures of steel, scrap, and pig iron. Scrap is a general term applied to ferrous materials that have been

a. Reduced in the manufacture of the steel in the steel plant itself or
b. Used and taken out of service.

CLASSIFICATION OF PROCESSES

74. Purification and Refining. The complete purification of pig iron would, of course, include the removal of all the elements alloyed with the iron. Actually, it is found impossible to remove all these impurities completely, and practically it is not wise or expedient to do so. The purest iron made today is carbonyl or electrolytic, but these are very expensive and even they contain traces of impurities. The major elements in pig iron are carbon, manganese, phosphorus, sulfur, and sili-

TABLE 22

CLASSIFICATION OF FERROUS PRODUCTS

(According to Process of Manufacture)

A. Produced directly from the ore or oxide.
 1. Pig iron.
 2. Ferromanganese.
 3. Sponge or powdered iron.

B. Produced from pig iron by casting direct or remelting and casting.
 1. Without heat-treating, purifying, or mixing with other materials.
  a. High-carbon cast iron.
   (1) Gray iron castings.
   (2) White iron castings.
 2. By mixing pig iron with other ferrous products by remelting or heat-treating after casting.
  a. High-carbon gray iron castings.
   (1) Plain gray iron castings.
   (2) Annealed gray iron castings.
  b. Low-carbon gray iron castings.
   (1) Plain iron castings.
    (*a*) Untreated.
    (*b*) Annealed.
   (2) Alloyed cast irons.
    (*a*) Pearlitic.
    (*b*) Austenitic.

C. Made by partial purification of pig iron without additions.
 1. Washed metal.
 2. Puddled wrought iron.

D. Made by partial purification of pig iron with subsequent refining or additions.
 1. Aston process wrought iron.
 2. Acid Bessemer steel.
 3. Acid open-hearth steel.
 4. Acid electric steel.

E. Made by complete purification of pig iron followed by deoxidation treatments or additions.
 1. Basic open-hearth iron.
 2. Low-metalloid steel.
 3. Ingot iron.

F. Made by complete purification of pig iron followed by additions and treatment to adjust the composition as well as deoxidize.
 1. Basic steel.
  a. Basic open-hearth steel.
  b. Basic Bessemer (Thomas) steel.
  c. Electric-furnace steel.
  d. Duplex steel.

G. Made from refined products with or without additions.
 1. Cement steel.
 2. Crucible steel.
 3. Induction furnace steel.

con; the minor ones such as copper, nickel, and chromium (through contamination by scrap in the blast furnace or open hearth). In view of the fact that these same elements, or most of them, are desired in steel, the amount depending upon the use to which it is to be put, purification from a metallurgical standpoint is taken to mean only the removal of undesirable elements or the excess of the elements desired in the steel. It is unfortunate that, owing to the chemical properties of the various elements, selective removal is seldom possible, and very frequently the combinations are such that in order to remove one element the operator must remove a second and then put back into the steel a sufficient amount of the second metal to meet the specifications of the customer. Consequently, the term refining is really preferable to purification. On the above bases the refining processes can be classed as selective or non-selective, oxidizing or reducing, basic or acid, low-temperature liquid phase, high-temperature liquid phase, solid-liquid phase, solid-gas phase, and liquid-gas phase, depending upon the methods or processes used.

75. Commercial Methods of Refining. The two cheapest substances for purifying pig iron are air and iron oxide; and the two chief methods of purification, the pneumatic or Bessemer, and the open-hearth or Siemens processes, are attempts to meet the different conditions imposed by the fact that one of these reagents is a gas and the other a solid. Depending upon the character of the slag used, they may be termed acid processes when there is a large percentage of silica or basic processes when lime or iron oxide is predominant. By the processes of the first class only carbon, silicon, and manganese are removed, whereas methods of the second class remove phosphorus and, to a somewhat limited extent, sulfur. The basic Bessemer process has been named after its inventors, the Thomas-Gilchrist in England or the Thomas on the continent of Europe.

76. Classification of Steels. The word steel is a very general term for a ferrous alloy; and because it is marketed and used by brands, by chemical or physical specifications, a wide variety of classifications is possible. Even in the early days of the steel industry there were many different kinds of steel, dictated by the needs of the individual, and later developments have only served to multiply this almost endless variety of products. The classification chosen for this textbook in Table 23 is a slight modification of the one suggested by C. B. Francis in *The Making, Shaping, and Treating of Steel*. In general the term "kind" refers to the process of manufacture, as basic open-hearth steel, basic Bessemer steel. The word "class" refers to divisions based on size or service, as heavy goods, light products, structural, heat-resistant, tool. The word "type" denotes such qualities as grain size or chemical composition; for example, a fine grain, high-carbon alloy steel. The term "grade" is based on the carbon content or physical properties, such as a high-tensile structural steel.

TABLE 23

Classification of Steels

A. According to processes and methods of manufacture.
    1. Cement.
    2. Crucible.
    3. Acid Bessemer.
    4. Basic Bessemer.
    5. Acid open-hearth.
    6. Basic open-hearth.
    7. Duplex.
    8. Electric furnace.

B. According to use.
    1. Structural.
    2. Corrosion, heat-resistant, and stainless.
    3. Tool.
    4. Spring.
    5. Boiler, flange, fire-box.
    6. Rail.
    7. Pipe, skelp, welding.
    8. Sheet, sheet bar, tin bar.
    9. Casehardening.
    10. Electrical.
    11. Strip.
    12. Hoop.
    13. Free-cutting, screw stock.
    14. Forging.
    15. Cast.
    16. Wrought.

C. According to composition or grade.
    1. Plain.
        a. Ingot iron, basic open-hearth, low metalloid.
        b. Simple, plain, straight, ordinary carbon.
            (1) Hypoeutectoid.
                (a) Dead-soft.
                (b) Low-carbon.
                (c) Medium-carbon.
            (2) Hypereutectoid or high-carbon.
    2. Alloy-treated.
    3. Alloy.
        a. Simple or ternary.
            (1) Copper.
            (2) Low-manganese.
            (3) Manganese.
            (4) Silicon.
            (5) Nickel.
            (6) Chrome.
            (7) Molybdenum.
            (8) Vanadium.
            (9) Tungsten.

TABLE 23 (*Continued*)

b. Quaternary.
    (1) Chrome-nickel.
    (2) Chrome-vanadium.
    (3) Chrome-molybdenum.
    (4) Copper-nickel.
c. Complex alloy.
    (1) High-strength corrosion-resistant.
    (2) Corrosion, heat-resistant, stainless.
    (3) Low-alloy tool.
    (4) High-speed.

D. According to quality.
  1. Methods of forming.
    a. Casting, cast.
    b. Hot-forming.
      (1) Special forging.
        (*a*) Hammer-forging.
        (*b*) Pressing.
        (*c*) Drop-forging.
      (2) Cold-forming.
        (*a*) Cold-drawing.
        (*b*) Cold-rolling.
        (*c*) Deep-drawing.
        (*d*) Special machinery
  2. Special inherent properties.
    a. Corrosion-resistant.
    b. Heat-resistant.
    c. Abrasion-resistant.
    d. Non-aging.
    e. Shallow hardening.
    f. Deep hardening.
  3. Microscopic structure.
    a. Pearlitic.
      (1) Coarse grain.
      (2) Fine grain.
    b. Martensitic.
    c. Austenitic.

In order not to lengthen this discussion unduly and yet place the reader in position to interpret intelligently the technical literature, detailed definitions will be given for only those steels not readily identified by the mere name.

Cement steel is made by carburizing bars of wrought iron or soft steel. Duplex steel is made by partially purifying pig iron of medium-high phosphorus content in an acid Bessemer converter, then transferring it to a basic open-hearth where the purification is completed. Skelp steel is a dead-soft or low, plain carbon steel especially suitable for the manufacture of pipe by welding. Alloy-treated steels are carbon steels to which some other element or elements are added to improve their quality without changing markedly their characteristics. Alloy steels are those to which, in addition to carbon, another element or other elements are added in sufficient amount to modify the properties, to a marked degree, over those exhibited by the carbon steel.

EFFECTS OF ELEMENTS ON STEEL

77. General. Besides the gangue all iron ores commonly contain relatively large amount of manganese, phosphorus, sulfur, and silicon, and small amounts of other elements, such as chromium, nickel, copper, and zinc. These are, to a greater or less extent, reduced in the blast furnace and enter the pig iron. In recent years, because of the large amount of scrap that is being returned to the steel plants from industry, there has been a sharp rise in the residual metals thus introduced, such as chromium, nickel, vanadium, molybdenum, and copper. Still other metals, tungsten or cobalt, for example, may be introduced to add new properties to those ordinarily possessed by steel or to enhance the old ones; descriptions of the effects of such special metals are left to textbooks on metallography and physical metallurgy. For the purposes of this discussion, only those normally introduced by the steel-making processes are considered; namely, carbon, manganese, sulfur, phosphorus, silicon, copper, tin, antimony, and the gases.

78. Carbon. So characteristic and beneficial is the effect of this element on iron that it is commonly used as one of the bases of nomenclature for steels. For example, a steel containing 0.1 per cent carbon, or less, is known as very mild steel; one containing 0.26 to 0.60 per cent carbon, a medium steel; and one containing over 1 per cent carbon, a very high carbon steel. The effect of carbon, in such plain carbon steels, is to increase the hardness and strength, decrease the ductility, and render the steel more responsive to heat treatment. In a general way the addition of each 0.1 per cent carbon to steel, up to 0.85 per cent, affects the physical properties as indicated:

> Yield point is raised 4000 pounds per square inch.
> Tensile strength is raised 9400 pounds per square inch.
> Elongation is reduced 4.3 per cent.
> Reduction of area is reduced 7.3 per cent.

Above 0.85 per cent carbon this general rule does not hold because of the presence of a new constituent—cementite.

79. Manganese. Manganese is primarily a cleansing, desulfurizing, or deoxidizing agent for steels. As early as 1856 Mushet noted its power to overcome the bad effects of oxygen and sulfur. These effects are discussed in more detail in Article 292. Incidentally, below 0.30 per cent the deoxidizing power of manganese is very small, and the amounts partitioned to desulfurizing, to carbon, and to alloying are so small that their effects upon the physical properties are scarcely noticeable. On the whole, small amounts of manganese add to the tensile strength of steel, give it better rolling and forging properties, but above 1 per cent it begins to produce hardness and brittleness. The range in plain carbon steels is from 0.30 to 1.0 per cent.

80. Effect of Phosphorus. In plain carbon steel phosphorus raises the tensile strength, increases the elastic limit, raises the elastic ratio, and improves slightly the resistance of steel to atmospheric corrosion, prevents sticking of thin sheets in the pack-rolling process, but does not appear to have much influence on the hardenability. Its bad effects are numerous, for in medium- and high-carbon steels phosphorus above 0.08 per cent tends to make the steel brittle, particularly at low temperatures. In low-carbon steels (carbon under 0.15 per cent) this embrittlement is not noticeable until the phosphorus is raised above 0.14 per cent. Above 0.25 per cent phosphorus, the embrittlement becomes pronounced, as indicated by low and erratic impact values. Steels containing undue amounts of phosphorus are particularly susceptible to banding by segregation in ingots made of high-phosphorus material. Steels in general may contain 0.005 to 1.40 per cent phosphorus, but most contain less than 0.110 per cent.

81. Sulfur. Within the range of 0.02 to 0.2 per cent, sulfur, accompanied by sufficient manganese, has practically no effect on the tensile properties of the steel in the direction of rolling. Sulfur reacts with iron to form iron sulfide and with manganese to form manganese sulfide. The former melts at 1193°C. so that it remains liquid after the iron in the steel has solidified and is found as segregations around the grain boundaries; the latter melts at about 1600°C. and tends to precipitate out as a finely divided solid while the steel is still molten. This behavior explains why the sulfur in steel commonly makes it hot-short or brittle at high temperatures and why, combined with manganese, it embrittles the ferrite, thus imparting the free-cutting properties characteristic of the higher sulfur, higher manganese steels. On the whole, sulfur increases the tendency of the steel to corrode. The extreme range in plain carbon steels will be from 0.002 per cent to 0.350 per cent sulfur.

82. Silicon. Silicon in plain carbon steels is usually added solely as a deoxidizing agent, because in amounts up to 0.5 per cent its effects on the physical properties are moderate. Besides increasing the hardenability somewhat, each 0.1 per cent raises the tensile strength approximately 2000 pounds per square inch without affecting very much the ductility or the elastic ratio. However, silicon does tend to raise the elastic or proportional limit so that in steels containing about 1 per cent silicon, the proportional limit and the yield strength are almost identical. In amounts around 0.25 per cent it confers greater resiliency without increased brittleness and consequently is used extensively in spring steel. The usual range in carbon steel is from 0 to 0.5 per cent.

83. Copper. In low- and medium-carbon steels the tensile strength increases about 1180 pounds per square inch for each 0.1 per cent of copper added, with corresponding increases in hardness. In higher carbon steels this strengthening effect decreases to as low as 600 pounds per square inch. The yield strength is increased by copper more rapidly than the tensile strength, the increment being of the order of 1500 pounds per square inch for each 0.1 per cent in copper content for low, and about 750 pounds per square inch for the higher carbon steels. In amounts up to 2 per cent, copper has little effect upon the ductility of steel. The most important effect of copper is to increase the resistance of the steel to atmospheric corrosion. Its effect is materially increased by the presence of phosphorus so that the common grade of copper-bearing steel contains 0.2 per cent copper and 0.1 to 0.14 per cent phosphorus. Although it is possible that phosphorus acts through the formation of insoluble phosphates of both iron and copper, the most commonly accepted explanation of this action is the formation of a tightly adhering film of copper and copper oxide on the surface which acts as a protective coating to cut down the speed of corrosion. Copper above 0.2 per cent adds but little to the corrosion resistance. As copper is increased above 0.3 per cent, it begins to cause trouble in rolling by forming a copper-rich, low-melting-point alloy that penetrates the grain boundaries and makes it difficult to obtain satisfactory surfaces.

84. Tin and Antimony. These elements ordinarily do not occur in iron ores, but their presence is being felt in present steel-making practice because of the increasing amounts of detinned scrap as well as small amounts of bearing metal and other tin- and antimony-bearing alloys finding their way into steel scrap in the dealer's yard. Tin in rather small amounts increases considerably the hot shortness or brittleness of steel at rolling temperatures, although tin up to 0.1 per cent has no bad effects upon the other physical properties of the steel. Antimony is even worse in effect, for it has been found very difficult to roll steel containing as little as 0.03 per cent because of the hot shortness developed.

85. Gases. The large amount of gas that a molten metal can absorb is not commonly appreciated. For example, when a 1200-gram sample of ingot iron was melted in a vacuum furnace, 503 cubic centimeters of gas was obtained. In other words, it contained about 189 per cent by volume or 0.03 per cent by weight of the original iron. Incidentally, this gas was composed for the most part of carbon monoxide and carbon dioxide. Although a similar sample of raw converter metal gave a comparable amount of gas so far as volume was concerned, it contained 44 per cent carbon monoxide and 46 per cent hydrogen by volume. Much remains to be done on the effect of gases on the properties of steel. Authorities are generally agreed now that oxygen increases brittleness of steel and detracts from its rolling and forging properties. Nitrogen tends to make steel brittle and hard. Hydrogen is not known to serve any useful purpose.

BIBLIOGRAPHY

1. *Alloy of Iron Monographs* (a series). New York: McGraw-Hill Book Company, 1930 to date.
2. BULLENS, D. K., and Metallurgical Staff of Battelle Memorial Institute, *Steel and Its Heat Treatment.* New York: John Wiley and Sons, 1939. 2 vols.
3. CLEAVES, H. E., and J. G. THOMPSON, *The Metal Iron.* New York: McGraw-Hill Book Company, 1935. 574 pp.
4. *International Critical Tables.* New York: McGraw-Hill Book Company, 1926.
5. *National Metals Handbook.* American Society for Metals, 1939.
6. SAUVEUR, A., *Metallography and Heat Treatment of Iron and Steel.* New York: McGraw-Hill Book Company, 1935. 531 pp.

CHAPTER IV

THE IRON BLAST FURNACE

HISTORY

86. Development in Europe. Prior to the fourteenth century, the early hearth furnaces, similar to the Catalan forge (see Article 196), were the sole means of extracting metallic iron from its ore, and only then in the form of wrought iron. As early as the eighth century we learn of a new furnace called the Osmund, about 4 feet square and 10 feet high, and still later larger ones of circular cross section, but these still produced wrought iron. As a matter of fact, the discovery of cast iron, and the subsequent development of the blast furnace, was brought about by an accident, the result of the demands for larger and larger amounts of wrought iron.

One of the earliest furnaces consisted of a pile of ore and charcoal heaped on the ground and covered with mud to retain its form. Hollow reeds or other pipes were inserted in the pile and were connected to bellows, probably goat skins, which were equipped with a small hole in the upper surface and a thong for pulling the skin upwards and filling it with air. The furnace was lighted at the end of the blow pipes and kept burning by man power, the "blower" inflating the skin and then blowing the air into the furnace by putting his weight on the bellows, using his heel to close the air inlet hole. This method of reduction is still used in certain sections of Africa, China, and India.

As the furnaces grew in size from this small pit it became necessary to increase the pressure and amount of the blast. This in turn increased the temperature within the furnace and lengthened the cycle until a point was reached when, from the furnace on being opened, instead of a large lump of wrought iron, out gushed a stream of liquid slag and metal. To the chagrin and disappointment of the operators, this metal was quite unlike any that had been produced before. It was termed "sick iron" because it was hard and brittle. Years passed before methods were devised for purifying it to produce the attractive wrought iron that has been in use for many centuries.

T. T. Read* has pointed out that the belief that iron castings were

---

* T. T. Read, "Composition and Microstructure of Ancient Iron Castings," American Institute of Mining and Metallurgical Engineers, *Tech. Pub.* 882, 1938.

first made in Europe in the fourteenth century is erroneous. In China, in 1906, he examined nine castings whose inscriptions unquestionably indicated dates of casting from A.D. 500 to 1000. Analyses, given in Table 24, and microscopic study revealed a wide diversity of struc-

TABLE 24

CHEMICAL ANALYSES OF CHINESE CAST IRON

Per Cent

Specimen No.	Total Carbon	Combined Carbon	Graphitic Carbon	Si	P	S	Mn
1	3.35	1.05	2.30	2.42	0.205	0.067	0.13
2	3.22	0.96	2.26	2.39	0.17	0.077	0.23
3	3.35	0.33	3.02	1.98	0.312	0.063	0.78
6	3.96	3.35	0.61	0.09	0.231	0.022	....
8	3.84	1.49	2.35	0.08	0.097	0.024	0.02

tures—white, gray, and mottled irons. The most significant departure from modern irons was the uniform low phosphorus content, but other ornaments have contained as much as 0.52 per cent. As to the method of manufacture, little is known. Read feels sure that the Chinese first reduced the iron ore to iron and then melted this in a crucible furnace. It is significant that the Chinese invented the double-acting bellows.

It was probably about 1323 that the German Stückofen, Bauernofen or Blaufofen made its appearance in Europe; at least there is no specific mention of a blast furnace until the year 1340. Such furnaces, shown in Figure 12, were about 10 feet high and may be considered to be the immediate forerunners of the true blast furnace. In succeeding years metallurgists evolved a new type of furnace built of masonry which inclosed a shaft or vertical opening in the form of two truncated cones placed end to end, resembling in a crude way the lines of the modern blast furnace. The lower cone came to be known as the bosh and the bottom as the hearth of the furnace. In such a furnace, ore, flux, and charcoal were charged in at the top while air under very low pressure was blown in at the bottom. This method of reduction was introduced into England about the year 1500, where in 1619 coke was first used, to be followed by another innovation, the hot blast, about two hundred years later.

87. Development of the Industry in the United States. Although a furnace was built in the Jamestown Colony as early as 1619, it was

not until the Pilgrims settled in Massachusetts that the need for a local iron industry was recognized. Crude stone furnaces were built in the Cape Cod region. Practically all these early furnaces were built on the side of a hill, thus allowing room for the stock house and the stock piles to be located above the furnace; a trestle from the hill to the furnace top, along which the stock could be wheeled in buggies and dumped into the top of the furnace, facilitated the operation of

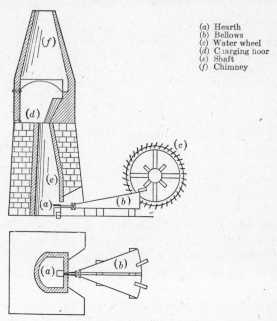

(a) Hearth
(b) Bellows
(c) Water wheel
(d) Charging floor
(e) Shaft
(f) Chimney

Fig. 12. Styrian Stückofen.

charging. The gases of combustion and reduction were generally exhausted to the atmosphere so that furnace operation was difficult and hazardous. For raw materials these furnaces used bog ores, charcoal, and sea shells. The first furnaces built in this region cast only about 2 tons of iron per day, although later improvements increased this output to as high as 20. Only the better ores in use contained 30 to 40 per cent iron, and these were often found cropping out of the hillside itself. Near-by deposits of micaceous schist were used to line these furnaces (fire brick was as yet unknown). In general it took about 3 tons of ore and 140 bushels of charcoal to make a ton of iron. Most charcoal furnaces operated with only one tuyère, and casts were made once or twice a day, the iron flowing from the furnace taphole, down runners, through sows, and into the sand molds. In those days pig iron was graded entirely by fracture because chemical analysis was not generally used until the coming of the twentieth century. These early eastern furnaces played an important part in furnishing ordnance during the Revolutionary War, and many were the attempts made by the British to capture or destroy them. After the War, as the years rolled by, the hardy pioneer families pushed on westward. The demands of these new districts, as well as the discovery of better deposits of ore and coal, resulted in the development, first in Pennsylvania and finally in Ohio, Indiana, and Illinois, of extensive iron-smelting industries.

On the outskirts of Lisbon, Ohio, there is a reservation of some 125 acres of woodland, an old mansion house of stone, and the remains of

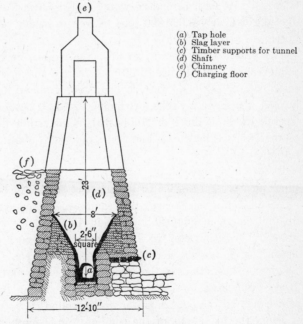

(a) Tap hole
(b) Slag layer
(c) Timber supports for tunnel
(d) Shaft
(e) Chimney
(f) Charging floor

Fig. 13. Early American Blast Furnace.

one of the earliest blast furnaces to be built in the Middle West. Because its construction and operation were similar to many such furnaces built in the early days of the industry and in order to throw light on the development of the modern blast furnace, a little space will be devoted to its discussion. The furnace referred to is the Rebecca

Stack, built in 1807 by Gideon Hughes. The original product of the furnace was a ten-plate wood-burning stove which served the pioneers for cooking as well as for domestic heating. The stove was the "Rebecca of New Lisbon" whose superiority is referred to in the diary of Benjamin Franklin in Philadelphia. Additional products of the furnace were plow iron, tools, pots, and kettles. Although the furnace did not operate after 1832, it continued to be kept in a good state of preservation, with the result that it was possible to reconstruct it as shown in Figure 13 (reconstruction made in 1892).

This furnace, in common with many of the early ones, was in blast for only nine months of each year, first because the weather of the winter months was too cold for outside work and second because the lining of the furnace was destroyed in less than one year, the outside walls being so heavy that the heat generated could not be dissipated. Contrast this with a modern water-cooled furnace with which a production of nearly 3,000,000 tons of iron in seven years of continuous operation is not unusual.

The practice was to cut wood, in the winter, in 4-foot lengths and pile them in conical piles of 30 to 40 cords. In the early spring, these piles, called "meilers," were covered with dirt and leaves, lighted, and burned for about 2 weeks, producing 27 to 30 bushels of charcoal per cord of wood, as much as 200 bushels being required to produce a ton of pig iron. Kidney ores and limestone were obtained from the surrounding hills.

In operation the cold blast was taken to the tuyère in tin or wooden pipes at a pressure of 0.5 to 1 pound per square inch. The melted iron collected below the hearth dam and was ladled out at intervals of about 6 hours in quantities of about 1000 pounds. Slag ran over the dam and was collected in flat cakes on the stones of the cast-house floor. The charge was fed by carrying the charcoal, ore, and stone in boxes and baskets over the runway to the top of the furnace stack. Blast-furnace gas was burned at the top of the furnace in a flame which lighted the landscape for miles around.

From the old books of the company, it is found that the capacity of this furnace was about 2 tons of iron per day, which sold at $90 per ton. An analysis of pieces of iron from the furnace shows carbon 3.54 per cent, manganese 0.18, phosphorus 1.23, sulfur 0.117, and silicon 1.32. The sulfur and especially phosphorus are high; the latter produces an iron that was easy to pour in the thin sections required for stoves, pots, and other colonial articles.

88. Changes in the Locality and Character of the Industry. The history of iron making in this country can be divided conveniently into the first or "Pioneer Period," extending from the building of the first blast furnace to the outbreak of the Civil War in 1861; the second or "War Period," covering the four years of the Civil War from 1861 through 1865; the third or "Reconstruction Period," extending from 1866 to the advent of the modern blast furnace in 1880; the fourth or "Modern Period," embracing the years from 1880 to the present time. For much of the pioneer period the life was that of the frontier, crude and extremely simple. Such settlements as had come into existence were largely along navigable streams and contained scarcely more than a few dwellings, a blacksmith shop, a tan yard, a general store, and sometimes a furnace or forge. Transportation was largely by river, since such roads as existed were impassable during much of the year to all but the man on horseback. Steamboats plied upstream to bring the products of civilization and returned with raw materials from the frontier. Blast furnaces of this early era were as simple as the life and conformed closely to that shown in Figure 13. As the years passed, these furnaces were gradually increased in size, but actually the only two improvements of importance were the hot-blast pipe stove and the substitution of steam-driven blowers for the original water power. With water power the operation of a plant depended upon the supply of water; consequently, during times of drought or flood the furnace was idle.

When the long-hovering war clouds broke over the country in 1861, the demand was the same as it is today—iron and more iron. The pressure of market demand as well as financial difficulties discouraged experimentation and development, with the result that, although a great many more furnaces were built, in both the north and south, there were few changes in design or size.

The years which followed in the wake of the Civil War were almost as barren of technical development as were the previous two periods. By reason of the political problems connected with reconstruction as well as the economic depression which descended upon the country, the furnace operators were quite content to let well enough alone. One new feature of furnace construction which came along at this time was the use of iron or steel mantles with iron-supporting columns instead of the old type of stone furnace. Sandstone hearths and open tops gradually gave way to fire-brick hearth and lining and closed tops, and steam-driven elevators took the place of the old hillside method of filling.

TABLE 25

Chronology of Iron and Steel in the United States

Date	
1619	First iron produced in North America at Jamestown.
1645	First successful furnace at Lynn, Massachusetts.
1720	First furnace installation in Pennsylvania.
1803	First furnace installation in Ohio.
1818	First furnace installation in Alabama.
1833	Pig-iron production, 165,000 tons.
1834	First use of hot blast in the United States.
1835	First successful use of coke in the blast furnace in the United States.
1839	First furnace installation in Illinois.
1839	First use of anthracite coal in a blast furnace.
1840	Pig iron production 286,000 tons from 804 blast furnaces.
1840	First wire rope manufactured, J. A. Roebling, Butler, Pennsylvania.
1840	First iron bridge, Frankfort, New York.
1840	Invention of rotary squeezer for wrought iron.
1842	First use of waste gas, Greenwood, New York.
1844	Iron ore discovered in Lake Superior district.
1844	First rail rolled, Mt. Savage, Maryland.
1846	William Talley discovered pneumatic process for malleable iron.
1850	Pig-iron production 563,755; steel 6078 tons.
1851	First wire nail mill.
1852	John Fritz invented 3-high rolling mill.
1859	First furnace installation in Michigan.
1863	First metallographic work, H. C. Sorby, Sheffield, England.
1865	First Bessemer steel rails rolled, Chicago, Illinois.
1867	First furnace installation on Pacific Coast, Portland, Oregon.
1869	First continuous wire rod mill, Worcester, Massachusetts.
1870	Pig-iron production 1,665,179; steel 68,750.
1870	First open-hearth furnace built in United States, South Boston, Massachusetts.
1880	World's record 185 tons pig iron, per furnace, per day, Braddock, Pittsburgh.
1886	First experiments with basic open-hearth process, Cleveland, Ohio.
1887	First butt- and lap-welded pipe.
1889	First tilting open-hearth furnace.
1892	Steel-ore ships appear on Great Lakes.
1900	First electric furnaces for steel making.
1901	U. S. Steel Corporation organized.
1902	First gas-engine power plant operated in United States on blast-furnace gas.
1904	Dry blast for furnaces, James Gayley.
1906	Largest steel plant built, Gary, Indiana.
1918	World's largest by-product coal plant, Clairton, Pennsylvania.
1919	First high-frequency steel furnace, E. F. Northrup.
1923	First cluster-type rolling mill.
1930	Aston process for wrought iron.

About 1880 a marked change took place in industry in the United States. The country had finally weathered the terrible economic depression, new frontiers were opened, new inventions demanded more metal, the standard of living of the people increased, railroad expansion started, giving rise to an unprecedented demand for iron and steel. The furnaces which up to this time seldom had a capacity of more than 100 tons per day were rapidly increased in size, and a wave of new improvements came along (see Table 25) to change radically the character of the whole industry. Furnace fuel changed from charcoal to coke,* permitting the construction of much larger stacks; skip or mechanical filling entirely replaced the old hand method; and mechanical devices for distributing the stock in the furnace produced more regular and uniform operation. Hot-blast stoves of modern design took the place of the old pipe stove, producing higher heat and having better fuel economy; blowing engines of more efficient type were driven by the surplus gas of the furnace, and the coke breeze formerly wasted from the coke ovens was utilized to produce power for the mills and mines. Pig iron was no longer cast in sand beds but handled through hot metal ladles over modern pig-casting machines, thus eliminating back-breaking labor and producing a greatly improved and more uniform product. A still more important development was the increased use of chemistry and research to promote the accurate control of the output and the development of new products and new uses for the old ones. By-product coke ovens displaced the old beehive ovens, with the resulting benefits of a better and more uniform quality coke and the recovery of formerly wasted products such as gas, tar, ammonium sulfate, and benzol. Furnaces increased in size, as indicated in Table 26, and closer attention was given to the proper preparation of raw materials, with the result that today a stack producing 1000 tons of pig iron per day is common.

In 1917 the United States Steel Corporation had a total of 127 furnaces which produced 17,315,914 net tons; in 1941 the furnaces had been reduced to 85 (a decline of 33 per cent) while the tonnage increased to 22,000,000 (27 per cent gain). The production per furnace increased 72 per cent, from 486 to 835 net tons per day. The largest of the furnaces in 1917 produced 644 tons per day, as against 1350

---

* Charcoal remained the predominant fuel until 1838, when it gave way to anthracite coal to be followed by coke. In 1874 of the 680 American furnaces in operation, 226 used anthracite. However, from the standpoint of tonnage, coke surpassed anthracite in 1875. In 1941 there were only four charcoal furnaces in the United States.

TABLE 26

FIGURES TELL STORY OF DIMINISHING BLAST FURNACES

Year	Total Blast Furnaces, December 31	Active Blast Furnaces, December 31	Blast Furnaces Built During Year	Blast Furnaces Abandoned During Year	Blast Furnaces Remodeled During Year
1918	435	351			
1923	418	231	1	11	5
1927	354	169		15	11
1929	316	156		19	17
1931	301	57		9	6
1932	291	42		10	3
1936	252	146		16	4
1940	231	206		1	

Year	Annual Capacity, December 31, Gross Tons	Average Daily Production, Gross Tons	Average Daily Capacity per Furnace, Gross Tons	Operations-Production Related to Capacity, Per Cent
1918	48,626,115	105,308	299	81.3
1923	52,146,430	109,659	341	76.6
1927	50,329,750	99,422	403	69.7
1929	51,490,680	115,808	443	82.8
1931	51,598,175	50,035	479	34.7
1932	50,313,975	23,699	486	16.7
1936	55,557,305	75,942	541	58.3
1940	57,609,590	129,856	683	82.6

1940

State	Number of Furnaces	Gross Capacity	State	Number of Furnaces	Gross Capacity
Pennsylvania	77	18 683,430	New York	15	3,814,720
Indiana and Illinois	42	12,153,010	Michigan	8	1,448,770
Ohio	48	12,981,080	Maryland	6	2,280,000
Alabama	19	3,588,890	Others	16	12,659,690
			Total	201	57,609,590

82 per cent of total capacity dependent upon Lake ores.

Blast furnace rated above 320,000 tons annual capacity—30.

Average daily capacity, per furnace, per day actual blowing time—751 tons.

for one of them in 1941. The largest hearth diameter in 1917 was less than 20 feet; today several have 28-foot hearths.

So much for the technological changes which have occurred. Meanwhile, as indicated in Figure 14, the geographic center of the steel industry, along with the young men of the period, was moving westward. As a matter of fact, this westward movement of the center of

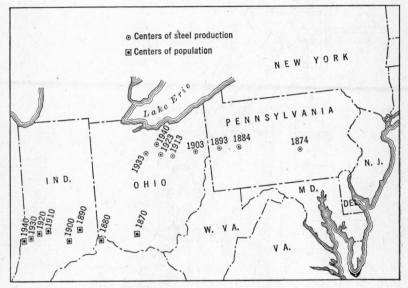

Fig. 14. Centers of U. S. Iron and Steel Industry.

the steel industry closely resembles a similar shift of the center of population of the country. Since 1870,* the center of population has moved 190 miles to the west from a point 48 miles east of Cincinnati to a point 3 miles southeast of Carlisle, Indiana. In 1874 the center of the steel-making industry was in east-central Pennsylvania; in 1893 in western Pennsylvania; and at the present time it is about 8 miles northeast of Mansfield, Ohio.† In part this change has been caused by the expansion of the general manufacturing industry to the western part of the country and in part to the discovery of the cheap high-grade ores of the Mesabi (see Chapter II).

* The first center was established in 1790 at a point 23 miles east of Baltimore, Maryland.

† This is the second eastern move in seven years, the most westerly point being Crestline, Ohio, in 1933. Fully 6 million tons of capacity were installed between 1936 and 1940, and much of this to the east and north of Ohio.

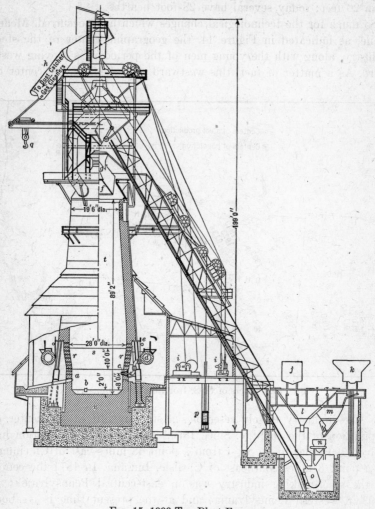

FIG. 15. 1000-Ton Blast Furnace.

a.	Cinder notch	*l.*	Coke bin
b.	Iron notch	*m.*	Ore bin
c.	Tuyères	*n.*	Scale car
d.	Bustle pipe	*o.*	Skip car
e.	Mantle	*p.*	Large bell counterweight
f.	Large bell	*q.*	Crane
g.	Small bell	*r.*	Cooling plates
h.	Down comer	*s.*	Bosh
i.	Hoists	*t.*	Shaft
j.	Coke transfer car	*u.*	Fire brick
k.	Ore transfer car	*z.*	Foundation

CONSTRUCTION OF THE BLAST FURNACE

89. General. The changing industrial conditions outlined above have brought about radical changes in the construction of the modern blast furnace from that indicated in Figure 13. Such a blast furnace shown in Figures 15 and 16 is now designed so that a mixture of ore, fuel, and flux in proper proportions can be charged through a specially constructed opening in the top of a cylindrical-shaped furnace and top gas and flue dust* withdrawn for recovery, retreatment, and use. At the same time heated air from stoves, which obtain their heat from the combustion of this top gas, is blown in near the bottom through openings called tuyères, forming carbon monoxide, which passes up through the openings in the charge to reduce the iron ore. The process is a continuous one except for the periodic removal of the impurities, in the form of slag, and of the metal, through large openings in the crucible of the furnace. In present-day Lake practice the production of a ton of pig iron involves the use of about 2 tons of iron ore, 1 ton of fuel, 4 tons of air, and 0.35 ton of flux and produces, besides the 1 ton of pig iron, 6 tons of gas, 0.6 ton of slag, and 75 to 375 pounds of flue dust. If these figures are translated into the daily requirements, we find that the blast furnace also requires a large and very efficient transportation system; the 1000-ton stack referred to above will require 3500 tons of charge, 100,000,000 cubic feet of blast, 6,000,000 gallons of water, and produce 500 tons of slag and 150,000,000 cubic feet of gas per 24 hours.† That the supply of water alone is a considerable one is indicated by figures of the American Iron and Steel Institute, which has calculated that the steel industry uses about 4 billion gallons of water per day,‡ or about four times as much as that consumed daily in all five boroughs of New York City.

While the central equipment in a blast-furnace plant is the furnace with its auxiliary apparatus for hoisting the materials to the top and handling the slag and molten metal, a considerable investment, and

* At the present high-wind rates Lake furnaces are making 350-375 pounds per ton of pig iron, of which 250 pounds is dry dust and 100-125 pounds sludge.

† This gas will have a heat content of about 95 B.t.u. per cubic foot and consist of 29 per cent by volume of combustibles (carbon monoxide and hydrogen) and 71 per cent of inerts (nitrogen and carbon dioxide).

‡ Divided as follows:

Making steam	45 per cent
Open-hearth, rolling mills	29 per cent
Blast furnaces	20 per cent
Coke ovens	6 per cent

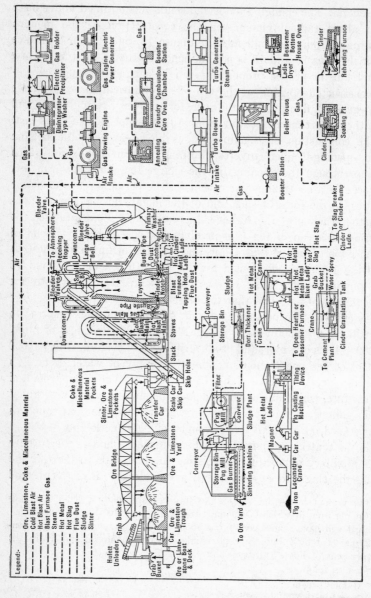

FIG. 16. The Manufacture of Pig Iron. (*Courtesy of Carnegie-Illinois Steel Corp.*)

much space, must be provided for auxiliary apparatus. Ladles or granulating pits must be provided for the slag; ladles or casting machines for handling of molten metal; blowing engines for compressing the air; stoves for heating the blast; dust catchers and gas cleaning apparatus for recovering the large quantities of flue dust; boilers or gas engines for furnishing power and for compressing the air; air-conditioning plants for removing a part of the moisture from the air; and stock houses, bins, ore bridges, car dumpers, docks, etc.

The modern blast furnace, shown in Figures 15, 16, 17, and 18, is circular in cross section, 90 to 100 feet high and lined with fire brick, held in a close-fitting steel shell which is divided vertically, for convenience, into three main parts. The bottom, cylindrical in form and some 10 to 12 feet deep, is termed the hearth or crucible; the second section, in the form of an inverted frustum of a cone, 9 to 12 feet in height, is called the bosh; and resting on the bosh, and extending up for a distance of about 70 feet, is the stack. Finally, the whole is capped by the furnace top, providing means for the introduction of the charge and the withdrawal of the gas and flue dust.

90. Foundations. The foundations of a modern blast furnace shown in Figures 15 and 17 must carry a total load of nearly 4000 tons, as indicated below:

Above mantle....................	235 tons
Bustle pipe.....................	35 tons
Uptakes, etc....................	125 tons
Brick lining....................	2348 tons
Charge.........................	1012 tons
Metal..........................	150 tons
Slag...........................	30 tons
Total......................	3935 tons

In view of this immense weight and the fact that a small amount of settling will crack the lining or throw the skip and the charging devices out of line, the stability of this foundation is of great importance. No generalization can be given as to size and depth; they will vary with the conditions of soil (sand, clay, or rock) on which the furnace is built. On a proper bed, the foundation is built up with several feet of concrete (this extends some distance outward beyond the floor of the furnace), on top of which is laid common brick of good quality and strength except directly beneath the hearth and walls of the furnace, where fire brick is used.

91. Hearth or Crucible. This portion of the furnace which contains the molten metal and slag is constructed of fire brick of the best quality, usually 60 inches or more in thickness and reinforced by means of strong bands and protected in places with water-cooled plates. The bottom is given a rough basin or cup-shaped cross section by corbeling or stepping out the lower four or five courses of brick toward

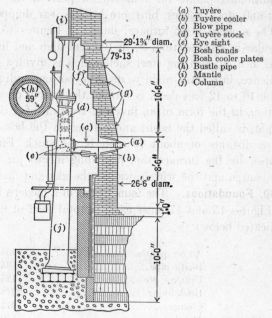

(a) Tuyère
(b) Tuyère cooler
(c) Blow pipe
(d) Tuyère stock
(e) Eye sight
(f) Bosh bands
(g) Bosh cooler plates
(h) Bustle pipe
(i) Mantle
(j) Column

FIG. 17. Hearth, Bosh, and Foundations.

the interior of the hearth. In the large furnaces the hearth will be 22 to 28 feet in diameter and 11 feet in depth. In view of the fact that the 7 to 10 feet of slag and metal within the crucible creates a considerable pressure on this hearth,* and because of the high temperature prevailing there, these refractory bricks must be reinforced by heavy metal jackets made of riveted steel plates or of segmental iron castings that are closely fitted and bolted together. Such jackets are always water-cooled: those of cast iron by internal circulating systems and those of steel by coolers set between the brickwork of the jackets. The upper diameter of this jacket is smaller than the diameter at the base so that the jacket will hold the walls of the

* The pressure caused by 8 feet of metal and 3 feet of slag will be about 30 pounds per square inch.

hearth in place by offering resistance to the buoyant forces of the bath and slag. The bottom of the crucible must be built up very carefully of high-grade fire brick with closely fitting joints in order to prevent intrusion of the metal. If such construction is not carried out, large sections of the bottom may be floated up by the heavy metal, thus endangering the whole bottom structure of the furnace. These bottoms vary in thickness from about 6 feet in the smaller furnaces to 12 feet in the larger ones. The bricks, at the end of the campaign of 4 to 7 years, may be almost entirely replaced by metal, which collects in the form of a solid mass (salamander), often weighing 50 to 100 tons.

92. Tapping Hole and Cinder Notch. The tapping hole or cinder notch is an opening about 6 by 8 inches on the inside, through which the molten metal may be drawn from the crucible. The outside dimensions are somewhat larger in order to permit the insertion of the tapping tools, and at this point the hearth jacket is usually protected by a water-cooled "dam plate." Furthermore, during the tapping of the iron, the metal parts of the furnace directly above the tapping hole are protected with a plate or chain screen (splasher).

There is usually only one cinder notch, located about 6 feet from the floor of the hearth and 4 or 5 feet above the tapping hole, generally placed 45 degrees from this opening if there are two notches, or 90 degrees if there is only one. Slag does not react explosively with water, as does molten iron; consequently, this opening can be protected from the corrosive action of the slag by means of a water-cooled metal casting. In the brickwork of the hearth, at the cinder notch level, is left a hole about 1 foot in diameter on the inside, increasing to about 2 feet on the outside, into which circular, cone-shaped hole is fitted the cooling devices—a cinder cooler, an intermediate or monkey cooler, and a monkey. A cinder cooler is a casting, made in the form of a hollow frustum of a cone, with a 1-inch space through which water circulates. Inside this and similarly shaped is placed the intermediate cooler and, finally, the monkey, which reduces the opening to about 2 inches in diameter. The intermediate cooler and monkey are made of cast bronze. During the operation of the furnace this opening is closed by means of a short iron rod called a "bott," fastened, for safety, to the end of a longer one.[*]

93. Tuyères. Tuyères, 10 to 16 in number, through[†] which heated air is blown into the furnace, are distributed symmetrically about the

---

[*] These are being replaced with mechanically operated "botts."
[†] Through these pass 40,000 to 80,000 cubic feet of air per minute.

upper circumference of the hearth just below the bosh. Indirectly, they also determine the height to which the slag in the furnace may rise above the slag notch; in most furnaces this is about 3 feet, allowing for the collection of 50 to 75 tons of slag. They are protected by tuyère coolers, similar to the cinder coolers, as indicated in Figure 17. The tuyère, shown in Figure 18, itself, which projects within the furnace, is made of copper or bronze, 4 to 7 inches internal diameter,

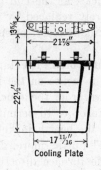

Cooling Plate

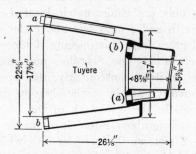

FIG. 18. Cooling Plates and Tuyère.
(a) Inlet (1¼″)   (b) Outlet (1¼″)

and, like the cooler, water-cooled to prevent corrosion and distortion. The life of a tuyère will vary from a few days to 10 months, depending upon furnace conditions and irregularities, raw materials, and condition of water.

In view of the fact that heated air must pass through these tuyères and connections and that the temperature of this air varies with operating and atmospheric conditions, special precautions must be taken to allow for expansion in order to keep this air system tight. Such a set of tuyère connections is shown in Figure 17. The blow pipe is a horizontal cast-iron pipe, 3 to 5 feet in length, both ends of which are turned to fit into double sockets in the tuyère and tuyère stock. This blow pipe connects with a tuyère stock, sometimes known as "leg pipe," "bootleg," or "pen stock," to which mechanical pressure is applied by means of a spiral spring so that the system may be held in place against the pressure of the blast as well as to compensate for the expansion and contraction which occur with changes in blast temperature. In the tuyère stock, and in line with the blow pipe and tuyère, is a small opening called a wicket (tuyère cap) through which a small rod may be inserted to clean the tuyères or through which, by means of a peep hole, conditions at the focus can be observed. The tuyère stock connects with the nozzle of the gooseneck, to which it is clamped by means of keys, and that in turn meets, at right angles, the neck of the bustle pipe. The bustle pipe, about 4 feet in outside diameter, and lined with fire-clay brick, encircles the furnace just below the mantle and distributes hot air to the tuyères. This, as well as all connections down to the blow pipe,* is lined with fire brick.

94. Bosh. The bosh is that part of the furnace, at the mantle level, just above the upper limits of the crucible, where the furnace attains its greatest diameter. Actually, it is the weakest part and must be very carefully constructed and maintained. Starting at the top of the hearth, the brickwork, which is normally about 27 inches in thickness, is stepped outward, externally, about 6 inches for each 12 inches of vertical rise. Each of these step-outs is supported by means of heavy steel "bosh bands." Between these bosh bands, or in large furnaces each pair of bosh bands, are inserted cooling plates called bosh plates. These bosh plates are in horizontal rows about 2 feet vertically apart, the plates in each row being about 2 feet apart and the plates in different rows staggered vertically so as to avoid making weak joints in the brickwork. The bosh plates, which are of course water-cooled, serve to protect the brickwork, because this point, being opposite the zone of fusion in the furnace, is likely to be corroded very rapidly by the hot slag.

At the upper limit of the bosh is the mantle, made up of heavy steel plates and angles, encircling the furnace. Upon it rests the weight of the stack, and this in turn is supported by a series of cast-iron or fabricated steel columns which rest on the main furnace foundation. Such construction permits the removal of the entire bosh and hearth without disturbing the rest of the furnace. This is frequently desirable, for it may become necessary to shut down the furnace for repairs to the hearth or crucible without disturbing the shaft.

* U. S. Patent 1362702 has been issued for a refractory-lined blow pipe.

95. Shaft or Stack. This comprises that part of the furnace located above the bosh but below the bells, and for convenience is divided into three almost equal parts, called the upper, middle, and lower inwalls. In order to meet local conditions, three different types of inwalls are employed; namely, the thick, the intermediate, and the thin.

A great many domestic furnaces are lined with thick walls up to 5 feet in thickness. They are inclosed with a heavy riveted steel shell about ½ inch thick and space allowed between the outside of the brickwork and the inside of the shell for loam or granulated slag that serves as a cushion in the expansion and contraction of the inwall. Such thick-walled furnaces not only serve to support the top but also seldom require water cooling.

In the intermediate type the walls are about 3 feet in thickness; and to cut down corrosion, cooling plates similar to the bosh plates* are inserted for a vertical distance of 20 to 40 feet above the bosh.

In the thin-walled type (few exist in the United States) the inwalls are only 9 to 18 inches thick, and not only must the shell be cooled throughout its entire length but also means must be provided for supporting the top on a separate structural framework. Cooling may be carried out by spraying the jacket with water and collecting this water in a large trough at the mantle level; the shell may be encircled by a series of deep, narrow, horizontal troughs through which water flows continuously from the top to the bottom of the stack; or the entire outer surface of the stack may be encircled with a spiral trough which is kept full of water by a series of feed lines.

The furnace "lines" and bosh angle will vary according to the type of lining employed. By lines is meant the contour formed by the inner edges of the vertical section through the center. In the old type of furnace the inwalls were straight and the boshes somewhat flat with corresponding sharp angles, but experience with the fine ores from the Lake Superior district has proved that much better furnace performance can be obtained with more nearly vertical lines. Consequently, in the latest type of furnace, shown in Figure 15, the lower inwall rises vertically for several feet, the bosh is steep, and the upper inwall drops vertically for a distance of about 10 feet from the stack line. With these changes have come corresponding ones in the bosh angle, which has gradually been increased to 79 to 85 degrees.

The brickwork forming the hearth, bosh, and inwalls of the furnace is referred to as the lining; and obviously, because of the very dif-

---

* Depending upon their location as well as conditions in the furnace, cooling plates will last 6 months to several years.

ferent thermal and mechanical conditions existing at these different levels, each requires a different type of brick. Fire-clay brick is universally used, and great care must be exercised because the life of the furnace depends in a large measure upon the lining, and the item of the cost of the brick is certainly not a small one. Although furnaces with approximately the same capacity show wide variations in the amount of brickwork used, a fair estimate for the modern 1000-ton stack is:

Bottom............ 131,000 9-inch equivalents ($9'' \times 4\frac{1}{2}'' \times 2\frac{1}{2}''$)
Hearth............ 43,900
Bosh.............. 48,900
Stack............. 353,800

This whole matter of refractories will be discussed in more detail in Article 182.

96. Double Bell and Hopper. In olden times the top of a blast furnace was "by day in a pillar of cloud . . . by night in a pillar of fire,"[*] for no attempt was made to collect the gas. Today every effort is made in top construction to equalize the distribution of the stock, to eliminate or compensate for irregularities in operation, and to hold at a minimum the dust carried over with the gas, and the gas lost to the atmosphere during charging. First the gas was used for burning bricks and heating small furnaces, but not until 1845 was it used to heat stoves. To collect the gas economically and easily an arrangement known as the bell and hopper was put into use in 1850; considerable gas was lost during the charging period, so later this was improved by introducing a second bell. Such a device is shown in Figure 19. Essentially this consists of a lower large bell and just above it a smaller bell and hopper, thus providing a gas-tight space between the two. The raw materials of the charge are first dropped into the upper hopper, whence it may fall into the lower one if the small bell is lowered. When sufficient charge has collected over the larger bell for charging into the furnace, the large bell is lowered, permitting the charge to fall into the furnace without the escape of much gas. These bells are usually supported from their top centers by means of a rod in a sleeve, each attached to a counterbalanced lever operated, or controlled, from the ground. The large bell is attached to the rod and the small bell to the sleeve. The bells are made of cast steel with a slope of 45 to 55 degrees, sufficient to permit the charge to slide off readily.

[*] Genesis XIII, 21.

The small upper bell has a revolving receiving hopper and just above that a stationary receiving hopper, which in turn receives ore from the skip hoist. The rotating hopper, carrying the small bell with it, can be revolved by a motor-driven reduction gear, which drives the rack fixed on the cast-steel plate carrying the rotating hopper. There

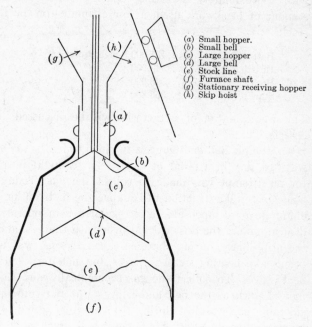

(a) Small hopper.
(b) Small bell
(c) Large hopper
(d) Large bell
(e) Stock line
(f) Furnace shaft
(g) Stationary receiving hopper
(h) Skip hoist

FIG. 19. McKee Revolving Top.

is an automatic switch gear which allows the rotation to take place through any angle to which it has previously been set, and, although the exact routine of charging can be varied at the discretion of the operator, one involving six stops, as indicated in Figure 20, is most commonly employed.

97. Other Top Openings. In order to provide for the escape of gases and flue dust from the furnace, two to four large openings, called offtakes,* are provided just beneath the large bell. From these openings, which are about 4 feet in diameter, fire-brick-lined pipes lead

* In recent construction these offtakes enter vertical "uptakes," closed at the top by explosion doors, to prevent large material from being thrown out of the furnace during slips or explosions and to reduce the load on the dust catcher.

downward to converge into one large pipe called the downcomer or downtake. Special openings, closed by explosion doors, are provided either in the offtake pipe or in the top itself. These serve to prevent ejection of the material from the furnace, to relieve pressure, and to prevent possible injury to the top by slips or explosion. Leading off the top is a "bleeder," a tall, vertical pipe usually inserted on the higher surface of the offtake pipe for the escape of surplus gas, in

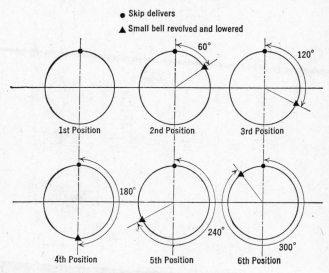

FIG. 20. Charging Rotation.

case it cannot be used in the stoves or boilers. Finally, a small opening, known as a "try hole," is provided in the top of the furnace through which passes a rod of steel called a stock indicator. This, by means of automatic devices at the base of the furnace, indicates continuously the level of the charge or stock line.

98. Skip Hoist. The old-time method of charging by barrows has been entirely superseded by automatic mechanical charging, whereby either a skip or bucket traverses an inclined fabricated steel structure extending from the top of a furnace to a point beneath the tracks of the stock house. In the skip type the conveying vessel is a small open-ended steel car called a "skip" that automatically dumps the material upon the little bell and hopper when it reaches the top of its journey. Such hoists are generally provided with double tracks so that the empty skip in descending helps in hoisting the loaded one on the other track. In the bucket type (offering a little more flexibility in charging) the solid materials are raised in a bucket suspended from a carriage which drops the charge directly into the space above the large bell.

99. Blast-Furnace Contour. The contour of an iron blast furnace, as shown in Figure 21, has changed materially during the past seventy years. It can be said that the furnace has approached very closely to the shape of a cylinder, the hearth has been made much wider, the

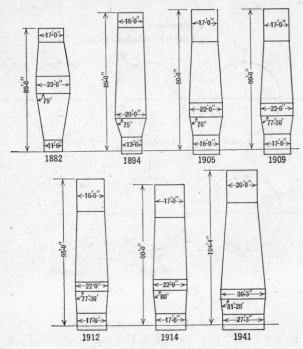

FIG. 21. Blast-Furnace Contour.

bosh lower, and the bosh angle increased. Although the change from the large bosh and small hearth was made necessary by reason of the change from coarse, hard ores and comparatively cold blasts to the soft, fine Mesabi ores and higher blast temperatures in modern practice, many other factors have served to contribute to this modification in contour. The change in height of the furnace, which has increased from about 60 feet to over 100 feet, has been due to:

1. More general use of coke of the by-product grade.
2. Changes in the chemical composition of the top gases.
3. Lower temperature of the top gases.

The inwall batter will be determined by the character of the ore in so far as it affects swelling, deposition of carbon, and the friction of the charge with the walls of the furnace. The relationship between the tuyère level and the slag notch or tapping hole will be determined by the probable slag volume, the quantity of iron to be produced, the pressure on the brickwork and casing, and the tapping interval. The effect of contour on flue dust losses and coke consumption has also been a contributing factor.

100. Modern Furnace. At this writing (March, 1942) the No. 3 Carrie Blast Furnace of the Carnegie Illinois Steel Corporation,* located at Munhall, Pennsylvania, is a good example of a modern furnace and is the largest, not only in content but in monthly production. This furnace, making basic iron, is 26 feet in hearth diameter and 105 feet high; it has a bosh angle of 81° 30', a stock line diameter of 20 feet, a big bell diameter of 14 feet 8 inches, 16 tuyères, and a total content (cinder line at the tapping hole to bottom of closed big bell) of 47,414 cubic feet.

This furnace, operating on Mesabi ores, produced 41,782 net tons of pig iron in January, 1942, an average of 1347 tons per day. For the 90-day period, December, 1941, to February, 1942, the furnace averaged 1330 tons per day.

The wind blown varied from 76,000 to 80,000 cubic feet per minute, the flue dust and sludge produced about 225 pounds per ton of iron, and gas produced 100,000 cubic feet per minute (at standard conditions). The charge consists of 20,000 pounds of coke, 49,000 pounds of ore and roll scale, 7000 pounds of basic open-hearth slag, and 10,000 pounds of limestone (10 to 15 per cent of this is dolomite).

STOVES AND UTILIZATION OF BLAST-FURNACE GAS

101. General. The early type of blast-furnace stove employed cast-iron, U-shaped pipes inclosed in a fire-brick structure, around which pipes the gases from the blast furnace were burned and circulated. This old type of recuperative stove labored under the shortcoming that it was impossible to heat the blast higher than 490°C. without the cast-iron pipe quickly burning out. When Neilsen first applied the stove to blast-furnace practice, in 1824, at the Clyde Iron Works, it required about 8 tons of coal to produce a ton of pig iron with cold blast. He raised the temperature of the blast to 150°C. with a reduction in fuel consumption to 5 tons of coal per ton of pig iron. By 1833, this had been further reduced to 2.6 tons at 600°F. In 1857

* Private communication.

Cowper and Whitwell applied Siemen's regenerative principle to the hot-blast stove, with the result that today, with blast temperatures ranging from 600 to 800°C., the coke consumption is 0.7 to 0.9 ton per ton of pig iron.*

102. Stoves. The blast-furnace stove during the past 70 years has become pretty much conventionalized in the shape of a cylinder of

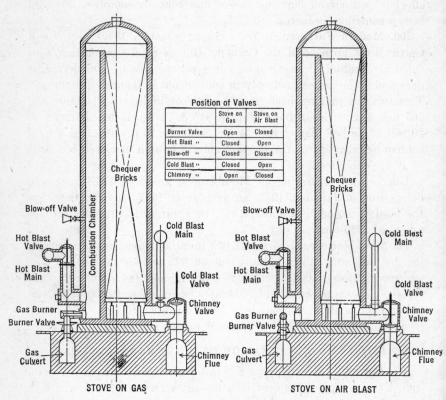

Position of Valves	Stove on Gas	Stove on Air Blast
Burner Valve	Open	Closed
Hot Blast "	Closed	Open
Blow-off "	Closed	Closed
Cold Blast "	Closed	Open
Chimney "	Open	Closed

STOVE ON GAS   STOVE ON AIR BLAST

FIG. 22. Blast-Furnace Stove.

boiler plate about 22 feet in diameter by 100 feet in height filled with a checkerwork of fire brick as shown in Figure 22. This checkerwork is heated by the combustion of blast-furnace gas and subsequently gives up a part of its heat to air from the atmosphere, passed through it in the reverse direction. Common practice is to provide four stoves for each blast furnace, on the basis that, as the number of stoves in-

* With a consumption of 1700 pounds of coke per ton of pig iron, about 120,000 cubic feet of top gas are produced per ton of pig iron.

crease: (1) the velocity of the gas, and hence the rate of heat transfer, falls off; (2) the heat losses through radiation increase; and (3) leakage increases. The operator hesitates to use as few as two stoves per blast furnace because of (1) the necessity for frequent cleaning, (2) little reserve capacity, and (3) deterioration of the fire brick because of higher temperatures during a part of the cycle. Internally the combustion chamber extends from the bottom to the top of the stove and may be located at the center in the so-called center-combustion stoves or at the circumference in the side-combustion ones. The arrangement of the flues also furnishes a means of classifying stoves into two-, three-, or four-pass stoves, depending upon the number of times the gases from the combustion chamber pass through the regenerative flue system. Practically all stoves are now of the two-pass type; and the combustible gases being burned at the bottom of the stove, it follows that in two-pass stoves the products of combustion, passing through the checker, must leave the stove at the bottom. Hence the opening to the stack, on two-pass stoves, is there.

During all these years stove construction and practice have been for the most part faulty and unscientific because stove design has been dictated more than anything else by the degree of cleaning of the blast-furnace gas. The universal presence of large quantities of flue dust and the necessity of building a stove which would operate with dirty gas have been the chief factors in determining the size and kind of stove which would be able to transmit to the blast the desired quantity of heat during a period sufficiently great to make stove changes convenient. The heating surface, as well as the volume of checker brick, was limited by the necessity of having large openings and thick walls. Large openings were a means of delaying, but not preventing, the "plugging" of the checkers, whereas the thickness of the walls was habitually increased because of the abuse given the top of the checker construction during the frequent periods of cleaning and to compensate for the fusing of the combustion chamber, walls, and checkers by the flue dust (clean-out doors are provided at convenient points to facilitate the removal of the dust). Under such conditions heat transfer to and from the stove was slow and inefficient; glazed and sintered surfaces were unfavorable influences; and it was seldom that all the checkers were unobstructed. More important even than these disadvantages was the large size of the individual flue and the comparatively great free area through the checker passages as shown in Figure 23. The principles of a hot-blast stove design, leading to improvements in this condition, are discussed in Article 104.

103. Burners and Valves. The burners employed are usually very simple in construction, consisting of a movable gooseneck mounted on a rack attached to the terminal of a vertical section of an underground gas flue so that the horizontal portion extends into a gas port in the side of the stove. A plate or valve cover is attached to the base of the gooseneck so that racking the gooseneck back and forward automatically closes or opens the connection to the gas main. The essential valves for controlling the gas and air are:

1. The gas valve described above.
2. The chimney valve located at the base of the stack and preventing the escape of air through that opening when the stove is on blast.
3. The cold-blast valve located in the airline.
4. The hot-blast valve, which controls the exit of the blast from the stove.
5. A blow-off valve, which relieves the pressure and provides the removal of the air on changing the stove from air to gas.
6. A mixer valve, used to maintain a "straight-line heat" by mixing cold blast from the main with hot blast from the stove in varying proportions during the period the stove is on blast, so that the desired hot-blast temperature can be maintained with a minimum of variance.

104. Stove Linings. The brick for these linings need not be very refractory because the temperature in the stove is relatively low,

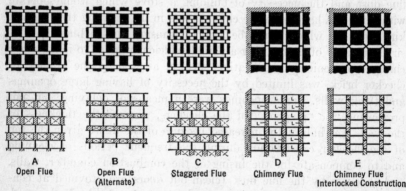

A	B	C	D	E
Open Flue	Open Flue (Alternate)	Staggered Flue	Chimney Flue	Chimney Flue Interlocked Construction

Fig. 23. Conventional Checker Brick. (*Courtesy Carnegie-Illinois Steel Corp.*)

except in the combustion chamber, where a brick possessing fairly high refractory properties must be used. It is obvious that the checkerwork brick must have high thermal capacity and heat conductivity. Formerly, these checkers were built of brick of the conventional rectangular form as shown in Figure 23 and supported by brick arches built into the bottom of the stove. Improvements in gas cleaning,

together with intensive research on stove design, such as those of
A. J. Boynton[6] and F. T. Kinney,[8] have made possible certain generali-
zations regarding stove design. It can now be said that heat transfer
in a stove will vary:

1. As about the 0.8 power of the velocity of the gas, expressed in pounds
per second per square foot of free area.

2. As the 0.5 power of the arithmetic mean absolute temperature of the
gas in °F.

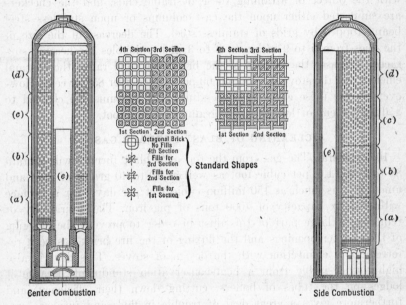

FIG. 24. Brassert Stove. (*Courtesy of H. A. Brassert and Co.*)

(a) 1st section of brick   (d) 4th section of brick
(b) 2nd   "   "   "   (e) Combustion chamber
(c) 3rd   "   "   "

3. As the 0.2 power of the surface factor expressed in reciprocal feet (the
area of the surface through which heat transfer is taking place divided by
the volume of the open space through which the gas is flowing).

4. Directly as the average specific heat of the gases and of the refractory
at constant pressure.

So much for theoretical consideration, but practical ones of equal
importance demand that there should be:

1. The maximum volume of brick in a minimum space so disposed as to
present the largest heating surface and still maintain high and equal velocities in all parts of the stove.

2. Flues of as small cross section as possible, particularly in the cooler parts of the stove.

3. Continuity of checker flues, facilitating inspection and repair.

4. Turbulence, without excessive pressure drop.

5. Adequate structural strength; but past experience has shown that nothing less than 2-inch thickness can be entertained if the proper structural stability and long life of the lining are to be expected.

Brick of many special shapes, shown in Figure 24, are now in use with the object of attaining these desirable ends, and the checkers are supported either upon the cast columns or upon stainless steel beams topped by grids of stainless steel. The decrease of the size of the flues from 5 to 9 inches to 2 to 3 inches doubles the heating surfaces, increases the volume of the brickwork, and raises the thermal efficiency of the stove from about 60 per cent to over 85 per cent. However, to use these checkers successfully, the gas must be cleaned to a dust content of less than 0.3 grain per cubic foot.

CLEANING OF BLAST-FURNACE GAS

105. General. The gas from the top of a blast furnace will contain 85 to 100 B.t.u. per cubic foot as well as 10 to 40 grains of dust and amount to as much as 150 million cubic feet per day,[*] for a furnace with a daily capacity of 1000 tons of pig iron. The desirability of removing a large part of this dust in order to prevent the clogging of the checker openings and the fluxing of the fire brick has been referred to in connection with the design of stoves. This dust is also highly undesirable from a heat-conservation standpoint because it lodges on the tubes of boilers, cutting down their efficiency, and furthermore gives a great deal of trouble in flues and furnaces employed for general heating purposes. As a result, the trend today is toward as complete cleaning of this gas as is consistent with a moderate cost.

106. Uses of Blast-Furnace Gas. A modern, large steel plant usually has its own coke-oven plant so that blast-furnace and coke-oven gas are both available and applicable to any of the iron- and steel-making processes, including the generation of power. The coke-oven gas is ordinarily high grade enough so that it may be used as a domestic or municipal fuel, and therefore its use about the plant will be dictated by local conditions and prices. Blast-furnace gas, either alone or mixed

---

[*] The amount of flue dust will vary widely (75 pounds to 500 pounds per ton of pig iron produced, depending upon the character of the charge, the rate of blowing, and the lines of the furnace).

with coke-oven gas, is commonly used about the plant for the following purposes:

1. The burning of blast-furnace gas in stoves for the regenerative heating of air for the blast furnace is the oldest and, metallurgically, the most important of uses. It is universally performed with unmixed blast-furnace gas and normally requires, for a blast temperature of 730°C., not over 25 per cent of the total gas generated by the blast furnace.

2. Unmixed blast-furnace gas is frequently used about the plants for steam-raising purposes.* With the high efficiency of the modern boiler, and with improvements in gas cleaning, this is at the present time the most important application in the steel plant.

3. There have been a number of large-scale installations of gas engines using unmixed blast-furnace gas for both blowing and power. Whereas the use and renewal of these plants still continue, the tendency in recent years has been to take advantage of the marked improvement in boiler construction and operation, and of the increased size and efficiency of the steam turbine, and to install the boiler-turbine units for both blowing and power.

4. In recent years there have been several notable installations involving the use of blast-furnace gas in the underfiring of coke ovens. This may be carried out with either straight blast-furnace gas or with a mixture of coke-oven and blast-furnace gases. The temperature requirements are moderate— 800 to 1370°C.

5. Another very promising use is the mixing of blast-furnace gas with coke-oven gas for open-hearth fuel to obtain temperatures of 1700-1900°C. It appears that no single fuel has obtained the heat economy in the open hearth which is possible with such mixtures, but the proper use of these fuels requires a variation in the percentage of coke-oven gas contained in the fuel mixture in accordance with the stage of the open-hearth process.

6. Blast-furnace gas, either alone or mixed with coke-oven gas, is commonly employed for mill heating (1200-1350°C.). Not only is it an effective use for excess gas, but in mill heating the proportions can be varied at will in accordance with the temperature of the steel entering the furnace, the temperature to which it is desired to heat, as well as the required speed of heating and the size of the steel. Any excess gas is usually burned in stack bleeders into the atmosphere, particularly at large furnace plants (over five furnaces).

107. Dust Catchers. The principle involved in the construction of the dust catcher is that of greatly reduced velocity† accompanied by sudden change of direction. As commonly built, it consists of a mild

---

* Normally 100,000 cubic feet of gas is equivalent to 650 pounds of coal (13,000 B.t.u. per pound).

† The velocity of gas at the inlet of the dust catcher is 40-60 feet per second; in the dust catcher 1-5 feet per second.

steel shell about 25 feet in diameter by 35 feet in height, as shown
in Figure 25, with a conical bottom and a dome top. Although dust
catchers, in the past, were lined with fire brick, the tendency now is
to build them without this lining. The discharge of the dust is by
means of a conical valve at the bottom. Usually such a dust catcher
retains all the particles coarser than about 20 mesh. This dust, which
consists of fine particles* of ore, coke dust, and limestone (see Table

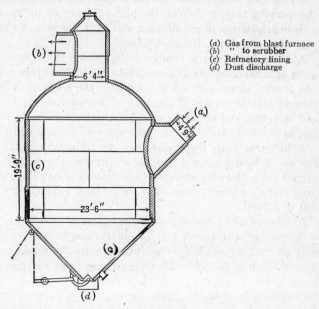

(a) Gas from blast furnace
(b) "   to scrubber
(c) Refractory lining
(d) Dust discharge

FIG. 25. Dust Catcher.

27) can be drawn off, briquetted, or sintered and made a part of the
blast-furnace charge. From the dust catcher the gas, now cleaned to
about 3.5 grains per cubic foot, enters a large gas main from which
it may be distributed for use about the plant, because certain uses
permit gas of this dust content to be employed directly for heating
purposes. In view of the fact that the difficulty of removing dust
increases very rapidly as the particle size decreases, plants are generally designed to clean the gas in two stages: a primary stage in
which only the coarser particles are removed and a secondary one

* Although irregularities in operation may throw particles as coarse as ¼ inch
in diameter into the dust catcher, normally all the dust will pass a 14-mesh
screen and 75 per cent a 65-mesh screen.

TABLE 27

ANALYSES OF FLUE DUST AND SLUDGE*

(Lake Ores)

Product	Per Cent					
	Fe	P	Insol.	CaO	C	S
Flue dust (normal)	36.8	0.21	13.8	7.8	15.2	0.28
„ „ „	45.8	0.09	14.0	2.9	10.8	0.18
Flue dust (extreme)	21.6	0.22	11.9	13.2	30.6	0.16
„ „ „	22.1	0.21	17.8	9.6	26.5	0.17
Sludge	48.2	0.09	12.4		5.8	

* Private communication.

where as much of the remaining dust as practicable is taken out. Under normal conditions the average dust content of the gas leaving the furnaces varies from 10 to 40 grains per cubic foot, that leaving the dust catcher contains 3 to 10 grains, that leaving the primary cleaners 0.06 to 1.0 grain, and that leaving the secondary cleaners 0.005 to 0.1 grain. In general it may be said that a dust content of not more than 0.01 grain is desirable for gas engines and 0.2 to 1.0 grain for stoves and boilers. The methods used to obtain the above result may be conveniently divided into the dry-cleaning and the wet-cleaning processes. In the former, the principal aim is to remove the dust without cooling, thus conserving the sensible heat which may be an important item if the gas does not carry too much moisture. In the latter method the aim is to wet the particles, agglomerate them, and wash them out of the gas with water.

108. Wet Cleaning. For primary wet cleaning the Feld washers have been very commonly used. This washer consists of a stationary steel shell divided into about five compartments and an equal number of revolving pans, one for each compartment, attached to a central revolving shaft. The gas enters at the bottom, ascends through the different compartments, while clean water is admitted at the top to flow downward through each compartment and be sprayed from each pan by centrifugal force toward the shell, thus cutting across the gas stream, wetting and agglomerating the particles of dust. Secondary wet cleaners of the Thiessen disintegrator type consist of a type of fan that disintegrates the water introduced in small jets into a spray which is forced to travel in one direction while the gas is forced through the same channels in an opposite one.

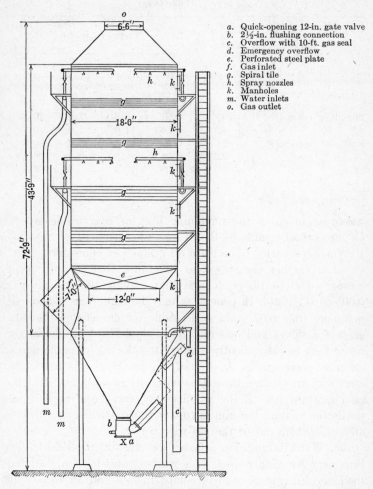

a. Quick-opening 12-in. gate valve
b. 2½-in. flushing connection
c. Overflow with 10-ft. gas seal
d. Emergency overflow
e. Perforated steel plate
f. Gas inlet
g. Spiral tile
h. Spray nozzles
k. Manholes
m. Water inlets
o. Gas outlet

FIG. 26. Brassert Washer.

In addition to the Feld, Thiessen, and McKee* washers, still more highly refined washers of the Brassert type, shown in Figure 26, have been developed. This 3-stage washer consists of a shell 9 feet in diameter by 70 feet in height. The gas enters the washer at the

* At a large Lake plant (13 furnaces) the McKee cleans the gas to 0.06-0.18 grain per cubic foot.

bottom and passes through two banks of 6-inch spiral tile. These banks have a set of 6 sprays operating at a pressure of 10 pounds per square inch and should clean the gas to 0.25 grain per cubic foot. The gas then passes through stationary disintegrators operating at 150 pounds per square inch, and then to the eliminator section, which consists of one layer of 4-inch spiral tile which is periodically flushed by 7 sprays. The gas passes downward through the spiral tile, and through the whirling action imparted to it by the tile loses much of the entrained water it contains. The total water consumption is of the order of 30 gallons per thousand cubic feet, and gas can be cleaned to 0.15 grain of dust per cubic foot. The pressure drop through such a washer will be about 14 inches of water.

109. Dry Cleaning. The secondary dry cleaners have included bag filters, but these have not been particularly successful because of the great volume of gas to be filtered as well as the high temperatures and moisture contents frequently encountered in blast-furnace operation. In recent years the Cottrell electrical precipitation method has been installed in a number of plants. In this method of dry cleaning, used very extensively in non-ferrous smelters, the dust-laden gas passes through narrow channels or ducts across which a high-tension, direct-current electric field (about 75,000 volts) is maintained. The dust particles in passing through this electric field may be made to assume an electric charge and be attracted to an oppositely charged surface. The precipitated fume builds up, as a layer, on this and, when of sufficient thickness, may be dislodged at intervals by mechanical hammers. This dislodged material falls from the electrodes, is collected in hoppers below the treater, from which it can be removed mechanically and returned to the main system for retreatment. Usually it is briquetted, or sintered, and returned to the blast furnace as a part of the charge. Large Cottrell treaters consist of large rooms through which the gas may be passed and in which are suspended a number of vertical plates, chains, pipes, or wires.

110. Condensation Cleaning of Blast-Furnace Gas. Even with the great amount of attention which has been given to the cleaning of blast-furnace gas in the past few years, it a curious commentary on what in patent parlance may be called the "state of the art" that few operators have given any consideration whatever to the utilization of what is perhaps the most essential constituent of blast-furnace gas; namely, its humidity or water vapor content. Because of the microscopic nature of the fine particles it is a common objective of all the cleaning systems to increase the mass of the individual particles of dust or fume by driving them into a film or drop of water or loading them with electrons. It seems curious that few have tried to take advantage of the water in the gas and bring about this same separation by causing the water vapor in the gas to condense upon these particles. In every case where blast-furnace gas is cooled below its dew point, water vapor is condensed and particles wet thereby. R. R. Harmon[18] has carried out a great deal of experimental and development work which tends to show that this new condensation method, as outlined below, gives great promise of success. The essential steps are:

1. Intensively scrub the gases to remove all solids yielding to mechanical treatment while the gases are at a temperature above the final dew point.

2. Simultaneously with the scrubbing operation, transform all sensible heat of the gases into latent heat by evaporation of the maximum amount of the water. This is accomplished and safeguarded by recirculation of hot water through the primary scrubber, permitting ample time for complete humidification and preventing any condensation of water vapor during these two operations.

3. Regulate the humidity to maintain a uniform dew point of the gases.

4. Cool the stripped and humidified gases step by step to condense the water vapor on the residual fine particles, removing the larger particles in each cooling step to prevent subsequent condensation of vapor on them.

5. Regulate the degree of cooling in each condensation stage, or in other words control the distribution of condensed water vapor in the cooling stages so as to cause the wetting and immediate removal of the larger particles of dust in each stage and thus conserve water. As the gas passes from stage to stage, it becomes cleaner and cleaner, the only limit being set by the amount of water vapor remaining in the gas.

Although this method has not been tried out on a large blast furnace, tests on a reduced scale have given very encouraging results. A two-stage system embracing a humidifier or primary unit and a condenser or secondary unit was operated continuously for a period of weeks, treating gas from a furnace making basic iron. The gas from a dry dust catcher, varying from 1.5 to 3.0 grains of very fine dust per cubic foot, entered the humidifier, and with condensation cleaning of the above description this gas was cleaned over a range of 0.0004 to 0.030 grain per cubic foot, and at all times the gas leaving the secondary unit was dry.

111. **Use of Hot Water.** Another modification involves two stages: first, the hot washing, humidifying, and conditioning stage, and,

second, the condensing and cooling stage, the sludge being removed from the bottom of the first stage. Such a washer is shown in Figure 27.

The efficiency of cleaning gas with hot water is much greater than with cold water because the viscosity and surface tension of hot water is much less than cold water, and the ability of the washing media to wet the dust particle is therefore greatly increased. It is a

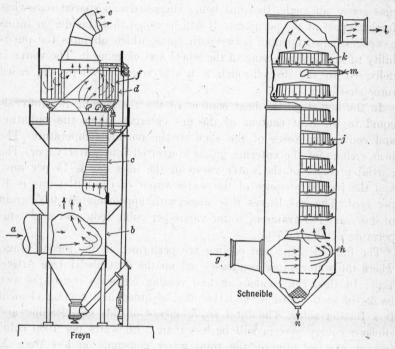

FIG. 27. Wet Washer.

a. Gas inlet
b. Tangential, 1st stage
c. Wood hurdle, 2nd stage
d. Cyclone drum, 3rd stage
e. Gas outlet
f. Rubber vanes
g. Gas inlet

h. Wet cyclone
j. Impingement plates
k. Entrainment separator
l. Gas outlet
m. Water inlet
n. Water and sludge outlet

well-known fact that if cold water is poured upon an impalpable powder, the water will form globules upon the surface of the powder; but if hot water is added, an emulsion is quickly formed. The degree to which any mechanical or static spray will atomize is a function of the surface tension and the viscosity of the fluid. It can be shown that the average size of the atomized water particle with hot water is much smaller, and the degree of cleaning in the wet type of gas cleaners varies with some function of the degree of atomization.

In the hot stage the rough cleaning is performed by two sets of stationary hurdles made of white pine, metal, or ceramic acid material. This hurdle surface will completely remove all large, coarse, or abrasive particles from the gas stream and humidify the gas. Final cleaning in this stage is accomplished by passing the gas through a Bassler rotor which consists of a cone disc with a large number of projecting pins set at an angle, the pins being staggered and spaced somewhat farther apart at the periphery. It will be noted that this design forms a wedge-shaped opening between the pins, which obviates the possibility of material adhering to the wheel and clogging it. The water is delivered to the disc through a nozzle which envelops the cased rotor shaft.

In the hot stage the heat content of the gas leaving the tower is equal to the heat content of the gas entering minus the radiation and convection losses of the shell to the outside temperature. The heat content of the entering gas is converted into water vapor. The partial pressure of the water vapor of the inlet gas is 15 per cent, and the partial pressure of the water vapor of the outlet gas is 40 per cent. The gas leaves this stage with approximately 0.05 grain of dust and 100 grains of water vapor per cubic foot, and at a temperature of about 75°C.

The final cleaning and cooling are performed in the second stage, where the water vapor condenses out on the dust nuclei (see Article 110). In this, the condensing and cooling elements consist of two banks of static hurdles, and the final cleaning and cooling element is a Bassler rotor. The total requirements of this gas-cleaning and sludge-recovery system will be less than 2 kilowatts per 1000 cubic feet of gas per minute, the total water consumption less than 22 gallons per thousand cubic feet of gas, and the waste water will not have more than 10 grains of suspended solids per gallon. The fine cleaned gas will have less than 0.015 grain of dust per cubic foot and less than 0.1 grain of entrained moisture.

112. Typical Gas-Cleaning Plants. A modern gas-cleaning plant, shown in diagrammatic form in Figure 28, is typical of Lake practice and follows out the general principles laid down. The dust from such a furnace, about 40 tons per day, even at a nominal value of $2.00 per ton, represents the saving of nearly $30,000 per year. In many wet-cleaning systems it is necessary to use as much as 2500 gallons of water per minute per furnace, more when secondary wet washing is carried out. In most districts this effluent must be clarified not only because of the value of the solids but also to conform with local laws. Federal and state authorities insist that this dust be kept out of navigable rivers and harbors, and the contamination of streams and lakes is being prohibited over a wider area each year.

Looked at from an economic standpoint, most plants aim at a recovery of 90 per cent of the suspended solids from the scrubber water, which usually corresponds to a solid content of about 15

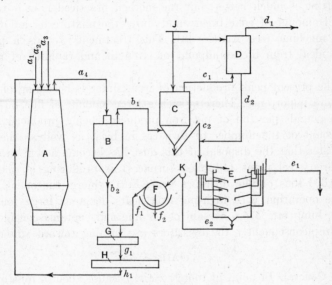

FIG. 28. Gas-Cleaning Plant.

A. Blast furnace. a_1. Ore. a_2. Coke. a_3. Limestone. a_4. Raw gas—10 gr./cu.ft.— 180#/ton pig.
B. Dry dust catcher. b_1. Gas—4–6 gr./cu.ft. b_2. Dry dust—90#/ton pig.
C. Primary wet washer. c_1. Gas—0.25 gr./cu.ft. c_2. Wash water—190 gr./gal.
D. Electrical precipitators. d_1. Clean gas— 0.01 gr./cu.ft. d_2. Dust.

E. Thickener. e_1. Water to sewer—15 gr./gal. e_2. Sludge—40–50% solids. 90# Dry wt./ ton pig. 90–95% recovery.
F. Filter. f_1. Filter cake—16–22% H_2O. f_2. Filtrate to sewer.
G. Pug mill. g_1. 10–11% H_2O.
H. Sintering machine. h_1. Sinter.
J. Water supply.
K. Pump.

grains per gallon. From the standpoint of stream pollution, still better clarity is desired, for rather dirty river or lake water will have a turbidity of only 12.

The thickened sludge may be run into a pit or basin, allowed to drain, and sent back to the ore yard (the plant illustrated furnishes 14,000 tons of cheap ore per year in the form of dust and sludge); it may be pumped into a dry-dust car and allowed to drain or, and this is the best practice, be filtered and mixed with flue dust or fine ore in a pug mill. This sludge may be thickened easily to 60–63 per cent solids; if it is to be filtered and sintered, 40 per cent is more economical. With vacuum filters the capacity is 800 to 1200 pounds of dry dust per square foot per day. Cake moisture will range from 16 to 26 per cent. The cake* is mixed in a pug mill with dry dust to give a resultant moisture of 10 to 11 per cent.

This mixture may be nodulized but there is a tendency to glaze over the surfaces of the particles and slow down the penetration of the reducing gas in the blast furnace. From a theoretical standpoint briquetting is much better, but the method practiced now is to add a small amount of coke breeze and sinter the mixture on a Dwight-Lloyd machine (see Article 48). This treatment[17] yields a porous sinter, ideal from the standpoint of strength and rapidity of reduction.

At the present peak production of iron, sinter is becoming of more and more importance. There is such a large amount of flue dust (up to 375 pounds per ton of pig iron produced) being produced today on account of the number of furnaces in blast as well as the high wind rates that the disposal of this dust has become a real problem. One large steel plant (13 blast furnaces) is producing at the rate of 750,000 tons of flue dust per year. Furthermore, the open-hearth furnace operating with high-pig iron heats demands large tonnages of dry, lump ore. Most Mesabi ore is fine and contains considerable moisture; consequently the operators are turning toward sinter.

AIR

113. General. In point of tonnage, air, because about 4 tons of this raw material is used in the production of 1 ton of pig iron, is one of the major items in blast-furnace operation. Unfortunately, too, air is even more variable in character than any of the other raw materials, and this variability is under less positive control. As a matter of fact, the blast-furnace operator watches the weather with even a keener interest than the baseball-club manager, knowing that the efficient operation of his furnace depends partly upon the moisture content of the air. James Gayley, in 1904, realized the importance of this uniformity in blast-furnace operation and built the first refrigerating plant to freeze the moisture out of the air and thus eliminate

* Dry basis screen analysis of the wet dust:

+40 mesh	0.33 per cent
+60 mesh	1.28
+80	3.15
+100	4.04
+200	15.68
−200	84.32

this variable. The success of the dry blast was definitely proved, but it was abandoned in 1916 by reason of the high investment and maintenance costs involved. The chilling effect of water vapor on the blast furnace is obvious when one considers the very high heat of decomposition. This lowering of the temperature at the tuyère zone and in the zone of fusion of the blast furnace will markedly affect the character of the iron being produced by the furnace (particularly the silicon content).

The better knowledge obtained through the development of air conditioning in other branches of industry and the demands of industry for a more closely controlled iron caused the Woodward Iron Company of Woodward, Alabama, to attack the problem anew in 1939 and install a precompression, chilled-water system on one of their blast furnaces, hoping to overcome the high and widely fluctuating humidity and maintain a constant moisture content in the blast of about 3 grains per cubic foot. There was a marked improvement on this one furnace, and the experience at this plant demonstrated the adaptability of modern air-conditioning equipment to this use.

To be still more specific, it can be said that for a furnace producing 550 tons of pig iron per day, with 50,000 cubic feet of blast per minute, each grain per cubic foot decrease in the water means a reduction of 5 net tons of water or, under very humid conditions, dry blast prevents, per day, 30 tons of water from entering the blast furnace. Without dry blast, variations in moisture content are fought by varying the temperature of the hot blast. General practice is to allow 15 to 25°C. increase for each grain per cubic foot. This requires that reserve capacity be left in the stoves in anticipation of such a sudden rise. The charge requires 10 to 12 hours to reach the hearth, with the result that the weather must be accurately predicted or ample leeway left in the stoves for the purpose of keeping the furnace regular until the burden can be changed to conform to whatever weather may be expected in the next 12 to 18 hours. As regards coke consumption, it is estimated that one grain per cubic foot accounts for about 48 pounds of coke per ton of pig iron.*

There is available a wide variety of fully developed and practical air-conditioning equipment, each having widely varying characteris-

---

* On the other hand, many blast-furnace operators question this. For example, at one large steel plant they plotted data for the years 1939 and 1940, and with the average moisture in July and August of 5.5 to 7.0 it was found that the "coke practice" was as low in these months as it was during months when the moisture was 2.0 to 3.5 grams per cubic foot.

tics. Points of difference include the form, shape, and principle of the equipment; the amount of, and the form in which energy is applied; the points at which this energy is applied; and the extent of dehydration as indicated:

1. Removal by condensation before compression.
2. Removal by condensation after compression.
3. Dehydration with solid absorbents.

114. Jones and Laughlin Steel Corporation Plant. In April, 1941, the Jones and Laughlin Steel Corporation* put in operation a conditioning system similar to that of the Woodward Iron Company on one of their large furnaces which has a hearth diameter of 28 feet 6 inches, height of 90 feet, bosh diameter of 30 feet, and is equipped with 18 tuyères, through which 80,000 cubic feet of air pass per minute. The operation of this furnace has been noticeably smoother and more uniform than the other four blast furnaces which are not equipped with air conditioning, and, from the data shown in Table 28 there

TABLE 28

CONTROLLED MOISTURE IN BLAST-FURNACE AIR*

| Period | | Per Cent Increase in Iron Production | Per Cent Decrease in Coke Consumption | Humidity gr. cu. ft. Natural Air | | | Air Conditioned |
With Air Conditioning	Without Air Conditioning			Min.	Max.	Avg.	
April, 1941, to September, 1941	Monthly Average for 1940	8.22	3.03	1.355	9.962	5.087	3.298
June, 1941	June, 1940	14.55	4.31	2.746	9.066	5.666	3.351
July	July	16.67	5.46	3.064	9.962	6.702	3.642
August	August	14.84	3.04	3.064	8.782	5.757	3.499
September	September	18.46	0.25†	2.849	9.655	5.398	3.251
Avg. June–September, inc.	June–September, inc.	16.07	4.26†				

* *Steel*, Nov. 10, 1941.
† Coke not representative.

* *Steel*, Nov. 10. 1941

has been apparently a decided improvement in both iron production and coke consumption.

115. The Blaw Knox Process. This system, shown in diagrammatic Figure 29, is designed to remove both the water vapor and dirt from

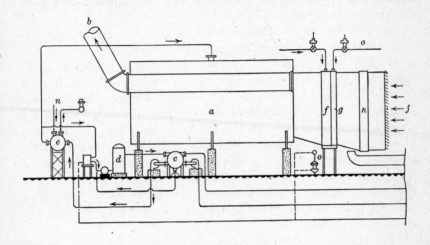

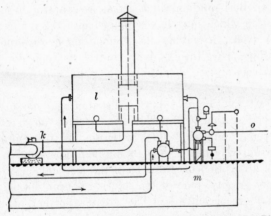

Fig. 29. Blaw Knox Air-Conditioning Plant.

a. Contactor	f. Air cooler	l. Regenerator
b. Conditioned air to blower	g. Air heater	m. Heat exchanger
c. Sump tank	h. Air filter	n. Water inlets
d. Filter	j. Air inlet	o. Steam inlets
e. Cooler	k. Fan	

the blast air, controlling the air going to the blowing engines at any predetermined vapor content and temperature.

Air at atmospheric temperature, humidity, and pressure enters the air filter where dirt is removed, after which the air passes through heating and cooling coils which either heat or cool the air, depending on the setting of a dry-bulb controller in the outlet air. This compensates for the difference of temperature in the atmospheric air, making it uniform and in conformity with the control point. After the air passes through the heating and cooling coils, it enters the plenum chamber of the dehumidifier and then through the next section, where it comes in contact with the dehydrating solution and gives up its water vapor, and at the same time is equalized to the outlet air temperature setting. This contact section consists of Raschig rings held in place by two parallel open-mesh screens. The air passes horizontally while the liquid drops vertically. Contact between the air and liquid takes place on the surface of the rings, as a result of which entrainment of solution is avoided. The heat generated by the absorbing action is taken up by the solution trickling down over the contact bed. Under certain conditions of humidity, when the inlet moisture is extremely low, moisture must be added to maintain a constant grain loading which is done by means of a steam jet just ahead of the dehumidifier.

After passing through the contact bed, the air continues through a dry bed composed of Berl saddles which act as a separator to stop any particles of solution which may have dropped into the air paths from the open-mesh screen. Air leaving the dehumidifier flows through the outlet collecting pipe, past the dry-bulb control thermometer, to the blowing apparatus at any predetermined moisture and temperature condition.

The dehydrating salt solution is fed to a distributing pan at the top of the contact bed section. From this pan it flows down over the ring packing, where it makes contact with the air, then into a solution sump located directly below the dehumidifier. The solution is partly diluted by the absorption of water from the air, and, in order to maintain the proper gravity, part of the solution is sent through a regenerating cycle and reconcentrated. The greater portion of the solution after leaving the solution sump is pumped through a solution cooler where the heat of solution is transferred to the water used for cooling.

That portion of the solution to be reconcentrated is first filtered and then passed through a heat exchanger, picking up heat from reconcentrated solution being returned to the sump. The partially heated solution then goes to a steam heater where the solution is heated to the proper reactivation temperature before it is sprayed over the contact bed of the regenerator. In this contact bed the solution meets air being blown up through it. In meeting this air, the solution gives up the moisture that has been absorbed in the dehumidifier. The air passes through a stack to the atmosphere, and the solution drains back through the heat exchanger where it in turn gives up its heat to the cold solution coming to the regenerator and finally blows back into the sump under the dehumidifier.

The plant is fully automatic and, under the usual conditions, air can be supplied to the stack at any desired moisture content down to 1.5 grains per cubic foot.

ACCESSORY EQUIPMENT

116. Mud Gun. When a blast furnace is tapped and the iron has almost ceased to flow from the tapping hole, it becomes necessary to close this hole in order that iron and slag may again collect in the crucible. This is a rather difficult task, for, under the pressure of blast in the furnace, gases are pouring forth from this hole. To accomplish this closure, a clay or mud gun hung on a crane at the side of the runner is provided. It could, of course, be closed by hand (as a matter of fact, it used to be); but it is much quicker and more convenient to do this mechanically. The old type of mud gun was provided with a steam cylinder operating a ram, which in turn forced a quantity of clay, mixed with a little coke dust, into the tap hole. This was done under considerable pressure so that the clay formed a plug that closed this opening. This first plug of clay could then be backed up with more of the same mixture fed into the clay gun in the form of moist balls. Such a mechanically operated gun is preferred by furnace men because it permits the furnace to be kept on blast even while the hole is being plugged. Actually, it was a bit more convenient to shut off the blast momentarily in order that this closure might be effected more easily. Recently, a new type of mud gun operated by electricity (the Brassert) has been developed, which is a notable advance over the old steam type. It operates more evenly, greater pressures are available, and it has been found that the furnace can be kept on blast during the casting period. And, although this delay is at worst only of a few minutes duration, the gross amount of delay is considerable when calculated in terms of tons of iron (nearly a ton per minute in a large furnace).

117. Runners. These are metal castings, laid end on end to form deep troughs, through which slag or metal may be conducted away from the furnace. These troughs are given a heavy coating of loam or clay wash before casting or lined with sand to insulate and protect the trough from the hot metal. The iron or casting trough fits up close to the iron notch at the upper end, and at the lower end is the dam, skimmer, and "big gate," by means of which the trough is drained after the cast. The molten iron comes from the iron notch into the trough and is separated from the slag by the skimmer. The iron flows under the skimmer and over the dam into the iron runner which carries it to the hot metal ladles, and the slag is skimmed off the top and flows to one side into the slag runner, which carries it to the cinder ladle cars or to the granulating pit.

118. Slag Disposal. Although blast-furnace slag does have some industrial uses, as railroad ballast, road material, and in the manufacture of Portland cement, ordinarily its disposal is an item on the debit side of the ledger. Most of it will be transported, while still molten, in unlined cast-iron ladles, to a convenient spot and dumped. It has been found that after this material has weathered for several months the slag may be crushed and reclaimed for use. When the slag is used for certain other purposes, notably for making Portland cement, it is usually granulated by causing the slag to flow from the furnace into a large concrete-lined pit partly filled with water. Just before the stream of molten slag enters the water in the granulating pit, it is met by a small stream of high-pressure water coming from behind and against the stream of slag so that the slag is well broken up. This also furnishes a method of regulating the fineness of the slag for certain markets. Sometimes in order to form small hollow globules that are light in weight and highly insulating, air or a mixture of air and steam is blown against the slag.

119. Stock-House Equipment. The stock house is the large space under the trestle and bin devoted to the mechanical devices which are used in charging the furnace. Skip tracks are provided at the furnace so that the skip can be lowered far enough below the floor of the stock house to receive materials from the chute. This chute in turn is fed by means of a small trolley car which runs on tracks that extend the full length of the bin. This car is provided with a scale in order that the ore and limestone may be accurately weighed. Almost universally, coke is measured by volume.*

120. Pig-Casting Equipment. The old method of casting pig iron in sand, whereby pig iron received its original name, has been pretty well superseded by mechanical methods. Not only are these cheaper in

---

* Very recently there is a trend toward weighing the coke for greater accuracy.

the long run, but they also furnish a better grade of pig iron by reason of the fact that no inclusions of sand result. A Thomas pig-casting machine consists of an endless chain, carrying a series of hollow molds or troughs, the edges of which overlap slightly in order to prevent undue spillage of the molten metal. This molten metal is brought to the machine in a large ladle and poured slowly into a trough provided with one or more skimmers from which it flows into this line of slowly moving molds. Ordinarily, these have been prepared by either "liming" or "smoking" in order to prevent sticking of the iron. The pigs may be cooled by carrying the iron directly through a trough of water, dumping the half-cooled pigs upon a conveyor, or cooling them by jets of water impinging on the bottoms of the molds.

121. Cinder Cars. When the furnaces were small, the slag from a blast furnace was usually run into shallow boxes or pits and disposed of by hand, when sufficiently cooled. In the early eighties cinder pots (steel-plate tanks lined with brick) were put into use. Later cast-iron pots were developed, and still later cast-steel ones. Today cast-steel pots are almost always used for blast-furnace slag, but for open-hearth slag many still use cast iron because molten steel, which is often carried over the side, adheres to the wall of the cast-steel pot but not to the cast-iron. The life of a cinder pot (400 to 450 cubic feet capacity) seems to depend upon how many times it is filled and also upon how long the hot slag stays in the pot before it is dumped. In many plants, 3000 fillings are expected from a cast-steel pot. The dumping problem is not a simple one, for cinder pots, being conical, are by nature top-heavy when full of slag. As a result, a certain amount of power is required to start the pot, but once started the momentum may overturn the car; therefore, it is necessary to control the speed of dumping, which is ordinarily done by means of oil, air, or steam cylinders. Another type of cinder car in use has no dumping device but is tipped by means of an overhead crane; and still another type, known as the end dump car, is dumped in the direction of the railroad tracks when these cars are used to build up and extend the cinder dump.

122. Hot-Metal Cars. The early type of hot-metal ladle was a simple ladle lined with fire brick, but the tendency in recent years has been toward the mixer type or closed ladle, the real advantage of which is that its construction permits building ladles of very large capacities. Standard railroad clearances limit upright ladles, with covers or semi-open tops (conical), to capacities of about 75 tons, whereas mixer-type cars have been built with a capacity of 160 tons and designs perfected for one of 300 tons. Of the different types developed, the cylindrical ladle with conical ends lends itself most admirably to the design of large units.

Mixer ladles are lined with either fire brick or stone, whichever material affords the lowest cost per ton of metal handled, depending upon service conditions, slag composition, and how long the metal is held in the ladle. If used between blast furnace and mixer, an average of 100,000 tons per lining can be expected; but, if the ladle is used as a mixer at the open hearth, about one-half of that is a fair average. The lining seems to have a certain maximum carrying capacity per day. If the ladle is made to carry more or less, the life of the lining will be affected. Because of the heat-retaining properties of the ladle, metal has been held in a molten state for 48 hours and at the end of this period was still fluid enough to be poured without forming more skull than can be melted by the following cast. Consequently, this type of ladle is adapted to transporting molten metal long distances, up to 10 or 15 miles. Mixer cars are also used to handle hot metal for the manufacture of ingot molds from direct blast-furnace iron, and, with the improvement in the blast-furnace technique, this practice may be extended to other fields. Mixer cars do not make any appreciable amount of scrap; permit a minimum of runner length, of attending labor, and of reduced lining costs and car upkeep; and allow a whole cast to be taken in one ladle.

STOCK DISTRIBUTION

123. General. It is evident that in such a heterogeneous mass as the charge of a blast furnace, in which the size of the particles varies from the finest dust up to lumps 4 inches in diameter,* and the specific gravity of the particles varies as much as iron ore and coke do, there is bound to be some segregation when these materials are dropped into the receiving bell at the top of the furnace. On the whole the larger lumps of ore and stone will have a tendency to roll and collect, either around the edges or to one side or the other. The same segregation will occur when the bell is lowered and the charge is dropped into the furnace. This tendency results in a more or less open and continuous channel being formed through the charge, and in extreme cases this channel may extend from the top to the bottom

---

* Coke is usually screened on ¼ inch with a maximum of 4 inches; limestone is sized between 1 and 4 inches; and ore varies from the finest dust to 4 inches.

of the stack. These channels offer less resistance to the passage of the blast than the remainder of the furnace column, with the result that a disproportionate quantity of the reducing gas passes through them. Furthermore, the velocity in them will be high and give rise to greater amounts of flue dust.

124. Character of Work. Changes in methods of charging or in the physical characteristics of the materials charged have more direct influence on the upper shaft than on any other part of the furnace. Consequently, it is timely to consider the work done in this part of the furnace which consists of (1) drying and preheating the charge, (2) first steps of reduction, and (3) calcination of the limestone. All these reactions require a supply of heat; the more uniform the gas-solid contact in this zone, the more effective will be the heat transfer and the sooner the work will be accomplished, within certain limits. The advantage of doing as much work as possible in the upper part of the furnace is not apparent until the secondary reactions ("solution loss") represented by the reaction

$$CO_2(g) + C(c) \rightarrow 2CO(g); \quad \Delta H = 40{,}800 \text{ cal.} \tag{1}$$

are considered. This reaction does not occur at any appreciable rate below 850°C., but when it does occur, it results in the loss of solid carbon to the process unless the resulting carbon monoxide is converted to carbon dioxide either through reduction or carbon deposition farther up in the shaft. In view of the fact that none of the solid carbon entering the gas stream, through the medium of solution loss, is ever completely recovered in the upper part of the furnace, a distinct loss in efficiency is involved if any reaction producing carbon dioxide is allowed to occur at elevations in the furnace where the temperature exceeds 1000°C. The ideal conditions, therefore, require the completion of the reduction of iron ore and the calcination of limestone in the upper part of the shaft where the temperature is below 1000°C.; the more intimate the gas-solid contact in the upper part of the furnace, the more nearly will conditions approach these ideal ones.

The so-called direct reduction (that is, reduction by carbon rather than by carbon monoxide gas) is another factor to be considered. The exact mechanism of this direct reduction is still under debate, but for the moment we are concerned only with the overall effect, which is

$$Fe_2O_3(c) + 3C(c) \rightarrow 2Fe(c) + 3CO(g); \quad \Delta H = 118{,}000 \text{ cal.} \tag{2}$$

That is, carbon is taken from the coke to produce carbon monoxide, whereas the work could be done just as well, with less carbon, by producing carbon dioxide at lower temperatures. If reduction is completed at low temperatures no iron ore is left to be reduced at the higher ones; consequently, there are no secondary reactions that tend to diminish hearth temperatures. To maintain these hearth temperatures—those necessary to complete desulfurization and reduction of silica—as much of the coke as possible should be burned at the tuyères.

125. Support of Charge Column. This is made up of five elements: upward pressure of the gas; friction of the charge on the sides of the shaft; vertical upward thrust against the charge from the converging slope of the bosh walls; buoyant effect of the molten iron and slag on the hearth; and the film effect (dragging) of the pasty zone against the walls at the top of the bosh (possibly a part of friction).

126. Variables in Charging. Operators, in using conventional apparatus, and designers, in devising new methods of charging, are limited in the number of factors they can vary at will, being able to manipulate the following:

1. Size and angle of the bell.
2. Height of the bottom of the bell above the stock-line.
3. The sequence of depositing materials on the big bell.
4. Speed and height of the big bell drop.
5. Size of the constituents of the charge.
6. The sintering of a portion of the ore.
7. The moisture in the ore.
8. The bell clearance.

127. The Effect of the Variables on Charging. C. C. Furnas[14] and T. L. Joseph[27] carried out, a number of years ago, an investigation in which laboratory experiments were conducted on blast-furnace models to determine the effect of the above variables on charging. Their findings were:

1. The average size of the particles at the center may be decreased by decreasing the time of depositing material on the bed, which in turn may be done by:
   A. Keeping the stockline close to the bell.
   B. Increasing the bell angle.
   C. Increasing the speed and distance of bell drop.
   D. Increasing the bell clearance.
2. The average size of the particle at the center is increased by:

A. Reverse filling*—coke on the big bell first.

B. Mixing—alternating skips of ore and coke.

C. Decreasing the size of the ore charge.

D. Decreasing the bell clearance.

3. Unit charging (charging ore and coke separately) seems to have little effect.

128. Shaft Conditions. In the past ten years, thanks to S. P. Kinney[30, 31, 32] and his associates, much light has been thrown on conditions in the shaft of an iron blast furnace, which work is discussed in some detail in Articles 131-152. With furnaces having moderate top diameters, let us say a stockline diameter of 17 feet, a bell of 13-foot diameter is customarily provided. This dimension, coupled with the size of the charge ordinarily used, resulted in placing the ore in the furnace in the form of an annulus, the outer periphery of which coincided with the walls of the furnace while the inner diameter was 4 to 5 feet. The central core thus formed contained but little ore, but was composed chiefly of coke, for the most part of the size somewhat above the average for the charge. The permeability of this central core was reduced by its slow motion but it still was excessive, even when the furnace retained the 17-foot diameter referred to. It is timely to note that this dimension originally related to a maximum diameter at the bosh of the furnace of 22 feet. Now this diameter has since been increased to nearly 28 feet, which should require a stockline diameter of 23 feet if the original differential and gas and charge conditions were to be preserved. Furnace designers, however, have refrained from making such an extreme change, with the result that, today, in no case does the stockline diameter exceed 21 feet. This relative constriction of this dimension has resulted in a high velocity of gases through the top and a tendency to increase the proportion of flue dust formed. Designers have realized that when charging by means of an ordinary bell an increase in stockline diameter would involve either an open center of large diameter or a failure to seal the walls with ore.

Investigation has proved that the combustion of coke takes place

* Normal charging refers to the usual method of charging a furnace: the ore is placed on the big bell, the coke is placed above it, then the bell is lowered and the hopper discharged.

Reversed charging refers to the reversed order: coke is placed first and the ore layer above it.

Unit charging refers to discharging a coke unit alone or an ore unit alone from the hopper.

within about 42 inches of the tuyère nose (see Article 141). Assuming a nominal hearth diameter of 26 feet and a projection of the tuyère into the furnace 9 inches beyond the hearth wall, the distance between opposite tuyère noses would be 24 feet 6 inches, and the inert circle inside the limit of combustion activity of the tuyère would be approximately 17 feet. The descent of the stock in the furnace is caused,

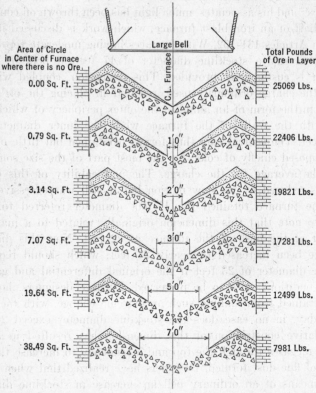

FIG. 30. Extent of Ore Layers in Furnace with Peak under Edge of Bell. (*Courtesy American Institute Mining and Metallurgical Engineers.*)

first, by the gasification of the coke and, second, by the shrinkage in volume of the charge in the furnace. Since the ore is charged into the furnace in the form of an annulus, next to the wall, these two causes of shrinkage affect the same parts of the furnace volume. Descent is most rapid above the tuyères, while in the center of the furnace, at the bottom, the only movement is that caused by the absorption of carbon by the molten iron on the hearth (this movement may conceivably amount to nothing if carburization of the iron is complete in the upper region of the furnace). Movement of the stock in the upper levels is also at a maximum next to the walls and a minimum at the center. This central movement, although relatively small, is a maximum at the stockline and a minimum at the hearth.

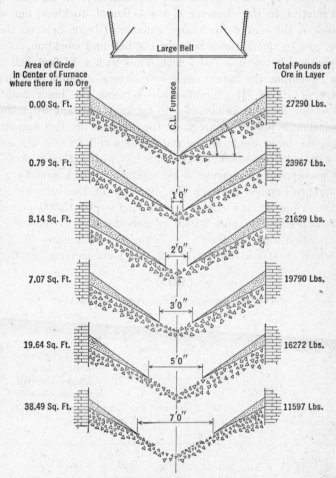

Fig. 31. Extent of Ore Layers in Furnace with Peak against Wall. (*Courtesy American Institute Mining and Metallurgical Engineers.*)

Figure 35 indicates that the velocity of the gas, its temperature, and carbon monoxide content are all a maximum in the center of the furnace and a minimum in the annulus between an assumed central cylinder and the outer wall of the furnace. There is a tendency for these quantities to increase at points close to the wall, a fact which indicates that any attempt to seal the center by a reduction in the diameter of the bell will result in hard working of the gases on the walls of the furnace and the consequent rapid deterioration of the lining. The width of the annulus which can be covered by ore discharged from the bell depends in some measure on the size of the charge relative to the diameter of the bell and stockline, but within the limits of the size of the charge capable of being held on the bell at once, and of the distance between the bell and stockline, its maximum width is between 6 and 7 feet. Thus with a 13-foot bell and a 17-foot stockline the inner circle of the ore annulus will have a diameter of 4 feet. If the difference between the inner and outer circles of the annulus is assumed to be kept constant by increasing the ore charge proportionately to the increase in the area of the annulus, the inner circle of the ore annulus will have a diameter of 6 feet with a 19-foot stockline and of 8 feet with a 21-foot one. These figures presuppose an increase in bell diameter, which would maintain a constant difference between the diameter of the bell and of the stockline, while the ore charge would increase to 15,000 pounds for the 17-foot stockline and 20,650 pounds for the 21-foot stockline. These relationships are shown in Table 29 and Figures 30 and 31, from which it should be noted that with an increase in stockline

TABLE 29

EFFECT OF BRASSERT REVOLVING DISTRIBUTOR*

Diameters, in Feet		Width of Annulus, Feet	Area, Sq. Feet			Relative Weight Ore Charge and Area Annulus, Per Cent	Relative Area of Ore-free Center, Per Cent	Area of Ore-free Center as Percentage of Area of Furnace
Outer Annulus	Inner Annulus		Ore Annulus	Ore-free Center	Furnace Top			
17	4	6.5	214.44	12.56	227	1.00	1.00	5.53
18	5	6.5	235.35	19.65	255	1.10	1.56	7.70
19	6	6.5	254.65	28.35	283	1.19	2.26	10.05
20	7	6.5	275.40	38.60	314	1.28	3.75	12.30
21	8	6.5	295.70	50.30	346	1.38	4.01	14.53
22	9	6.5	316.30	63.70	380	1.48	5.08	16.77
23	10	6.5	336.46	78.54	415	1.57	6.27	18.92

* Communication from H. A. Brassert and Company.

diameter from 17 feet to 23 feet the area of the top increases 85.5 per cent, that of the ore annulus 56.8 per cent, and that of the central ore-free circle 626.5 per cent while the ratio, area of ore-free area to that of furnace top, increases from 5.53 per cent to 18.92 per cent.

It is further evident that ore placed within the central area, while it will be rapidly reduced by ascending gases, will not experience contact with gases at the high temperature which exists in front of and immediately above the tuyères where final reduction and melting take place. Experience has indicated that the amount of ore which may be placed at the center of the furnace is comparatively small. On the other hand, the placing of relatively small coke in the center of the furnace involves no such difficulties as does the similar placing of ore. The coke does not require to be reduced nor smelted, but merely to be heated to a temperature which is limited by its position in the furnace. The size of the coke so placed should be sufficiently small to produce the desired reduction in the amount of gas but sufficiently great to permit the passage of an adequate supply of gas to heat the central column. The coke could be screened into two sizes, charging a larger size with the ore and limestone so that it rests within the annulus corresponding to the area covered by the ore, and charging the smaller coke so that it comes to rest in the inner circle of the top.

Such dispositions of the charge cannot be made, of course, with the conventional double bell and hopper. As a matter of fact, there are many operators who believe that the early furnaces were under better control than modern ones by reason of the fact that with hand filling, ore, coke, or limestone of any size could be placed at any point within the furnace top.

129. Brassert Top. A successful attempt to carry out such distribution is embodied in the ingenious top designed by H. A. Brassert and Company, and shown in Figure 32. In this figure (1) is a receiving hopper for blast-furnace stock, (2) is a throat casting in which each skip load of the furnace charge is received and temporarily held, (3) is a small bell which seals the space formed by (2) against furnace gas and provides means for dumping the charge into the lower hopper, (4) is an annular bell rod which carries the small bell, (5) is a gas seal, (6) represents the drive which rotates the hopper (2). All these elements are usual in blast-furnace top construction. In place of the usual bell, casting (7) is provided, and extension (8) fastened to (7), and a central bell (9). The central bell (9) rests on the casting (7) and is held by the rod (10), which is forced down by the springs

(10a) so that contact is maintained between the bell (9) and the casting (7). The vertical motion of the rod (10) and bell (9) is limited by the stop (11) to one or two inches. The casting (8) is supported by the spider (12) and the annular rod (13). A circular hopper (14)

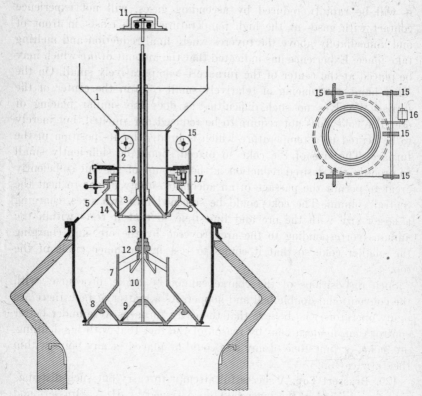

FIG. 32. Brassert Top. (*Courtesy of H. A. Brassert and Co.*)

1. Receiving hopper
2. Throat casting
3. Small bell
4. Annular bell rod
5. Gas seal
6. Drive to rotate hopper
7. Casting ⎱ Large bell
8. Extension ⎰
9. Central bell
10. Central bell rod
11. Central bell rod stop
12. Supporting spider
13. Annular rod
14. Circular hopper
15. Circular hopper sheaves
16. Motor
17. Circular hopper rods

is provided, which is supported by rods (17), preferably three. The support of these rods and their vertical movement are accomplished by means of the motor (16), the sheaves (15), and the gear reduction (16a). The method of operation is as follows:

If the hopper (14) remains in its upper position, ore, coke, or limestone is received in the throat (2) and dumped by lowering the bell (3) into the annular space around the casting (7) so that the charge rests on casting (7) and extension (8). When a sufficient amount of charged material has accumulated, means of discharging stock so held is provided by lowering the casting (7-8) and the material is deposited within the furnace in the customary form. If the hopper (14) is moved to its lower position, and the bell (3) subsequently lowered, small coke, or if desired, other material, is deposited within the casting (7). Lowering of the bell arrangement (7-8) places the material within the bell casting in the center of the furnace. This arrangement may be used with or without rotation of the members (2), (3), and (4), and with or without an electrically interlocked controller which determines the sequence of the charging operations. The preference is that both these features shall be included.

130. Importance of Voids. Much attention is being given, in connection with the charging of a furnace, to the preparation and properties of the raw materials, particularly the coke. This, besides furnishing most of the heat required for the operation and for reducing the iron ore, also provides voids (1) in the furnace stack for proper gas flow and (2) in the bottom of the furnace so that iron and slag can accumulate in the hearth. H. W. Johnson[25] points out that to the extent that a coke possesses the following properties it will fulfill these functions:

1. Initial size.
2. Range in size.
3. Uniformity in size in furnace.
4. Ability to withstand breakage.
5. Ability to withstand abrasion.
6. Type of fines produced after degradation.
7. Shape of pieces.
8. Behavior of coke pieces on reheating in furnace.
9. Resistance to abrasion and crushing at high temperatures.
10. Weight per cubic foot.
11. Percentage of voids effective for gas flow per pound of coke.
12. Uniformity from load to load.
13. Combustibility (defined as the average rate of gasification of coke per unit volume of the combustion zone of the furnace).

Mr. Johnson has also pointed out in a striking manner the way in which the system of filling affects the voids in the furnace and the character of the central column referred to above. Figure 30 shows a section through the top of a 17-foot furnace equipped with a 13-foot bell. When the ore and coke leave the bell, at, say, zero velocity, the top section consists of a layer of coke with a repose angle of 28 degrees and ore with 35 degrees. With an ore layer of 25,069 pounds, when the ore just reaches the center there is a thickness of 12¾ inches at the peak and 9⅛ inches at the wall. This difference in the thickness of the ore and coke layers determines, more or less, what the gas travel will be because the coke is large and produces voids whereas the ore is small and tends to fill them up. The other cross sections show how the diameter of this oreless column increases as the size of the charge decreases. Another factor is the segregation into coarse and fines. The small pieces of ore and coke are directly below the edge of the bell; the farther the pieces are from this vertical plane on either side, the larger they are. The areas with the maximum amount of coke will also contain the largest pieces of coke, and those with the minimum of ore will contain the largest pieces of ore. From this it follows that the minimum flow is directly under the edge of the bell, because there is a maximum thickness of ore layer for the thickness of coke layer and a concentration of the fines of both materials. If it becomes desirable to increase the flow up through the center, it can be done by increasing the voids, that is, placing less ore at the center. Figure 31 indicates that more or less the same condition will prevail when the charge possesses some velocity as it leaves the bell, causing the peak to form against the wall. It seems established, then, that the amount of gas flowing up the center of the furnace can be regulated by varying the size of the ore charge. This correction labors under the limitation that it does not compensate for lack of uniformity in the size of the material charged; that must be controlled by sizing.

CHEMISTRY OF THE BLAST FURNACE

131. General. A great deal of light has been thrown on the fundamental chemistry of the iron blast furnace through the splendid work of S. P. Kinney, C. C. Furnas, T. L. Joseph, P. H. Royster, and their associates.[14, 27, 30, 31, 32] Certain phases of this work were not only carried out in small experimental furnaces but facilities were also offered later by the industry so that the conclusions formulated in these smaller furnaces could be checked on a larger scale on a furnace shown in Figure 33. During relining holes were cut, as indicated, on five planes from just above the tuyère line to just below the stockline. Means were provided for taking stock and gas samples and measuring temperatures and velocities. The writer has attempted to present the results of this research in a brief and concise manner by discussing

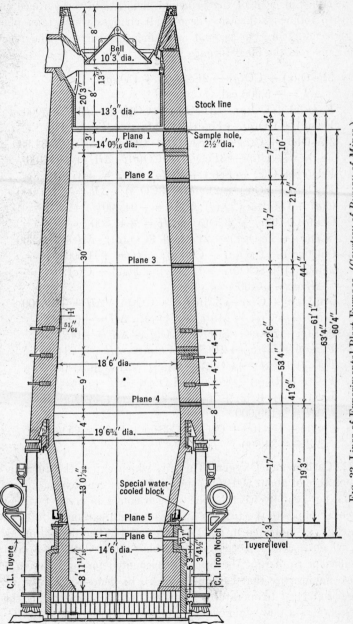

FIG. 33. Lines of Experimental Blast Furnace. (*Courtesy of Bureau of Mines.*)

the behavior of each of the principal elements in the furnace charge and then following through the overall changes which take place in the descending ore charge and ascending gas current. The reactions taking place in the blast furnace are:

$$3Fe_2O_3(c) + CO(g) \rightarrow 2Fe_3O_4(c) + CO_2(g);$$
$$\Delta H = -5{,}900 \text{ cal.} \tag{3}$$

$$Fe_3O_4(c) + CO(g) \rightarrow 3FeO(c) + CO_2(g); \quad \Delta H = +5900 \tag{4}$$

$$FeO(c) + CO(g) \rightarrow Fe(c) + CO_2(g); \quad \Delta H = -3900 \tag{5}$$

$$3Fe_2O_3(c) + C(c) \rightarrow 2Fe_3O_4(c) + CO(g); \quad \Delta H = +34{,}900 \tag{6}$$

$$Fe_3O_4(c) + C(c) \rightarrow 3FeO(c) + CO(g); \quad \Delta H = +47{,}400 \tag{7}$$

$$FeO(c) + C(c) \rightarrow Fe(c) + CO(g); \quad \Delta H = +37{,}600 \tag{8}$$

$$Fe_2O_3(c) + 3C(c) \rightarrow 2Fe(c) + 3CO(g); \quad \Delta H = +111{,}000 \tag{9}$$

$$C(g) + O_2(g) \rightarrow CO_2(g); \quad \Delta H = -94{,}400 \tag{10}$$

$$CO_2(g) + C(c) \rightarrow 2CO(g); \quad \Delta H = +41{,}500 \tag{11}$$

$$3CO(g) + Fe_2O_3(c) \rightarrow 2Fe(c) + 3CO_2(g); \quad \Delta H = -4{,}300 \tag{12}$$

$$CaCO_3(c) \rightarrow CaO(c) + CO_2(g); \quad \Delta H = +41{,}800 \tag{13}$$

$$2Fe_2O_3(c) + 8CO(g) \rightarrow 7CO_2(g) + Fe(c) + C(c);$$
$$\Delta H = -49{,}400 \tag{14}$$

$$Mn_3O_4(c) + C(c) \rightarrow 3MnO(c) + CO(g); \quad \Delta H = +29{,}000 \tag{15}$$

$$MnO(c) + C(c) \rightarrow Mn(c) + CO(g); \quad \Delta H = +64{,}400 \tag{16}$$

$$SiO_2(c) + 2C(c) \rightarrow Si(c) + 2CO(g); \quad \Delta H = +145{,}000 \tag{17}$$

$$P_2O_5(c) + 5C(c) \rightarrow 2P(c) + 5CO(g); \quad \Delta H = +234{,}000 \tag{18}$$

$$H_2O(g) + C(c) \rightarrow CO(g) + H_2(g); \quad \Delta H = +31{,}400 \tag{19}$$

$$FeO(c) + H_2(g) \rightarrow Fe(c) + H_2O(g); \quad \Delta H = +6200 \tag{20}$$

$$K_2CO_3(c) + 4C(c) + N_2(g) \rightarrow 2KCN(c) + 3CO(g);$$
$$\Delta H = +139{,}000 \tag{21}$$

$$FeS(c) + CaO(c) + C(c) \rightarrow CaS(c) + Fe(c) + CO(g);$$
$$\Delta H = +34{,}800 \tag{22}$$

132. Carbon and Oxygen. The air, which enters the furnace at a temperature of about 500° C., contains 20.8 per cent oxygen by volume or 23.2 per cent by weight. The oxygen comes in contact with white hot coke* opposite the tuyères and reacts with carbon to form carbon monoxide, as indicated in reactions 10 and 11. The deposition of carbon, which is always noticeable in a blast furnace and may at times be sufficient to disrupt the brick, is accounted for by reaction 14. It is also noteworthy that carbon may also be deposited by the reverse of reaction 11 at temperatures below 600°C. and, penetrating the ore, may serve as a powerful reducing agent, especially above 750°C. The decomposition of limestone yields large amounts of carbon dioxide

---

* In Lake practice about 14 million B.t.u. are required per long ton of pig iron.

which may so alter the carbon monoxide-carbon dioxide relationships in the furnace as to cause iron to be reoxidized. In a general way, in order to be of a reducing character, the volume of carbon monoxide in the furnace gases must equal or exceed twice the volume of the carbon dioxide. This matter of the character of the gases will be discussed later on in this chapter in connection with the experimental work referred to above.

133. Iron. In some respects the iron blast furnace can be considered as a gigantic gas producer, for actually most of the reduction of the iron oxide is carried out by means of carbon monoxide gas. At temperatures ranging from about 250 to 700°C., the reduction of ferric oxide by carbon monoxide takes place in three steps, being successively reduced to magnetic iron oxide, ferrous oxide, and finally to iron. Apart from theoretical considerations, which lead us to believe that such a progressive reduction takes place, it is noteworthy that on certain furnaces operating entirely on hematite ores, a considerable amount, sometimes up to 70 per cent of the iron in the flue dust, is present as magnetic iron oxide.

Carbon also reduces oxides of iron at relatively low temperatures (450 to 700°C.), but it is probably a minor factor in the process, by reason of the fact that, in order for such reduction to take place, a particle of iron oxide must come in contact with a particle of carbon. Obviously the chances of this taking place are infinitely less than those for carbon monoxide to penetrate into the porous iron ore and effect a similar reduction.

134. Manganese. Although small amounts of this element are found in the limestone and the coke ash, most of that entering the furnace does so as a part of the ore charge, in which it occurs usually as the dioxide and sometimes as manganese oxide (Mn_3O_4). These manganese compounds are reduced by carbon, at the high temperatures prevailing near the tuyères, as indicated in reactions 15 and 16. This reduction is never complete; its extent will be a function of the chemical composition of the slag as well as the temperature at the tuyères. Under normal conditions 50 to 75 per cent of the total manganese charged into the furnace will be found in the molten iron, the highest proportions being found with basic slags and high hearth temperatures.

135. Sulfur. Sulfur enters the charge mainly in the coke, although small amounts may be found in the ore and the limestone. A part of this sulfur combines with the iron as iron or manganese sulfide; the rest may be acted upon, at very high temperatures, by calcium oxide and carbon, as shown in reaction 22, to form calcium sulfide which may be absorbed by the slag if it is sufficiently basic. The conditions under which 'this elimination may be carried out will be more fully discussed under the section devoted to the regulation of the pig iron.

The demand for iron and steel of very low sulfur content has resulted in some fruitful experimental work utilizing calcium carbide. The melting point of the pure compound is about 2300°C., but the technical grade melts at a lower temperature. It is believed that metallic calcium is formed so that there is a solid-liquid reaction (somewhat slower than a liquid-liquid) with the subsequent formation of calcium sulfide. In a small ladle no difficulty was experienced in reducing the sulfur, in 3 to 5 minutes, from 0.10, 0.11, and 0.06 per cent to 0.056, 0.015, and 0.007 per cent, respectively; but at steel plants having large ladles the results were not so good. The difficulty appears to be a matter of effective distribution and mixing.

136. Silicon. The amount of silica in the iron ore may vary from as little as 5 to as much as 40 per cent, depending upon the character of the iron being produced. Only a relatively small amount of this silica is ordinarily reduced, the amount being dependent upon the chemical composition of the slag and the hearth temperature (high temperatures and acid slags favor the reduction of the silica).

137. Phosphorus. Unfortunately, under normal operating conditions, this element is beyond the control of the operator, for all of it is reduced in the furnace, as indicated in reaction 18, and enters the iron as a phosphide. It follows then that any changes in the phosphorus content of the pig iron must be effected by changes in the burden rather than by operating conditions.

138. Slag-Forming Elements. Although small amounts of such elements as titanium, potassium, sodium, zinc, and barium are present in the charge, the principal slag-forming compounds are calcium oxide, magnesium oxide, aluminum oxide, and silicon dioxide. Calcium and magnesium enter the furnace largely as carbonates, although, if the limestone is impure, small amounts of these may be present as silicates and under these conditions would undergo no chemical change in the furnace. They would simply constitute a load on the furnace, absorbing heat and diminishing the fluxing power of the limestone. Calcium carbonate, beginning at about 800°C., and progressing very rapidly at 950°C., decomposes according to reaction 13; the carbon dioxide thus formed joins the furnaces gases, and the calcium oxide and magnesium oxide react with silicon dioxide to form a suitable slag, if the charge has been properly proportioned.

139. Changes in the Solid Charge. The current of hot gases* as it reaches the top of the furnace is, under ordinary conditions, at a temperature of about 150°C. The first change therefore is simply one of drying, during which first the hygroscopic water and, as the charge sinks in the furnace and the temperature increases, the water of constitution are driven off from these solids. As the charge continues to descend it meets an upward-rushing current of hot gas containing, besides hydrogen and water, varying proportions of carbon monoxide and carbon dioxide. Although the proportions of carbon monoxide and carbon dioxide may vary suddenly owing to local conditions, on the whole the amount of carbon monoxide present in the furnace gas increases steadily until the tuyères are reached, where the gas consists almost entirely of nitrogen and carbon monoxide. It follows, then, that with increasing temperatures and greater concentrations of carbon monoxide, ferric oxide is successively reduced to magnetic iron oxide (begins at 450°C.), to ferrous oxide, and finally to iron (complete at 750°C.). It should be noted, in this connection, that the physical form of the iron ore will have a great effect upon the temperatures at which these reactions are completed and the rate at which they go on, the ones referred to being for fine particles of ore. Lump ore because of its low heat conductivity and low porosity will descend to much lower levels in the furnace before these reactions are complete. The decomposition of limestone, reaction 13, begins at about 800°C. and is complete at about 1000°C. The reduction of carbon dioxide by carbon begins at about 900°C., and is practically complete at 1000°C., so that very little carbon dioxide exists within 25 feet of the tuyères.

After these reactions have gone on, there remains in the descending mass sponge iron, gangue, coke, and decomposed limestone as well as, under certain conditions, particles of unreduced ore. The sponge iron is well named because, being porous, it begins at once to absorb carbon, manganese, silicon, sulfur, and phosphorus from the charge. In the lower levels, and at a temperature of about 1130°C., this alloy, now of the approximate composition of cast iron, melts to flow down over particles of white hot coke to absorb the remaining carbon and to

---

* It is worthy of note that although the solids may be in the furnace 5 to as much as 12 hours, the gases pass through the stack in 2 to 10 seconds. One cubic foot of gas generated at the tuyères carries only enough heat to bring one ounce of stock up to the temperature of the crucible.

come to rest in the crucible of the furnace. Meanwhile the particles of calcium oxide, aluminum oxide, silicon dioxide, magnesium oxide, manganese oxide, calcium sulfide, etc., fuse together to form the final slag which, in flowing down through the interstices of the furnace to meet both molten iron and coke, tends to absorb most of the impurities of the charge.

140. Changes in the Ascending Gas Current. Let us now reverse the process and follow the changes in the air as it is blown in through the tuyères. Entering at a temperature of about 500°C., the air comes in contact with hot coke, and, although it may react with carbon to form carbon dioxide, this is immediately reduced by excess carbon to form carbon monoxide so that, immediately in front of the tuyères, the furnace gas consists almost entirely of carbon monoxide and nitrogen (about 32 per cent carbon monoxide). As the gas rises through the furnace, further additions of carbon monoxide will be made by reason of reactions 6, 7, 8, and 9, but also at the same time additions of carbon dioxide will be made through the decomposition of limestone as well as the reduction of particles of iron ore which may have reached this low level in the furnace. In spite of these increases in carbon dioxide, the gas will still be sufficiently reducing in character, as it passes up through the upper reaches of the furnace, that it will successively reduce the iron oxide, as outlined above, to iron. The gas coming off the top of the furnace, under Lake practice, will vary between the following extremes: carbon dioxide, 13.8 to 16.1 per cent; carbon monoxide, 23.2 to 25.1; hydrogen, 3.1 to 4.8; and nitrogen, 55.8 to 57.1.

141. Combustion of Coke. The early conception of an iron blast furnace was that of a huge stove in which the combustion of the coke and production of carbon monoxide went on continuously up through the furnace, but the work of Kinney, Royster, and Joseph[30, 31, 32, 33] has proved that to be erroneous. This combustion takes place in a very limited volume in the form of ellipsoids, as indicated in Figure 34, with a central zone about 82 inches in diameter, in which no combustion takes place. If gas flow and composition are uniform across the tuyère plane, the carbon monoxide content of the gas at this point should be about 32 per cent. Gas samples at a point 30 inches above the tuyères show that only a trace of oxygen (0.4 per cent or less), is present, indicating that the oxygen has been consumed in the process of combustion by the time it reaches this point in the furnace. It is also believed that the penetration of the combustion zone in the vertical direction is about the same as that in the horizontal direction at the tuyère level. On this level the oxygen disappears at a distance of 30 inches measured on a horizontal line drawn from the center of the nose of the tuyère to the center of the furnace at the tuyère level. Figure 34 shows the approximate size and shape of this combustion zone in which A represents that part of the combustion zone where free oxygen is found and volume A' that part where some carbon dioxide is present. The free oxygen has been consumed before it can

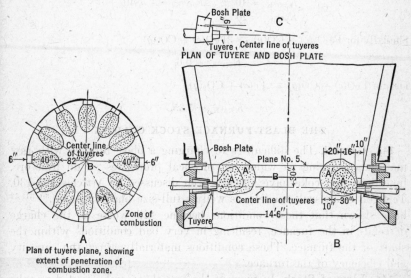

FIG. 34. Combustion Zones of Blast Furnace. (*Courtesy of Bureau of Mines.*)

enter the latter zone. Outside of this zone (in B) both oxygen and carbon dioxide disappear and the gases at this point are composed almost entirely of carbon monoxide, water, and nitrogen. Theoretically, if no secondary reactions, such as the direct reduction of iron ore by carbon or the formation of cyanide (shown in reactions 6, 7, 8, 9, and 21), take place in the bosh of the furnace, the gases at this point should contain 34.34 per cent carbon monoxide, a little water, and the remainder should be nitrogen. Gas at the tuyère plane contains about 32 per cent carbon monoxide, and whether these variations from theoretical conditions are due to side reactions (the decomposition of water, for example) or to physical conditions in the furnace has not yet been established.

142. Problem: 3. Calculate the equilibrium constants for the progressive reduction of iron oxide at 700°C.

$$3Fe_2O_3(c) + CO(g) \rightleftarrows 2Fe_3O_4(c) + CO_2(g)$$
$$S's = 3(21.5) + 46.2 \quad 2(35.0) + 51.1$$
$$\Delta S_{298°K.} = 10.4 \text{ cal.} \quad \Delta S_{973°K.} = 3.60 \text{ cal.}$$
$$H's = 3(-198.5)(-26.84) \quad 2(-266.9)(-94.45)$$
$$\Delta H_{298°K.} = -5910 \text{ cal.}$$
$$\Delta H_{973°K.} = -2310 \text{ cal.}$$
$$\Delta F_{298°K.} = -5910 - (298 \times 10.4) = -RT \ln K$$
$$K_{298°K.} = 10^{6.55} \quad \Delta F_{973°K.} = -5840$$
$$K_{973°K.} = 20$$

Similarly for $Fe_3O_4(c) + CO(g) \rightleftarrows 3FeO(c) + CO_2(g)$

$$K_{973°K.} = 9.6$$

and for $FeO(c) + CO(g) \rightleftarrows Fe(c) + CO_2(g)$

$$K_{973°K.} = 5.35$$

THE BLAST-FURNACE STOCK COLUMN

143. General. The difficulties of charging a blast furnace with raw materials differing as widely in physical properties as do iron ore, limestone, and coke have already been discussed in Articles 123-130. Tests on small-scale models, as well as full-size blast furnaces,[30, 31, 32] have shown that these conditions become still worse as the charge descends in the furnace, resulting in very bad conditions within the shaft of the furnace. These conditions materially affect the capacity and efficiency of the furnace.

144. Flow of Stock. In view of the fact that combustion does take place in localized zones in front of the tuyères, it seems reasonable to suppose that uniform flow of the stock across any plane parallel to the hearth is impossible and that the effect of these combustion zones must be transmitted to the stock column, perhaps even to its top. The experiments referred to show that, in seven tests, the average rate of flow of stock at the stockline was found to be 2.78 inches per minute. As contrasted with this, the individual rates measured at the same time over the iron notch, the cinder notch, and opposite the iron notch were 3.16, 2.92, and 2.93 inches per minute, respectively, whereas the rate measured from a point at or near the center of the top of the column was only 2.10 inches per minute. It is evident, therefore, that the flow of stock in the blast furnace column is not uniform, being much faster directly over the tuyères than in the center of the column —clear evidence of the existence of a relatively inert stock column in the center of the furnace as well as substantiation of the belief that the column of stock is partly submerged in and floating on the bath of slag and metal (there is a definite pendulumlike motion of the stock column at the instant of its receiving the charge).

145. Velocity of the Gas. Figure 35 indicates that there are similar wide variations in the velocity of the gas, which varies between the extremes of 74 feet at the inwall to 439 feet per second at the center of the column, just under the top of the stock. The low velocity at the inwall seems to bear some relation to the straight section above the batter of the furnace, and the high velocity at the center to variations brought about by charging the stock and to the resultant more open charge in the center of the furnace. These variations in velocity probably also bring about similar changes in temperature because a high velocity of gas indicates the passage of a large volume through a relatively porous portion of the stock column with corresponding high heat transfer. It is obvious, therefore, that because of segregation in the top of the charge column, as well as variations in the rate of its descent, reduction conditions are exactly the opposite of those desired. In the center of the furnace there is an inert mass through which is passing a rapidly moving current of carbon monoxide, a quantity far beyond the local demands of reduction. On the other hand, as one approaches the inwall of the furnace, where there may be more iron ore, and certainly a much more rapid movement of the stock, the gas velocity is less; as a matter of fact, the supply may be so small that a large amount of unreduced iron oxide may reach the lower zones of the furnace and be reduced directly with carbon.* Furthermore, the very high velocities in the center of the furnace, at the stockline, tend to produce undue proportions of flue dust because these gases, issuing at such a high velocity, sweep away the fine particles of ore into the offtake.

146. Carbon Monoxide—Carbon Dioxide Ratio. Figure 35 indicates that there are also wide variations in the reducing power of the furnace gases. It is significant to note that a portion of the gas at the stockline level is high in carbon dioxide in comparison with that generally found in the top gas. That it is found in one part of the plane might reasonably be taken to indicate that, under proper conditions, gas of a like carbon dioxide content might be obtained from all parts and the efficiency of the furnace markedly increased. In this connection it should be noted that up to the time these experiments were conducted the limiting carbon monoxide-carbon dioxide ratio of 2.0, as

* See Article 188.

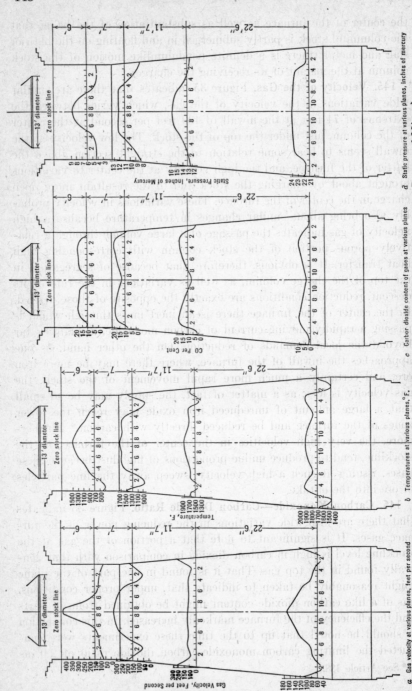

Fig. 35　Composition, Temperature, and Velocity of Blast-Furnace Gas. (Courtesy of Bureau of Mines.)

a　Gas velocity at various planes, feet per second

b　Temperatures at various planes, °F.

c　Carbon dioxide content of gases at various planes

d　Static pressure at various planes, inches of mercury

determined by Bell, has been commonly accepted. Apparently in modern furnaces this ratio in the top gases is of the order of 1.69 and in certain parts of the furnace may be as low as 1.29. Obviously, if such ratios are attained in one part of the furnace, it is reasonable to suppose that careful research may develop methods by which a lower ratio may be maintained in other parts, with a corresponding decrease in the coke consumption.

In general it can be said that the carbon monoxide content of the gas will be highest at the center of the furnace, somewhat lower along the inwall, and lowest at a point about halfway between the inwall and center of the furnace. Again we have the anomalous condition of a highly reducing gas passing rapidly up through the center of the furnace in contact with a slowly moving charge, while the gas of lowest carbon monoxide content is in contact with the most rapidly moving stock.

147. Temperature. Figure 35 indicates that there are comparable wide variations in the temperatures at different points on the horizontal plane. For example, at plane 1 it will be noted that the range is a considerable one, varying from 450°F. at the inwall to 1310°F. at the center. The points on the curve are somewhat scattered, probably because the plane is so close to the top of the stock and thus subject to variation through slight variations in the height of the stockline, the cold incoming stock, as well as irregularities in its flow. In a general way the same variation holds for plane 4, the temperature decreasing from 1670°F. at the inwall to 1380°F. at a point approximately 15 inches from the inwall, then increasing fairly uniformly to 1870°F. at the center of the furnace.

148. Reduction of Iron and Formation of Slag. Other experimental work carried out on a blast furnace at Holt, Alabama, with observation planes distributed approximately the same as those indicated in Figure 33, furnishes some interesting information on the progress of the reduction of iron oxides and the formation of the slag. The reduction of the iron oxides may be calculated from samples of the gas or of the stock. If both results are considered, it is found that at plane 4 (in this case 19 feet 3 inches above the tuyères) 80 to 85 per cent of the iron in the burden has been reduced from the oxide state to metallic (sponge) iron. On the other hand, only 6 per cent of the work of reduction was complete at plane 1, which was about 3 feet below the stockline.

Microscopic examination of stock samples from plane 4 indicated that they consisted in the main of three types of particles, which may be classified as:

1. Normal sponge iron.
2. Sponge iron containing comparatively little gangue matter.
3. Particles composed of metallic iron disseminated in gangue containing as high as 50 per cent foreign matter.

Slag formation occurs just above the bosh of the furnace. The slag constituents in their descent become more intimately mixed, become pasty as the temperature increases, and finally melt. Probably the slag at plane 4 never exceeds 3 to 4 per cent of the charge, and it is of very variable composition. Furthermore, it is usually impregnated with particles of metal, iron oxide, and carbon which are not released until these are liquated out in the crucible of the furnace. It should be emphasized at this point that these experiments have shown wide variations in the character of the slag at different times and in different parts of the furnace. For example, the observers found that flushes of average composition were frequently followed by flushes that were black and of an entirely different composition. The slag at the cinder notch may be normal while a runback into a tuyère pipe may be black and of another character. In other words, the slag is not completely formed until it reaches the metal bath, and the bosh and the hearth of the furnace are not very efficient mixing chambers so far as the slag-forming constituents are concerned. There may be a lean slag at one side of the furnace with a rich one at the other on a poorly working furnace, although normally such is not the case. In the upper part of the bosh where the slag first appears there is an excess of lime; the slag does not take up all of its silica until it has reached the level of the tuyères, where the silica in the coke ash is released. Holbrook's[23] work indicated that the elimination of sulfur is aided by the buoyant action of bubbles of carbon monoxide gas, and, consequently, the differences referred to may be ironed out in the crucible by agitation and diffusion.

149. Behavior of Impurities. Experiments on this Alabama furnace also brought out some very interesting data on the course of the reduction of the metalloids in the blast furnace. Incidentally, the metal produced from this furnace generally contained 2 to 3.5 per cent silicon, less than 0.05 per cent sulfur, 0.5 to 0.7 per cent phosphorus, 0.45 to 0.70 per cent manganese, and 3 to 4 per cent carbon. In a general way it will be observed from reaction 17 that the elimination of silicon is a function of temperature and the basicity of the slag, high temperatures favoring the reaction, and basic conditions of the slag retarding it. Experiments in electric furnaces have indicated that silicon is reduced by carbon at 1460°C. in the presence of iron, and ferrosilicon is formed at about 1200°C. From this it is logical to infer that, the temperature of plane 4 being about 853°C. and that of plane 5, 1350°C., the metal would take up a considerable part of its silicon by the time it had reached the latter plane. Observations check this in that the average silicon content of the metal at the cast was 2.92 per cent and at plane 5, 2.55 per cent; or in other words the metal had taken up 87.4 per cent of its silicon by the time it had reached plane 5 and an additional 11 per cent by the time it had reached the tuyères. As the temperature required to reduce silica is higher than that required to reduce other oxides, it would be expected that silicon would enter the metal in the lower part of the bosh of the furnace rather than higher up. The silica in the coke ash has apparently little effect on the amount of silicon entering the metal, although it will affect the coke consumption as well as the capacity of the furnace. The coke does not release its silica until combustion occurs in the relatively constricted zones in front of each tuyère. Before the metal reaches this level it has taken up the greater part of the silicon it will acquire, but the temperature of the combustion zone probably assists the last bit of silicon to enter the metal.

Manganese oxide is reduced, in the presence of carbon, at 1105°C. and ferromanganese formed at 1030°C. The manganese compounds present in the charge are never wholly reduced in the furnace, and the proportion of them that is so reduced depends upon the temperature and the basicity of the slag. Under conditions ordinarily prevailing, 50 to 75 per cent of the total amount of manganese charged will be found in the pig iron, the highest proportion being obtained with high hearth temperatures and a basic slag; however, a high manganese content may be obtained with lower hearth temperatures by increasing the proportion of this element in the charge. Manganese will enter the metal in the zone of fusion, but samples show that a small amount of manganese has entered the metal at plane 4. The average manganese content of the metal from fifteen casts was 0.53 per cent, and the metal samples taken from planes 4 and 5 contained 0.22 per cent and 1.10 per cent respectively. Approximately one-third of the manganese entered the metal while it was in the sponge-iron zone. It would appear, therefore, that considerable manganese is oxidized while the metal is passing through the tuyère zone, although this is complicated by the fact that, either in the slag or at the slag-iron interface in the crucible, manganese sulfide may form, enter the slag, and thus rob the iron of its manganese.

Phosphorus enters the furnace largely in the form of phosphates, and at a very high temperature and in the presence of coke these compounds may be completely reduced. On the other hand, phosphorus reacts immediately with iron to form the phosphide (Fe_3P), and hence the phosphorus in the iron can be controlled only through the selection of the raw materials. Results in this furnace agree with these statements. Samples from fifteen casts of metal gave an average phosphorus content of 0.64 per cent; samples taken from plane 4, 0.32 per cent; and from plane 5, 0.54 per cent. The results show that one-half of the phosphorus had entered the metal or was intimately in contact with it before plane 4 had been reached, and approximately 84 per cent had entered the metal by the time plane 5 was reached.

Reference has already been made to the porous, spongelike character of the iron produced by gradual reduction. For a long time it has been known that iron in this form will take up elements rather rapidly when heated in their presence. Experiments have shown that the order in which iron will absorb these elements is probably carbon, sulfur, phosphorus, manganese, and silicon. Analyses of metal samples indicate that the iron has readily absorbed a large amount of carbon by the time it has reached plane 4 and that the carbon in the metal from the cast contained an average of 3.39 per cent. At plane 4 the metal contained 1.29 per cent and at plane 5, 3.19 per cent, whereas four samples from the tuyère plane gave 3.68 per cent. In other words more than one-third of the carbon has been taken up by the metal by the time it reaches plane 4; the remainder is absorbed in the bosh of the furnace before reaching the tuyère level. With the gradual absorption of carbon, of course, the melting point of the alloy decreases, with the result that long before the iron reaches the tuyères it is in a perfectly liquid condition, and as such is in a still better condition to absorb the remainder of the impurities—sulfur, phosphorus, manganese, and silicon.

Sulfur elimination in the furnace depends upon the amount in the charge, the hearth temperature, the slag volume, the composition of the slag, and the length of time the metal is in contact with the slag. Much light has been thrown on the process of desulfurization through the work of Holbrook and Joseph. They melted metal and slag of varying sulfur contents in an induction furnace in order to observe the mechanism, as well as the extent, of desulfurization. So far as the first is concerned, they were able to show that the elimination of sulfur is directly connected with the buoyant effect of bubbles of carbon monoxide gas which adhere to the particles of iron as they descend through the slag as well as the rate of diffusion of calcium sulfide from the slag metal interface into the main body of the slag. They believe that through this flotative effect of the carbon monoxide bubbles, globules of iron may make several trips, up and down, through the slag before they finally come to rest in the crucible of the furnace. Another interesting point developed by them concerned the effect of

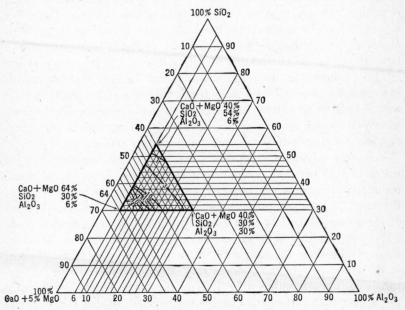

FIG. 36. Three-Component Diagram, CaO-SiO$_2$-Al$_2$O$_3$ + 5 per cent MgO. (*Courtesy of American Institute of Mining and Metallurgical Engineers.*)

magnesia, a question which has been vigorously debated by blast-furnace metallurgists for a number of years.

Figure 36 is a triaxial diagram taken from their paper, which indicates that a slag containing 5 per cent of magnesia must have the composition represented by the small shaded triangle to be desulfurizing at all; that is, a desulfurizing slag containing no magnesia must have a composition within the range 25 to 65 per cent calcium oxide, 30 to 60 per cent silica, and 5 to 35 per cent aluminum oxide. Furthermore, their work showed that if the basicity of a slag is expressed by the ratio $\dfrac{CaO + MgO}{SiO_2 + Al_2O_3}$, the slags having the highest desulfurization powers are those containing approximately 7 per cent aluminum oxide, 5 to 10 per cent magnesium oxide with a basicity between 1.2 and 1.4, 11 per cent aluminum oxide, and 1 to 5 per cent magnesium oxide with a basicity of 1 to 1.3, or 15 per cent aluminum oxide and 1 to 5 per cent magnesium oxide with a basicity of 1 to 1.2. Whereas laboratory experiments indicate that temperatures above the melting point have comparatively little effect on desulfurizing power, viscosity has a large one, and the viscosity, of course, will depend upon temperature and chemical composition, the alumina and magnesia being controlling factors, together with the ratio of lime to silica. This effect of temperature is not entirely borne out in practice, for it has been observed that, although the basicity of the slag is unquestionably a large factor in the elimination of sulfur from the metal, temperature is also an important one. In general it can be said that low sulfur irons can be obtained with high temperatures and a normal slag or with normal temperatures and a basic slag, whereas high sulfur irons (above 0.06 per cent) may be obtained with normal temperatures and an acid slag or relatively low temperatures and a normal slag.

If, in the Alabama experiments, we regard the tolerant limit on sulfur as 0.05 per cent, we find that at planes 4, 5, and 6 the metal contained approximately 140, 360, and 140 per cent, respectively, of the tolerant limit; at plane 4 the metal had taken up 3.33 per cent of the sulfur which had been charged into the furnace, and at plane 5 the metal had taken up 12 per cent of the available sulfur. Although these results show the ease with which the metal can take up sulfur in the upper part of the furnace, they also show that the metal continues to take up sulfur while it is in the bosh. This is attributable to the fact that part of the metal is not covered by slag and therefore subject to contamination with sulfur produced from the combustion of the coke at the tuyère level.

150. General Effects of Hearth Temperatures. Although the general effect of raising hearth temperature is to lower the sulfur and increase the silicon, manganese, and carbon, there are other factors affecting control that are difficult to estimate because: (1) to insure free-blowing iron and easy casts the lowest permissible hearth temperature is about 1370°C. while the highest is not over 1540°C., making a working range of less than 200°C.; (2) the manganese in the iron depends largely upon the amount present in the charge; (3) silicon tends to exclude carbon; (4) the amount of carbon in contact with the metal will vary considerably; and (5) the difference between top and bottom temperatures in the hearth may also vary.

151. Resistance of Iron Ores to Decrepitation and Mechanical Work.
Kinney has pointed out that economy in blast-furnace practice depends largely upon efficient gas-solid contact in the shaft of the furnace. If efficient work is not done in the shaft, the hearth and bosh can scarcely be expected to function properly, let alone complete the work. A condition may readily be imagined where the particles of ore in the shaft are so large that the time entailed in the descent of these materials into the bosh is not sufficient to permit proper reduction and preparation prior to the time the ore enters the bosh of the furnace. Still another condition may be pictured where the density of the stock column and the flow of stock are such that the ore will take one course and the gas another. Both these conditions will result in insufficient contact between the gas and the ore. It is obvious that fine ore particles occurring in the ore, as charged or formed in the furnace due to heat and mechanical action, place a definite limitation upon the efficiency of the operation, and, of course, there is an economic loss of fine material as dust.

T. L. Joseph[27, 28] and E. P. Barrett* have done considerable work at the Minnesota School of Mines Experiment Station and have been able to show in a small model of the top of a blast furnace that:

1. Screen analysis of an ore does not indicate its behavior when subjected to abrasion and heat.
2. Average decrease in average particle size for iron ore is 18 per cent due to cold work and 38 per cent due to hot work.
3. Imported manganese ores are little affected by cold work but much changed by hot work.
4. Limestone is very resistant to cold work and hot work at temperatures up to 760°C.

BLAST-FURNACE BURDENING

152. General. The amounts of ore and limestone charged per ton of fuel are referred to as the "burden," the fuel or coke being constant in amount; and any increase in ore and limestone above the normal is spoken of as a "heavy" burden while the reverse is a "light" one, and the regulation of these proportions is termed "burdening." Apparently the calculation of a furnace burden, given the weights and analyses of the raw materials, ought to be a comparatively simple stoichiometric problem. Actually, however, there are a number of factors such as the

---

* T. L. Joseph and E. P. Barrett, "Resistance of Iron Ores to Decrepitation and Mechanical Work," American Institute of Mining and Metallurgical Engineers, *Tech. Pub.* 372, 1930.

velocity of the gases, the viscosity of the slag, the contour of the furnace, and the distribution of the materials which are not fully known and sometimes not even under the control of the furnace operator. In connection with some of these, it should be noted that the important factor is not so much the composition of the substances as their behavior in the furnace. There are, however, certain fundamental factors in burdening any blast furnace. They are:

1. The presence of sufficient elements, such as silicon and manganese, to give a cast iron of the proper analysis.
2. The determination of the amount of flux to yield the required slag (composition) which will absorb the impurities, notably sulfur.
3. The determination of the proper amount of flux to yield a slag of a chemical composition which will insure the proper fluidity and the fusion temperature.
4. An adequate weight of slag per ton of iron to absorb the impurities.

153. Fuel. This is determined solely by experience and may vary from 1400 to 2500 pounds of coke per ton of pig iron. Ordinarily, the charge of coke, of the order of 11,000 pounds, is kept constant while the other ingredients of the charge are varied in order to produce a slag or iron of the proper composition.

154. Regulation of the Ore Mixture. We are concerned primarily with four elements: phosphorus, manganese, silicon, and sulfur. Phosphorus is entirely reduced within the furnace and joins the iron; consequently, any variation in phosphorus content must be accomplished by varying the character of the ore. From 20 to 55 per cent of the manganese is eliminated, and such elimination is favored by low temperatures and acid slags; 95 to 98 per cent of the silicon is eliminated in the slag, elimination being favored by low temperatures and basic slags; and 80 to 98 per cent of the sulfur is removed. Sulfur removal is favored by increasing:

1. The slag ratio; that is, making the slag more basic. (Incidentally, this usually raises the melting point.)
2. The slag volume.
3. The slag fluidity.
4. The manganese content.
5. The temperature.

155. Slag Volume. The minimum value of slag volume is determined by the degree of sulfur elimination, and any excess over this required amount represents a loss because it requires about 560 pounds of coke to melt and superheat a ton of slag. Slag volumes on Mesabi ores will range from 1100 to 1300 pounds of slag per ton of iron, contrasted to English practice, with their low-grade ores, where slag volumes will range from 3200 to 3600 pounds.

156. Iron Yield. Losses on the whole are about 7 per cent of the iron charged and may be due to:

1. Flue dust.
2. Slag which may contain either metallic iron or ferrous oxide.*
3. Oxidation during tapping.
4. Scrap formed in pig beds or casting machines.

157. Blast-Furnace Slags. In blast-furnace slags, compositions of which are shown in Table 30, it is found that usually silica plus alumina

TABLE 30

Cast Irons and Accompanying Slags*

(Per Cent)

Product	Cast Iron					Slag						
	Si	S	P	Mn	C	Fe	Mn	SiO_2	Al_2O_3	CaO	MgO	S
Basic	1.09	0.027	0.179	1.81	4.61	0.34	1.18	34.67	14.58	44.78	3.21	1.36
Blowing	1.54	0.028	0.118	0.65	4.41	0.38	0.59	35.28	14.50	45.88	2.21	1.31
Malleable	2.29	0.025	0.183	0.84	4.32	0.42	0.40	34.90	14.24	46.02	2.51	1.56
Spiegel	0.87	0.021	0.474	20.71	5.02	0.50	4.78	31.95	12.66	37.62	9.61	1.05
Ferrosilicon, 10–12 per cent	12.10	0.010	0.105	1.83	2.02	0.15	0.15	30.20	22.20	41.10	5.45	1.55
Ferromanganese, 79–81	2.09	0.020	0.295	81.50	7.00	0.15	3.90	32.45	12.20	35.00	13.85	2.20

* Private communications.

equal about 48 per cent of the slag, with the alumina varying from 10 to 15 per cent of the whole. After enough to satisfy the sulfur is deducted from the lime, the sum of the remaining lime, together with magnesia, will also be about 48 per cent of the total weight, with magnesia seldom, if ever, exceeding 10 per cent of the whole. This relation of acids to bases will generally vary through a range of about 4 per cent, any increase in one being followed by a corresponding de-

* Beginning in 1941, the very active demand for metal encouraged operators to work over old slag dumps. These were from both blast-furnace and basic open-hearth operations. One of these projects, using a power shovel and crude concentrating plant, recovered up to 5000 tons of iron per month.

crease in the other. The remaining 4 to 5 per cent of the slag is made up of calcium sulfide and small amounts of ferrous and manganese oxides. The ratio of bases to acids is taken as a measure of the basicity of the slag and, purely arbitrarily, slags with ratios of less than 1 are considered to be acid, those with ratios greater than 1, basic. A suitable blast-furnace slag must possess certain physical characteristics; notably, fluidity at the temperature of the furnace and a low melting point. The efficiency of the slag is dependent upon its basicity or its power to absorb sulfur. Reaction 22 shows that each percentage of sulfur neutralizes 1.25 per cent of calcium in the slag, and ordinarily the quantity of sulfur in the slags ranges from 1 to 2 per cent.

158. Calculation of the Furnace Burden. Let us assume that the materials at our disposal are the ones shown in Table 31, bearing in

TABLE 31

COMPOSITION OF MATERIALS FOR BLAST-FURNACE BURDEN

Constituent	Per Cent		
	Limestone	Ore	Coke
SiO_2	1.50	7.54	5.0
Al_2O_3	1.30	1.32	3.0
CaO	50.00	0.68	1.0
MgO	3.82	0.44	1.0
Mn		0.54	
P	0.01	0.073	0.01
S			0.50
Fe		54.04	
C			89.0

mind that the analysis of a material is always carried out upon a dried sample whereas the material charged into the furnace is in its natural condition. For instance, an ore which contains 60 per cent iron when dried at 100°C. contains only 54 per cent iron in its natural condition, if in that condition 10 per cent moisture is present in the ore. Ore and stone are calculated in long tons (2240 pounds) and fuel in short tons (2000 pounds). It will be assumed also that it is desired to produce pig iron containing 1.50 per cent silicon and 94 per cent iron and that a slag with a ratio of acids to bases of 1 to 1.1 is to be produced. The following sample calculations* are employed in determining the burden.

Efficiency and Slag-Forming Constituents of Stone

    Acids:

Silica	1.50
Alumina	1.30

            2.80 pounds acid present

$$2.80 \times 1.1 = 3.08 \text{ pounds bases needed}$$

    Bases:

Lime	50.00
Magnesia	3.82

            53.82 pounds bases present
             3.08 pounds bases needed

            50.74 pounds available base

$$\text{Efficiency of stone} = \frac{100.00}{50.74} = 1.97$$

The slag-forming constituents of the stone are equivalent to the sum of the percentages of silica, alumina, lime, and magnesia, which equals 56.62 per cent of the stone.

Stone for Fuel, Slag Formed, and Available Carbon

    Acids:

Silica	5.00
Alumina	3.00

            8.00 pounds acids present

    Bases:

Lime	1.00
Magnesia	1.00

            2.00 pounds bases present

$8.00 \times 1.1 \;=\; 8.80$ pounds bases needed for acids in ash of fuel
$8.80 - 2.00 \;=\; 6.80$ pounds bases to be added
$6.80 \times 1.97 = 13.40$ pounds stone needed to flux ash from 100
                    pounds of fuel

* "Burdening the Blast Furnace," R. P. Hudson, *The Rolling Mill Journal,* September, 1930.

The stone required to flux the sulfur in the fuel may be found by multiplying the percentage of sulfur in the fuel by the molecular weight of lime divided by the atomic weight of sulfur, multiplied by the efficiency of the stone, thus:

$$0.50 \times 1.75 \times 1.97 = 1.72 \text{ pounds of stone required to flux sulfur}$$
$$\text{in 100 pounds of fuel}$$

Then the stone required for the ash (13.40) plus the stone required for the sulfur (1.72) equals 15.12 pounds of stone required per 100 pounds of fuel.

The pounds of slag formed by the ash and sulfur of the fuel is obviously equivalent to the sum of these impurities plus the stone needed to flux them, thus:

$$8.00 + 2.00 + 0.50 + (15.12 \times 0.5662)^* = 18.90 \text{ pounds of slag}$$
$$\text{per 100 pounds of fuel}$$

Theoretically, the slag requires 25 per cent of its weight in carbon to melt it. Therefore:

$$18.90 \times 0.25 = 4.72 \text{ pounds of carbon required to melt the slag}$$

Then the carbon of the fuel (89.00) minus the carbon required to melt the slag (4.72) equals 84.28 per cent available carbon.

Flux Required for Ore—Slag Formed

There are in the ore:

Acids:

Silica	7.54
Alumina	1.32
	8.86 pounds

Bases:

Lime	0.68
Magnesia	0.44
	1.12 pounds

The percentage of iron in the ore (54.04) divided by the percentage of iron to be contained in the pig (94) equals a yield of 57.49 per cent.

If 1 per cent silicon is the equivalent of 2.14 per cent silica, 1.50 per cent silicon equals 1.50 times 2.14, or 3.21 per cent silica. Therefore:

$$3.21 \times 57.49 = 1.85 \text{ per cent silica for iron per 100 pounds pig}$$

* The slag-forming constituents of the stone are 0.5662 of the weight of the stone.

Then the silica in the ore minus the silica for pig equals the silica to be fluxed, thus:

Acids in the Ore:

Silica	7.54
	1.85 for pig
	5.69 to be fluxed
Alumina present in ore	1.32
	7.01 pounds acids to be fluxed

$$7.01 \times 1.1 = 7.71 \text{ pounds bases needed}$$

The ore contains 0.54 per cent manganese, which is present as manganese oxide; one per cent manganese being equal to 1.2913 per cent manganese oxide.

$$0.54 \times 1.2913 = 0.70 \text{ per cent manganese oxide contained in the ore}$$

This is a base and, therefore, the sum of the bases contained in the ore is as follows: lime (0.68) plus magnesia (0.44) plus manganese oxide (0.70) equals 1.82 per cent bases. Theoretically, 2/3 of the manganese oxide will enter the iron and 1/3 will enter the slag. Therefore:

Bases in the Ore:

Lime	0.68
Magnesia	0.44
⅓ manganese oxide	0.23
	1.35 per cent

The bases needed (7.71) minus the bases present (1.35) equals 6.36 pound bases to be added.

$$6.36 \times 1.97 = 12.53 \text{ pounds stone required per 100 pounds ore}$$

$$\frac{94.00^*}{54.04} = 1.7407 \text{ tons ore required per ton pig}$$

$$1.7407 \times 0.1253 = 0.2181 \text{ ton stone per ton pig for ore}$$

The slag-forming constituents of the ore are:

$$\frac{7.01 \text{ (acids to be fluxed)} + 1.35 \text{ (bases present)}}{100} \times 1.7407 \text{ (tons}$$

ore per ton pig) = 0.1455 ton slag from ore.

The slag-forming constituents of the stone (56.62) divided by 100 and multi-

* Percentage of iron in pig iron.

plied by tons stone per ton pig for ore (0.2181) equals 0.1235 ton slag from stone. Then slag from ore (0.1455) plus slag from stone (0.1235) equals 0.2690, the total slag due to ore.

Fuel Consumption

The fuel consumption is calculated as follows:

Required for formation and melting of slag (0.2690 × 0.25) 0.0672
Required for reduction, impregnation, and melting pig
  containing 1.50 per cent silicon (estimated)........... 0.6850
                                                         ————
          Total parts carbon required for pig and slag........ 0.7522

0.7522/0.8428 (available carbon) × 2240 = 2000 pounds coke per ton pig

Slag per Ton Pig

From ore	0.2690 × 2240 =	602.56
From fuel	0.1890 × 2000 =	378.00
		————
Total slag per ton pig		980.56 pounds

Stone per Ton Pig

For the ore	0.2181 × 2240 =	488.54
For the fuel	0.1512 × 2000 =	302.40
		————
Total stone per ton pig		790.94 pounds

Furnace Charge

With a fuel charge of 5000 pounds the burden becomes as follows:

Coke...................	5000
Ore....................	9750
Stone..................	1975

The charge is calculated thus: With a coke charge of 5000 pounds, and 2000 pounds required to produce a ton of pig iron, it is evident that the fuel charge will smelt 2.5 tons of pig. The amount of ore required to produce one ton of pig iron is 1.7407 tons, and to produce 2.5 tons of pig iron is 4.35 tons. This is equivalent to 9744, say 9750, pounds of ore. The stone per ton of pig is 790.94. Then for 2.5 tons pig the stone required will be 1977, say 1975, pounds to give round numbers. They are within the limits of accuracy and simplify the division of the charge into a certain number of skips of material composing the burden.

The carbon content of pig iron cannot be controlled, but usually averages about 4 per cent. The phosphorus and manganese, however, can be controlled. Practically all the phosphorus contained in the charge will be found in the resulting pig iron. The percentage of phosphorus may be calculated as follows:

From ore	$0.073 \times 1.7407 \times 22.4$	$= 2.8470$ pounds per ton
From coke	0.010×20.00	$= 0.2000$ pounds per ton
From stone	0.010×7.91	$= 0.0791$ pounds per ton

Total   3.1261 pounds per ton

The pig iron, therefore, will contain 0.016 per cent phosphorus.

The manganese content may be found as follows: The ore contains 0.54 per cent manganese or 0.70 per cent manganese oxide. Of this amount only two-thirds of 0.70 (0.47) per cent is available for the iron.

$$0.47 \times 1.7407 \text{ (total ore)} = 0.82 \text{ per cent manganese oxide or}$$
$$0.635 \text{ per cent manganese}$$

The pig iron, therefore, will contain 0.635 per cent manganese.

Theoretical Slag Analysis

By the use of Table 32 the percentage of the various ingredients in the

TABLE 32

TABULATION OF VARIOUS INGREDIENTS FOR CALCULATING PERCENTAGE OF EACH IN THEORETICAL BLAST FURNACE SLAG ANALYSIS

	Silica, per Cent	Lb.	Alumina, per Cent	Lb.	Lime, per Cent	Lb.	Magnesia, per Cent	Lb.	Manganese, per Cent	Lb.
Ore	5.69	554.78	1.32	128.70	0.68	66.30	0.44	42.90	0.23	22.43
Coke	5.00	250.00	3.00	150.00	1.00	50.00	1.00	50.00		
Stone	1.50	29.63	1.30	25.68	50.00	987.50	3.82	77.45		
Total		834.41		304.38		1103.80		170.35		22.43

theoretical slag analysis can be calculated in order to check the slag composition.

$834.41 + 304.38 + 1103.80 + 170.35 + 22.43 = 2435.37$ pounds slag per charge

$$834.41/2435.37 = 34.26 \text{ per cent silica}$$
$$304.38/2435.37 = 12.49 \text{ per cent alumina}$$

$$46.75 \text{ per cent acids in the slag}$$

$$1103.80/2435.37 = 45.32 \text{ per cent lime}$$
$$170.35/2435.37 = 6.99 \text{ per cent magnesia}$$

$$52.31 \text{ per cent bases in the slag}$$

$$22.43/2435.37 = 0.92 \text{ per cent manganese oxide, or}$$
$$0.71 \text{ per cent manganese in the slag}$$

These calculations are not exact because sulfur has not been taken into consideration. It varies from about 1 to 2 per cent.

Blast Requirement—Probable Tonnage

The blast required may be readily calculated if the size of the hearth is known. With average burdens and blast temperatures, a furnace hearth should consume 6000 pounds of coke per square foot of hearth area in 24 hours. If the hearth diameter is 12 feet, the area is 113 square feet. The coke consumed will then be 678,000 pounds per 24 hours.

If 60 cubic feet of blast is required to burn a pound of coke, the total is:

$$678,000 \times 60 = 40,680,000 \text{ cubic feet of blast per 24 hours or}$$
$$28,250 \text{ cubic feet per minute}$$

The theoretical tonnage may be calculated easily. The coke consumed in 24 hours is simply divided by the weight of the coke charge. This will obviously equal the number of charges consumed by the furnace in 24 hours. If this be multiplied by the number of tons of pig iron contained in the charge, the product will evidently be the output of the furnace per 24 hours. Thus:

$$678,000/5000 = 135.6 \text{ charges per day}$$

The charge contains 2.5 tons of pig. Therefore:

$$2.5 \times 135.6 = 339 \text{ tons of pig per day}$$

159. Discussion of Methods of Calculation. There are several other methods of numerical calculation[5, 13, 42*] in use by furnacemen. It should be stated, however, that any method is to be used only as a tool for investigating the results to be expected from a given set of raw materials or in estimating approximate costs under untried conditions or in checking up on fuel consumption. In actual operation over long periods of time, however, burdening is much simpler. For instance, in the above example, the ratio of the ore to the fuel is 1 to 1.95, but this will vary more or less with the temperature of the furnace and with external conditions. In all cases, the weight of the fuel charge is fixed, and, if the analysis of the fuel and stone is constant, it is necessary only to calculate the amount of stone required to flux the ash and sulfur of the fuel once; it need not be done again. All variations in the burden, thereafter, will evidently be in the ore and flux. It is known just how much stone is necessary to flux 100 pounds of ore; therefore, it is necessary only to vary this amount when the weight of the ore is changed.

* *"Textbook of Metallurgical Problems,"* Butts, McGraw-Hill Book Co., p. 178.

In most cases several different kinds of ores, scrap, scale, etc., are employed in the mixture. This does not make the calculation more difficult, though. The proportion of each ore in the burden need only be multiplied by its analysis to obtain the "weighted average analysis" of the ores.

It must be admitted that the knowledge of slags is purely empirical. It is known what character of slag is desirable under given conditions only because thousands of trials and analyses by furnacemen have indicated its characteristics. In the above calculation, a slag has been chosen with a ratio of acids to bases of 1 to 1.1. In making iron of a higher or lower silicon content, a different ratio may be desirable. This is also true when charcoal is used as a furnace fuel instead of coke.

Slag calculations may be performed mechanically, by means of movable scales and by the use of the slide rule. These methods, however, have not been generally adopted. Certain graphical methods are desirable, though, when operations are carried on for long periods under fixed conditions.

The blast requirement of a furnace may be easily calculated from the theoretical point of view. In practical work, though, the physical characteristics of the ores and the combustibility of the coke must be considered. Unfortunately, at the present time these factors cannot be accurately expressed by equations or formulae. Also it is difficult to estimate the probable tonnage accurately, because this factor depends more or less upon the rate of driving, humidity, and the volume of blast blown. Ordinarily, an increase in blast volume causes an increase in tonnage, but it simultaneously causes an increased flue dust loss so that the tonnage cannot be accurately estimated. Any variation in the moisture content of the air also has a bearing on the fuel consumption and indirectly on the amount of pig iron produced.

160. Effect of Sinter and Scrap. An increasing amount of sinter is being used in blast-furnace burdens, most of which has been produced from flue dust. Since the proportion will increase, particularly when a greater amount of our ores is beneficiated, the Republic Steel Company has conducted some tests to determine what effect such changes will have on the capacity of the furnace. In these tests varying proportions of flue dust, gas-washer sludge, and fine Mesabi ore were used (usually 40 per cent flue dust and 60 per cent fine ore). About 450 tons of sinter, containing iron 57.80 per cent, silica 12.10, phosphorus 0.096, manganese 0.98, and alumina 2.01, were produced per 24 hours. Tests on two furnaces indicated that the production of iron increased about 7 per cent and coke consumption decreased about 8 per cent. The furnace worked more smoothly and produced less flue dust. The conclusion was reached that there is not much advantage in using more than 50 per cent sinter in the burden because of a less intimate gas-solid contact.

Commonly blast furnaces use 5 to 10 per cent scrap in the charge, which may be either steel or cast iron. The Bethlehem Steel Company conducted experiments using up to 100 per cent scrap in the burden and reached the conclusion that there is no fundamental reason for any difference in the quality of the pig iron produced from ore and that from scrap. Due allowance must be made for the higher residual element content (Cu, Ni, Cr).

GRADES OF PIG IRON

161. General. In a sense the term pig iron is a misnomer, for the product long ago outgrew its name. In the early days of the iron and steel industry in this country, the entire product of a blast furnace was sand-cast pig iron, but today over 60 per cent is used in the molten condition for the manufacture of steel or to be cast directly in molds; only about 9 per cent is marketed in the form of pig iron. Formerly, pig iron was graded entirely by fracture, but that method has been superseded by chemical analysis and metallographic examination, the important elements being, and about in order of their importance, silicon, phosphorus, sulfur, and manganese. The different grades with their approximate analyses are given in Table 21.

162. Foundry Iron. This is graded on the basis of the silicon content from No. 1, which is coarse-grained, graphitic iron, to No. 6, which is the white iron. Above 3.25 per cent silicon, it is classified as a high-silicon pig iron; and above 5 per cent silicon, it is known as a silvery iron. The X grades are "softer"; that is, they contain more silicon and hence more graphite than the corresponding numerical grades. Silicon also affects remarkably the rate of graphitization in the manufacture of malleable iron. Silicon tends to decrease shrinkage and prevent blowholes in castings, and in amounts greater than 4.5 per cent increases the resistance to corrosion. Unless sulfur is increased considerably, the smallest amount of silicon possible in foundry irons is about 0.2 per cent, although it is seldom lower than 0.7.

163. Silvery Iron. Silvery pig iron[4] is a variety first made in the old charcoal furnaces mentioned in connection with the article on history, and differed from the ordinary grades of charcoal iron in that its silicon content was never less than 5 per cent. Today silvery iron contains as high as 17 per cent silicon and is an important source of silicon for cupola charges containing low-silicon pig, much gray iron scrap, or steel. Its use in the foundry has grown steadily with the advent of high-strength gray irons, of duplex melting, and of scrap charges. The low carbon content of silvery iron makes it attractive for melting in cases where the carbon content of the charge and of the iron produced must be held to a minimum. Various grades of silvery iron containing high manganese, phosphorus, or other common alloying elements such as copper, chromium, or nickel provide an effective means for introducing such elements into mixtures melted in the cupola. Although silvery iron is made in a blast furnace, its production is distinguished by many features not common to the conventional smelting operation. Burdens consist of relatively large percentages of siliceous ores, of coke, limestone, and special grades of coal. The coal is necessary as a fuel in order to hold the smelting zone down, keep the top cool, provide richer reducing gases, and higher furnace temperatures. The fact that slag volume is high helps not only to purify the iron but also to raise its temperature. Furthermore, the capacity of a modern silvery iron furnace will be only about 200 tons of 8 per cent silicon iron per day. These furnaces, too, differ from the ordinary furnaces by being water-jacketed from top to bottom in order to protect the refractories from the more intense smelting temperatures.

164. Malleable Iron. The production of malleable cast iron consists of two distinct steps. The first step is the production of white iron castings, which are brittle and hard, and the second is annealing or graphitizing the white iron so as to secure a ductile product known as "malleable cast iron." The annealing or graphitizing changes the combined carbon to free carbon in the form of what is known as "temper carbon." To accomplish this, the silicon must be kept low (that is, 0.75 to 1.50 per cent) and the sulfur less than 0.05 per cent because it tends to prevent the formation of temper carbon in the annealing process. Phosphorus averages around 0.2 per cent; if too low, the iron is not fluid enough to penetrate into the small mold sections characteristic of this type of casting; if too high, the resulting iron may be brittle and unreliable.

165. Gray Forge. This grade, used chiefly in the production of wrought iron by the old puddling process, is characterized by fairly low silicon (about 1.50 per cent) so as not to delay the elimination of phosphorus. Phosphorus should be about 1.0 per cent; if higher, the finished iron will contain more than the limiting amount of phosphorus, which is ordinarily 0.2 per cent. Manganese is usually less than 1 per cent, for if it is higher than this there will be too much slag, which not only represents a waste of iron oxide but also slows up heat transfer in the furnace as well as affecting the phosphorus content of the iron.

166. Bessemer Pig Iron. In this grade phosphorus, sulfur, and to a less extent manganese are the important elements. Phosphorus in the iron varies from about 0.085 to 0.10 per cent. Substantially all the phosphorus remains in the blown metal; consequently it must be low enough so that the final steel may meet the rigorous specification of a maximum of 0.10 per cent phosphorus. The sulfur averages about 0.04, varying from 0.03 to 0.08 per cent. The manganese usually runs under 0.60, for if it should run much higher a thin slag would result which slops out of the converter onto the floor of the shop, causing trouble as well as loss of steel.

167. Basic Pig Iron. This is the grade of pig iron which is suitable for refining in the basic open-hearth process to produce ordinary steel. The effect of variations in the composition of the pig iron on the open-hearth process is discussed in more detail in Article 292. For the present a generalized statement may be as follows: Sulfur should be low, of the order of 0.04 per cent or less, for the operator cannot depend upon much sulfur elimination in the conventional process; the silicon should be less than 1.25 per cent, for if it is much higher it not only produces a large volume of slag and thus cuts down heat transfer but also erodes the banks of the furnace; there should be sufficient manganese, 1 to 2.5 per cent, in order to give the proper residual manganese in finished steel; and the phosphorus may be present in any quantity, although it is normally below 0.6 per cent in order not to lengthen the process unduly.

168. Basic Bessemer Iron. This is the raw material, which may be reduced by the basic Bessemer process, and should contain sufficient phosphorus for the after blow—normally about 2 per cent. This product is of little importance in this country, for our reserves of high-phosphorus high-grade iron ore are not sufficient to warrant extensive use of this process.

EFFECT OF ELEMENTS ON CAST IRON

169. The Effect of Silicon on Cast Iron. Silicon reduces progressively the amount of carbon in the eutectic from 4.25 per cent in silicon-free iron to about 3.50 per cent when 3 per cent of silicon is present. There is a progressive reduction of the melting point from 1530°C. for pure iron to 1205°C. for 20 per cent silicon. For any given carbon content an increase of the silicon from 1 to 3.5 per cent progressively changes the structure of the cast iron from hard, brittle, white iron to mottled, pearlitic, and finally gray. Although these structures are further modified by the degree of superheat in casting as well as by mold temperatures, the important influence of silicon on cast iron is its graphitizing effect on the carbides. It promotes and assists the decomposition of the combined carbon to ferrite and graphite. In its absence nearly all irons have a white or cementitic structure. It is present in the iron, usually in solid solution as a silicide (Fe_2Si or $FeSi$). The common range is 0.7 to 3.5 per cent silicon.

170. Effect of Manganese on Cast Iron. Manganese in pig iron may assume two forms: manganese carbide (Mn_3C), which is associated with iron carbide in the pearlite, and the sulfide (MnS), which occurs as small, slate-colored inclusions throughout the metal. Within the ordinary plain-carbon ranges manganese has little effect on the mechanical properties of the steel. About 0.3 per cent of manganese above the amount theoretically required for combination with sulfur (which is 55/32 times the sulfur percentage) is necessary for mitigating the effects of that element. In most American steels sulfur runs from 0.06 to 0.12 per cent; hence the usual range of manganese is 0.5 to 0.8 per cent.

171. Effect of Phosphorus on Cast Iron. This element, probably present as Fe_3P, decreases the total carbon the iron will absorb, 1 per cent of phosphorus causing a drop of about 0.3 per cent in the carbon. It probably lowers the melting point of the eutectic, decreases the viscosity of the iron, but increases the loss of carbon as kish when the iron is held for a time in the liquid state. The range, in American irons, is from 0.1 to 0.9 per cent. It affects the depth and character of the chill in castings. In large amounts it is likely to yield unsound, porous, and brittle castings.

172. Effect of Sulfur on Cast Iron. Sulfur in pig iron is generally regarded as injurious, and, as the blast furnace affords the only positive means of reducing it, pig iron containing less than 0.05 per cent is desirable for making steel by the conventional processes. In castings it is varied from about 0.04 per cent to 0.2 per cent, and, since iron melted in cupolas always takes on some sulfur from the coke, due allowance must be made for this. Sulfur in iron forms iron sulfide, which is soluble in the metal and has a melting point that is lower than the other constituents of the iron. When present in iron sulfur has a threefold influence. First, it tends to hold the carbon in the combined condition; hence it can be used to increase the depth of the chill in chilled castings, but in malleable castings and other castings that are to be heat-treated it retards the graphitization if it is not fully neutralized as manganese, and may be very undesirable. The chill produced with sulfur is very brittle; low-silicon iron containing between 0.2 and 0.4 per cent sulfur cracks spontaneously when cooled rapidly. Second, the low melting point of the sulfide causes it to segregate as the iron solidifies, thereby causing the condition in casting known as "bleeding." Third, it increases the shrinkage of the iron to a marked degree, thus increasing the difficulty of making accurate castings and increasing the tendency to form cracks, which are a result of this high shrinkage. The range in commercial cast irons is 0.05 to 0.18 per cent sulfur.

HEAT BALANCE AND DISTRIBUTION OF THE WORK

173. **Heat Balance.** Table 33 has been compiled to show the amount of heat produced in the furnace, how it is consumed, and the distribution of this heat so far as work accomplished is concerned. The cal-

TABLE 33

HEAT BALANCE OF AN IRON BLAST FURNACE[33]

	B.t.u. per Ton of Metal	Per Cent
Heat Produced		
1. Combustion of carbon to carbon monoxide	7,371,759	51.0
2. " " " " carbon dioxide	4,784,637	33.1
3. Heat in blast (including moisture)	2,316,539	15.9
Total heat	14,472,935	100.0
Heat Consumed		
1. Reduction of iron oxides	5,577,086	38.4
2. Reduction oxides of manganese, phosphorus, and silicon	825,832	5.7
3. Calcination of carbonates	1,176,470	8.1
4. Dissociation of moisture	1,030,464	7.2
5. Carried off with iron	1,086,400	7.5
6. " " " slag	1,500,632	10.4
7. " " " gases (dry)	1,083,650	7.5
8. " " " moisture in top gases	651,819	4.5
Total heat accounted for	12,912,353	89.3
Heat unaccounted for	1,560,582	10.7

culations have been made on the basis that all the carbon is burned to carbon dioxide and all the hydrogen to water and that 80.5 per cent of the work of reduction of the iron oxide is done above the level of plane 4 (see Figure 33). This compilation indicates, in a general way, that 18.6 per cent of the available heat is consumed above plane 4; of this, 13.3 per cent is used in reducing 80.5 per cent of the iron oxide, 3.4 per cent in calcination, and 1.9 per cent in drying the charge. In the bosh and hearth 3.2 per cent is consumed in reducing iron oxide, 2.5 in reducing manganese oxide, phosphorus pentoxide, and silica, and 3.1 per cent in dissociating moisture. The table also shows that, although approximately 85 per cent of the carbon is burned at the tuyère level, more work is done in the stack above plane 4 than in the bosh and hearth. The importance of this will be discussed in more detail when the "solution loss" in the blast furnace is considered (see Article 188). It is indicated that 18.6 per cent of the heat is consumed in the stack, and 16.5 per cent in the hearth and bosh. The distribution of the total available heat in reducing the oxides is as follows: above plane 4, 13.3 per cent; hearth and bosh, 5.7 per cent. Further calculations show that of the total available heat, 19 per cent is used in the reduction, 1.24 per cent between the stockline and plane, 1, 2.36 per cent between planes 1 and 3, 11.70 per cent between planes 3 and 4, and 3.70 per cent in the bosh and hearth below plane 4.

174. Graphical Balances. Mr. Joseph F. Shadgen[40] has devised an original method, notable for its clarity and conciseness, for showing the actual performance data of a blast furnace. This furnace was located in the Calumet district, producing basic pig iron from Lake Superior ores, Michigan limestone, and by-product coke.

The three major issues in blast-furnace operation are heat values (B.t.u.), material quantities (tons or pounds), and the cost (dollars). Figure 37 shows the heat balance in the form of a rectangle in which the heat input is shown to equal the heat outgo. The large items are the heat content of the fuel charged and that of the gas evolved. The sensible heat items are relatively small (some 13 per cent), and the reaction of the reduction process itself accounts for about 24 per cent or only one-fourth of the heat supplied. The blast-furnace process is really efficient from the heat point of view, inasmuch as these surplus gases are utilized. The consistent utilization of these, originally termed by-product gases, has been a major development for the past thirty years, first in boilers, then in gas engines, and now in furnaces. The increase in stove efficiency has also been taken into account and is reflected by the spread between 7 per cent and 11 per cent, or 7 per cent and 13 per cent as the specific case may be.

Figure 38 illustrates in a graphical way the flow of materials through a blast furnace. Here, again, the rectangle furnishes the basis and expresses the old law—what goes in must come out—as the top and

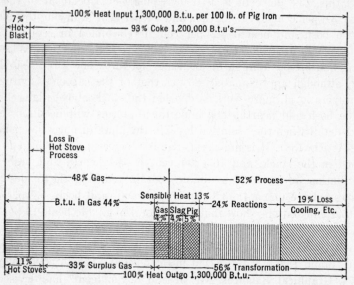

Fig. 37. Graphic Representation of Heat Values. (*Courtesy of The Iron Age.*)

bottom lines are of equal length. This picture makes the observer extremely air-gas conscious. It shows the enormous proportions of the weights and volumes of gases handled. This fact catches the eye of even the untrained observer and reminds one of some peculiarities that have become so familiar as to have been overlooked or taken for granted. It will be observed that over 50 per cent of the weight that goes into the blast furnace is air and over 75 per cent of the output is gas. In addition this graphical picture shows the transformation of the various constituents of the burden. It is simple to follow the changes of oxygen to carbon monoxide and carbon dioxide and the split-off of the carbon into the pig iron and the gases. This, or similar graphs made on a large scale, can be used to great advantage in burden calculations, daily comparison sheets, and monthly operating data. They are, of course, most valuable in comparing performances between plants located in various sections of the country.

Figure 39 applies these graphical balances to the dollars and cents

values of the blast-furnace process. Naturally, the rectangle as a basis
becomes impossible because of the transformation whereby the raw-
material values had to be increased. In other words, the product values
must be greater or else there will be no profit. The money balance
starts with the sum of the material values AA, and progressively adds
the labor charge, BB, the maintenance cost, CC, the amortization,
DD, and the present profit, EE, to arrive at the product's value, FK.

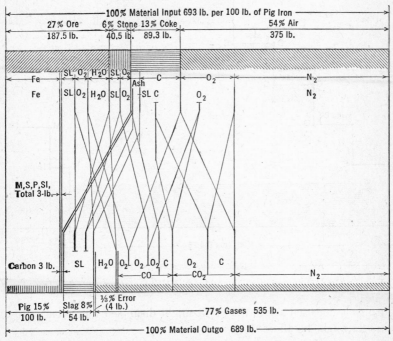

FIG. 38. Graphic Representation of Raw Materials. (*Courtesy of The Iron Age.*)

Again, the proportions are strikingly apparent. The air, in spite of
large quantities, costs comparatively little; coke and ore are the pre-
dominating dollar items of AA. The labor item of BB, because of the
large tonnages handled by the blast furnace, is relatively small. The
item CC is elastic, the maintenance being largely determined by the
policy of the corporation, the load factor, etc. The write-off charges
DD are still more elusive; they are complicated by considerations of
capital structure, and the profits depend on market economic trends,
national influences, etc. This figure shows most clearly the contributory
values of the so-called by-products, slags (GH), and gases (HK). In

other words, if a slag does not contribute a value, *EF* (the profit) will be influenced very much; if *GH* or *NN* is nil, the profits will be sharply reduced. The same applies to the blast-furnace gases. If their

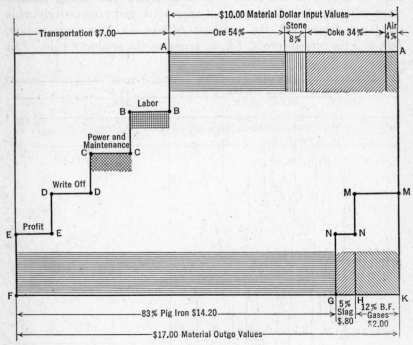

Fig. 39. Graphic Representation of Material Values. (*Courtesy of The Iron Age.*)

surplus is not used at all, the profit might disappear and even write-off charges might be affected.

OPERATION OF THE FURNACE

175. Blowing-in. The blowing-in of a blast furnace, ordinarily carried out in three steps (drying, filling, and lighting), is shown in some detail in Table 34. This sequence of operations will obviously vary with the condition of the furnace, the character of the ore, the kind of iron to be produced, and even the theories and experience of the operator.

New furnaces or ones with new linings must be carefully and thoroughly dried before they are put in service; otherwise the life of the lining will be materially shortened. The methods employed will vary from district to district. The easiest, although perhaps the most

TABLE 34

Record of Blow-in of "F" Blast Furnace*

Dimensions of Hearth

Hearth diameter	24 feet
Bosh diameter	26 feet 11 inches
Height	94 feet 6 inches
Stockline diameter	18 feet
Batter of stack	1⅛ inches per foot
Big bell diameter	13 feet 6 inches
Number of tuyères	16

Filling

Filling started at 12:30 P.M. April 11, and the furnace was full to within 11 feet below the bottom of the big bell at 10:00 A.M., April 12. Distribution within the top was found to be good. The stockline was established at 15 feet 6 inches below the stock rod hole in the hood. This was 24 inches below the ledge of the wear plates. The furnace was filled to this point and the stockline recorders set to read zero when the rod was at the level of the stock. The material charged was as follows:

(a) Four skips charcoal at 1500 lb. each
(b) Two skips charcoal at 1500 lb. each   } 3 charges.
    Four skips coke at 5000 lb. each
    Six skips coke at 5000.
(c) Two skips charcoal at 1500 lb. each; 6 skips coke at 5000 lb. each. This filled the furnace to the bottom of the tuyères, and at this point men went into the furnace and leveled off the coke and charcoal across the furnace.
(d) Four skips charcoal at 1500 lb.

After this bags of shavings and bundles of kindling wood were placed at the even-numbered tuyères, the odd tuyères being plugged.

(e) Five skips charcoal at 1500 lb.
    One skip charcoal at 1000 lb.

This used up the last of the charcoal.

(f) Twenty skips coke at 5000 lb. each.
(g) Twenty charges of the following burden:

1 skip blast-furnace cinder at 5000 lb.
2 skips coke at 5800 lb. (raised coke chutes).
1 skip stone at 1500 lb.

Burden 1—Earl 2000 lb., Beaver 2000 lb., blast-furnace cinder 4000 lb., siliceous ore
to   1000 lb., stone 3000 lb., coke 11,800 lb., followed by progressive changes in burden to
Burden 5—Earl 8000 lb., Beaver 8000 lb., blast-furnace cinder 4000 lb., siliceous ore 1000 lb., Limestone 4300 lb., coke 11,800 lb.

At this point the unit system of filling was begun.

Burden 6—Earl 35%   Ore 16,000 lb. per charge
       Beaver 30%   Stone 4400
       Kirby 10%   Silic. 1000
       Harper 20%   B.F. Cinder 1000 lb. per charge
       Scranton 5%   Coke 11,800 lb. charge

TABLE 34 (*Continued*)

RECORD OF BLOW-IN OF "F" BLAST FURNACE

OPERATION

Cast	Date	Time	Ladles	Tons	Cinder	Si	S	P	Mn
1	4/13	12:45P.M.	¼	3	7½	3.86	0.070	0.144	0.71
2		7:15	1½	40	4	5.40	0.032	0.141	1.12
3		1:30A.M.	5½	134	4½	5.04	0.047	0.150	1.33
4	4/14	6:00	4½	92	2½	4.43	0.039	0.150	1.37
5		11:30	5	100	7½	4.81	0.021	0.153	1.50
6		5:10P.M.	5	115	10	4.64	0.025	0.144	1.46
7		11:00	6½	143	7½	3.15	0.035	0.156	1.46
8		3:18A.M.	5¼	108	10½	2.66	0.023	0.189	1.48
9	4/15	8:35	5	132	8½	2.99	0.015	0.201	1.97
10		12:00M.	5½	118	8	3.12	0.015	0.198	2.06
11		5:40	5	131	8	2.58	0.016	0.192	1.88
12		10:00	5	126	9	2.23	0.021	0.189	1.83
13		3:45A.M.	5	143	9	2.20	0.021	0.183	1.74
14	4/16	8:10	6¼	147	7	1.40	0.021	0.198	1.53
15		1:35P.M.	6	165	14	1.77	0.022	0.207	1.92
16		6:05	4¼	105	11	1.47	0.020	0.192	1.73
17		10:50	5	147	12	1.15	0.022	0.195	1.62
18		3:15A.M.	5½	159	11	.95	0.033	0.195	1.47
19	4/17	8:10	6	168	11	1.35	0.025	0.210	1.67
20		1:30P.M.	6	168	11	1.35	0.026	0.192	1.56

SLAG ANALYSIS

Date	Time	Fe	SiO_2	Al_2O_3	CaO	MgO	Mn	S
4/13	7:30A.M.	0.22	36.40	14.50	45.00	2.09	0.39	2.33
	8:00	0.20	36.60	14.70	44.00	2.45	0.32	2.39
	8:40	0.28	36.60	13.90	44.40	2.23	0.34	2.38
	9:00	0.20	37.40	14.40	43.00	2.45	0.34	2.36
	10:30	0.24	38.00	14.90	42.60	2.38	0.41	2.38
	12:45 P.M.	0.36	40.60	14.50	39.80	2.38	0.54	2.22
	3:40	0.24	36.40	16.00	42.40	2:45	0.46	2.50
	5:10	0.20	34.60	15.10	44.00	2.52	0.46	2.45
	7:25	0.20	38.40	14.80	41.80	2.42	0.65	2.29
	10:30	0.24	36.60	14.80	43.20	2.66	0.60	2.22
	11:45	0.36	38.00	14.60	42.80	2.23	0.75	1.99
4/14	1:30 A.M.	0.18	36.50	14.90	44.00	2.45	0.56	2.34
	3:40	0.26	40.29	13.20	42.20	2.38	0.97	1.76

Furnace lighted and wind on   7:30 P.M. April 12

First flush   7:30 A.M. April 13

First cast   12:45 P.M. April 13

* Private communication from Lake plant.

dangerous, is carried out by means of a gas fire in the hearth. Unusual precautions must be taken to keep the gas burning, for, if the flame should go out, the furnace is likely to become filled with an explosive mixture of gas and air. The second method is to build three or four Dutch ovens at different points outside the hearth, fire these with gas-coke or a mixture of coal and coke, and allow the products of combustion to be drawn through the cooler-plate openings into the bottom of the furnace. This method, while safer, is obviously more trouble, requires more labor, and is probably more expensive. A third method makes use of the hot blast for drying by heating the stoves with blast-furnace gas as in normal operation and then blowing the air from the stoves to the bottom of the furnace through the regular connections as well as through a number of special pipes extending from the tuyères, inside the furnace, to the bottom. In all cases the heat must be applied gradually over a period of at least ten days to avoid the spalling of the lining; when possible, this period should be prolonged to two weeks or more.

After the drying is completed, the process of filling the furnace is started. In general this scheme consists of first placing wood and coke, or coke alone, in the bottom, to a height somewhat below the level of the tuyères, where some easily ignited material, preferably charcoal, is piled, then following this material with a large quantity of coke mixed with enough limestone to flux this ash, and gradually introducing ore with the proper amount of flux. Ordinarily, this initial volume of coke is about half the cubical contents of the furnace. Sometimes to get an easily fusible slag, as well as a good volume of it, blast-furnace slag may be introduced along with the ore.

The furnace may be lighted by filling the space immediately in front of the tuyères with light kindling wood. A light blast is turned on and the wood ignited by the hot blast (1000°F.). The wood soon burns away and the stock begins to settle, after which the blast pressure can be gradually increased. Some operators start with a fairly high blast pressure, for a few minutes, in order to drive the flames well in toward the center of the furnace and ignite the charge there. As soon as the stock gives signs of settling, the blast pressure is reduced to that normally used for the remainder of the blowing-in period, which is at first about one-fourth that used when the furnace is in full blast. During all this period great care must be exercised in handling the furnace, for not only are the gases toxic, but they are also highly explosive. Another factor connected with the lighting of the furnace is the heating of the stoves because the temperature of the hot blast, when the furnace is in full operation, should be 500 to 550°C., and it is, of course, a great help if the stoves can be heated nearly to this point for the lighting of the furnace.

176. Tapping. At the end of 12 hours, as indicated in Table 34, after the blast is on full, there will be a sufficient accumulation of slag to tap. This is done by removing the bott from the monkey and pricking through the solid slag, enlarging the opening until the cinder flows. The bleeder is then closed, for now the gas can be used in the stoves, boilers, or gas engines; up to this point, it has been exhausted into the atmosphere. Ordinarily, 25 to 40 hours will elapse before much iron accumulates, and, when this is ready to tap, a hole is bored by means of a long auger, or drill, almost through the clay plug of the tapping hole. The splasher having been put in place, the opening is then completed by driving a long pointed bar into the furnace or by burning out the iron plug with the oxygen lance. Samples of both iron and slag are taken because the iron is usually off-grade and ordinarily not marketable, and the slag analysis will indicate what changes in burden are needed to bring it back to the required composition. When the iron has ceased to flow from the tapping hole, the blower signals the engineer to reduce the blast, may even open the snort valve on the cold blast main to relieve the pressure, then swings the clay gun into position and closes the hole as previously described. As soon as the hole is stopped, the furnace returns to normal blast until the next tapping time, 4 to 6 hours afterward.

The sampling of the iron is a very important part of every tap, for the iron is graded by chemical analysis, and care must be taken to secure a sample that will be representative of the whole cast. This sample, therefore, is generally made up of a number of equal portions taken from the main runner at the farther side of the skimmer, and at periods corresponding to the first, middle, and last third of the cast. These samples consist of small castings made by pouring the metal into a mold. When cold, the small casting is broken with a hammer, and from the fracture thus exposed (if the test has been cooled properly) the foreman is able to judge very closely the quality of the iron. As a further check, one-half is sent to the laboratory, the other half kept at the furnace for reference. Chilled tests of all slags are also taken, carefully inspected at the same time, and likewise reserved.

177. Normal Operation. After about 2 hours of normal blowing (using Lake ores), the slag will rise to a point close to the tuyères and another flush will become necessary. A great many of the furnace plants today cast only four times per 24 hours, and, although five casts are quite common, the old six-cast cycle is practically a thing of the past. Normally only two flushes of slag are made on any casting schedule.

Charging of the furnace (see Articles 123-130) is usually done in "rounds," the basis of which is the weight of fuel in each round. Usually the coke in a round is measured by volume and not weight, but, of course, the weight·of the given volume is accurately determined. The weight of this coke unit varies at different plants, the ones most often used being 10,000, 12,000, and 15,000·pounds. Obviously, the relative weights of ore, fuel, and coke will vary according to the composition of the ore and that of the pig iron required. The manner of charging these materials is also subject to much variation. Sometimes it will be found that all the coke in a round may be charged, followed by the ore and limestone mixed together. At other times coke, ore, and limestone are charged separately.

The temperature of the furnace hearth is a matter of great importance because it is one of the two main factors which control the quality of the iron produced, particularly the percentages of silicon and sulfur, and the general operation of the furnace. The control of the hearth temperature is most easily obtained by controlling that of the hot blast temperatures, which may be raised or lowered by use of a by-pass. The period that a stove is on blast varies at different furnaces, depending upon the area of heating surface in the stoves and their number. If a furnace has four stoves with plenty of heating surface, the time on blast is usually not less than 2 hours and may be as much as 6 to 9 hours—hence the period on gas for the other three stoves would be 6 to 27 hours. Thus each stove is heated for 3 hours. In changing stoves the hot stove must be put on the furnace before the cold one is taken off. To put a stove on hot blast, the gas burner is racked back from the gas port, and the blow-off and chimney valves are closed, in addition to closing the gas inlet to the stove by means of a large door brick-lined on the inside. Then in quick succession the cold-blast valves and the hot-blast valves are opened, after which the blast is free to pass through the stove, which it does in the opposite direction to that by which the stove was heated. The cold stove is now taken off, the procedure being the reverse of that above, the cold-air valve is closed, and then quickly the hot-blast valve. To relieve the pressure in the stove, the blow-off valve is slowly opened, which permits the chimney valve to be opened. The stove is then ready for the gas, which is admitted by racking the burner forward.

178. Fanning. Formerly, it was regarded as highly undesirable, sometimes impossible, to reduce materially the tonnage produced by a blast furnace. Previous to the years of the recent economic depression (1930 to 1935), if market conditions dictated the lowering of the production to any material extent, the furnace was usually taken off blast and banked. At that time it was thought that any reduction in the blast pressure would result in the stock dropping through the bosh into the hearth, filling the bosh and hearth with cold material and making it difficult or impossible to start the furnace again. However, during the depression years referred to, when the demand for pig iron was only 10 to 30 per cent of normal, means had to be devised for curtailing the output of the few furnaces in operation.* Proving again the adage that "necessity is the mother of invention" it was found possible, if the furnaces were tapped dry and properly filled, to reduce the blast pressure to 1 or 2 pounds at the bustle pipe for several hours without chilling the hearth and to resume full blast at the end of that time without difficulty or injury to the furnace. To control output by this means—"fanning the furnace"—it was only necessary to work out a proper cycle of low- and high-blast operations with the time of each period so adjusted as to produce the required amount of iron and at the same time maintain proper smelting conditions in the furnace.

179. Irregularities in Furnace Operation. A prominent production metallurgist has said, "There are few situations in life where promptness and decision, forethought and good judgment, skill and experience are more needed than about a blast furnace in trouble." This tremendous and yet temperamental structure, like a man, works best with a cool head and warm feet, but it is frequently difficult to maintain these favorable conditions. Apparently modern science has placed at our disposal methods of control and regulation which should provide for easy and safe operation. but every furnaceman knows that even with these methods at his disposal a blast furnace can act in the most astonishing and unexpected manner. The most important of the difficulties which may be encountered in the routine operation of an iron blast furnace are:

1. Improper distribution of the charge, already discussed in connection with the construction of the blast furnace, caused by chimneying. This obviously brings about uneven reduction of the iron ore; but what is still worse

* In 1932 only 42 out of the 291 blast furnaces in the United States were in operation.

the hot gases follow the lines of least resistance, and, if these open channels happen to be near the walls, the condition becomes localized and the gases soon erode the walls adjacent to the area affected and give rise to a hot spot on the furnace shell. Water sprays applied at this point sometimes permit operations for a considerable period, and in recent years injections of fire clay slurry have been successful in building up the refractory lining at this point sufficient to continue operation for a considerable period.

2. Irregularities in charging may bring about a wedging of the stock in the upper part of the stack. This condition is further aggravated by the deposition of carbon, filling up the interstices of the stock, so that the gas can penetrate into it only with difficulty. When this condition does occur, the stock beneath this wedged portion may settle from that above and, sometime after that, the wedged portion may suddenly be released to give rise to what is known as a "slip," in which case the pressure of the gases produced by this slip may bring about a rise in pressure similar to a mild explosion.

3. Scaffolding is another condition brought about by irregularities in the working of the furnace. If the zone of fusion is suddenly lowered, the pasty mass at its top tends to adhere to the encircling wall with the result that a circular incrustation is formed projecting out into the center of the furnace. Naturally, this mass offers obstruction both to the rising gases as well as to the descending stock, and if this condition is not soon remedied, the blast gases may channel and result in serious damage to the lining on one side. This condition is also referred to as "hanging."

4. Loss of tuyères may be brought about by their burning out through the failure of the water or by the filling of the tuyères with molten material during a slip. In particularly bad slips a great deal of molten slag may be thrown up into the tuyères and even into the blow pipes and tuyère stock where it solidifies and stops the flow of air.

5. Another condition which may arise from a severe slip is a large amount of cold stock dropping into the hearth and thus lowering the temperature of the molten iron and slag to below the fusion point.

180. Banking and Blowing-out. Sometimes fanning is not sufficient to reduce production commensurate with market demand, in which case it becomes necessary to close down or "bank" a furnace completely for a few days or even weeks. This is done by charging coke blanks beginning a few hours before banking. After this has gone on for some time, the furnace is drained of iron and slag "dried up" (in furnace parlance). The connections to the rest of the plant are closed, the blast is shut off, the blow pipes and the tuyères removed, and all openings tightly bricked up. The bleeders, explosion doors, and finally the bells are opened, and the gas is allowed to pass out into the atmosphere. In this condition a furnace may remain inactive for several days or weeks. In starting up such a furnace it is filled with coke and a little ore, the ashes are raked out through a tuyère open-ing, the necessary connections made, and the blast turned on. In a week or more, depending upon the condition of the furnace, it will be operating normally.

In blowing-out the charging is stopped, but the blast kept on and the stock allowed to settle in the stack. Water is allowed to flow in through the try-holes in order to keep the top cool and prevent warp-ing of the bells. When the stock has descended to a point near the tuyères, the blast is shut off, the tuyères removed, and, when the furnace is sufficiently cooled, the rest of the stock cleared out with shovels.

181. Desulfurization with Alkali. The practice of external desul-furization has been current in England and Germany, where raw materials greatly inferior to ours are in use. In 1942 the demand for greatly increased production awakened interest in this method in this country (it was being considered in 1918 when the Armistice was declared). Tests run by the Pittsburgh Steel Company, summa-rized in Table 35, tend to prove that high-sulfur cokes can be used

TABLE 35

DESULFURIZATION WITH SODA ASH*

Method of Addition	Number of Tests	Pounds of Soda Ash, Per Ton Iron	Average Sulfur, Per Cent		Reduction in Sulfur, Per Cent	Efficiency, Per Cent
			Before Addition	After Addition		
A	282	8.2	0.0452	0.0279	38.1	13.93
B	85	7.3	0.0389	0.0272	30.0	10.56
C	36	8.6	0.0487	0.0330	32.4	12.12
Average	403	8.1	0.0440	0.0290	35.8	13.05

* "Desulfurization with Alkali," R. H. Sweetser, *Iron Age*, May 29, 1941.
A—Regulated feed in runner at cast house.
B—Addition to bottom of ladles.
C—Reladled at mixer from height of 25 feet.

without the necessity of carrying excessive slag volumes or strongly basic slags (which would affect silicon and manganese) because the extra sulfur can be easily and cheaply removed by the use of soda ash added to the runners or ladle. The other elements in the iron are not affected materially nor does the addition adversely affect open-hearth operation, but it does add to the cost of producing pig iron and means must be provided for removing the fume because it is a hazard to the operators. Whereas all irons were below 0.07 per cent sulfur, the indications were that the higher the original sulfur, the greater the percentage of reduction.

BLAST-FURNACE REFRACTORIES

182. General. The first blast furnaces built in this country in colonial times were lined with mica schist, but such a lining was so easily fluxed by the constituents of the charge that the short life of such linings was one of the major problems of the early operators. According to F. H. Norton, the first fire bricks were produced at Queens Run, Pennsylvania, in 1836. Other writers speak of brick having been molded and burned in Massachusetts about the year 1834. In 1841 a refractory plastic-clay brick began to be produced in Ohio near East Liverpool, and in 1871 the well-known Kentucky clay district was opened up and has since produced a large percentage of the linings for iron blast furnaces. In the early years of this century it was unusual for a furnace to produce more than 350,000 gross tons of pig iron per lining. Fifteen years ago this was up to about 500,000 gross tons, and at present 1,000,000 gross tons is considered an average figure; and some furnaces have produced 1,600,000 gross tons and better on a single lining. Although it is true that enlarged capacity of furnaces and improved general practice have accounted for some of this increase in tonnage, nevertheless better quality in fire brick must be given some credit for its share. Even these encouraging increases in the life of a lining do not convince us that we have reached the maximum life, and it is believed that a still better product can be produced and that the refractory industry of this country will, through its extensive research departments, ultimately develop a material that will far eclipse the records referred to.

It is obvious that a brick conforming to one set of specifications will not suffice for the lining of the entire blast furnace. The hearth and bosh require a brick of a very refractory composition capable of resisting high temperatures and the slagging effects of molten metal and slags, whereas other sections of the furnace should resist shock, attrition, or abrasion. The real problem lies in the shaft of the furnace, where one must employ a brick capable of resisting the abrasive action of the stock at temperatures as high as 1000°C. The brick forming the shaft or the inwall must also resist disintegration caused by carbon deposition. For the purposes of this presentation, the furnace can be divided into four zones:

1. Preparation.
2. Reduction.
3. Fusion.
4. Crucible.

183. Zone of Preparation. In this zone the temperatures will vary from 100 to 210°C., and the conditions are those involving the impact and mechanical abrasion of about 3000 tons of stock per 24 hours as it is charged into the furnace through the bell. It is true that the refractories in the upper part of the stack are usually protected with metallic wearing plates; nevertheless, the brick itself must have considerable resistance to such impact and abrasion. On the whole a plastic, hard-burned brick of close texture is usually employed.

184. Zone of Reduction. The temperatures encountered in this zone are from 210 to 1020°C., and here are encountered the hardest service conditions. Not only must the brick resist the abrasive action of the descending charge, but it must also resist the sand-blast-like action of the very hot, ascending gases. More often than not the first failure of a blast furnace lining occurs in this zone, as indicated in Figure 40. The brick in this zone must also resist disintegration caused by carbon deposition. A blast furnace has often been likened to a huge gas producer, being constantly filled with a gas containing a high percentage of carbon monoxide so that the bricks composing its lining are at all times permeated with this gas. It has been demonstrated that carbon monoxide gas, in the presence of free iron or ferric oxide, will break down according to the following reaction:

$$2Fe_2O_3(c) + 8CO(g) \rightarrow 7CO_2(g) + 4Fe(c) + C(c);$$
$$\Delta H = -49,400 \text{ cal.} \tag{23}$$

if held at a temperature between 788 and 878°F. Carbon may also be deposited at about 600°C. by metallic iron, thus:

$$Fe(c) + CO(g) \rightarrow FeO(c) + C(c); \quad \Delta H = -37,600 \tag{24}$$

or by the reversal of reaction

$$2CO(g) \rightarrow CO_2(g) + C(c); \quad \Delta H = -41,500 \tag{25}$$

Therefore, we must employ, for this zone, a fire brick free from all elements that possess catalytic properties that lead to the deposition of the carbon within the structure of the brick itself because these are certain to create internal strains that will ultimately cause the brick to be shattered or disrupted. On the whole, brick for this zone are hard-burned with the varying proportions of plastic and flint clays.

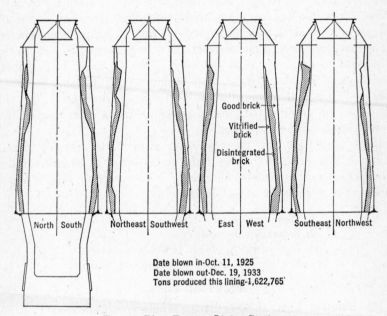

Good brick
Vitrified brick
Disintegrated brick

North | South   Northeast | Southwest   East | West   Southeast | Northwest

Date blown in-Oct. 11, 1925
Date blown out-Dec. 19, 1933
Tons produced this lining-1,622,765

FIG. 40. Blast-Furnace Lining Sections.

185. Fusion Zone. Here, just above the tuyères, the temperatures are very high (from 1000 to 1430°C.), and the brick is exposed to molten iron and slag as it trickles down over the lining of the furnace. Although the refractories are protected by cooling plates, nevertheless the refractory properties of these bricks are their most important property. They are usually made from mixtures of flint and semi-flint clays.

186. Crucible and Hearth. Here the temperatures are very high because the iron is usually at a temperature of about 1410°C. and the slag about 1380°C. By reason of the pressure of the charge and of the bath of molten slag and iron, the hearth is subject to static pressures of 25 to 40 pounds per square inch, with the result that slag and metal are forced into the interstices between the brick. By reason of this action, as well as the corrosive nature of the slag, most of the brickwork close to the hearth finally disappears, to be replaced by iron.* The mixtures used for the brick are usually those of flint and semi-flint clays.

187. Importance of Accurate Size and Shape. The brick should be not only of a homogeneous and proper structure, but accuracy of size and shape is also very important. It is just as essential to have these bricks laid up free from open joints that give easy access to the gas stream as it is to have their internal structure homogeneous. As a matter of fact, some designers have considered this sufficiently important to employ special shapes in order to break these joints. The demand on the part of blast-furnace operators is so insistent that we even find manufacturers, particularly those using the old hand method, grinding the finished bricks to size in order to meet the close tolerances now stipulated.

Brick sizes have also undergone a change in the last few years. Formerly, the bricks were very large, up to 3 feet in length, but the tendency now is towards smaller ones, of the order of 13½ x 6 x 3 inches. The reasons for these changes are:

1. They burn better.
2. Breakage is less costly.
3. It is easier to obtain better-fitting bricks.
4. The manipulation of these bricks is easier.

SOLUTION LOSS

188. Solution Loss. In 1874 M. L. Gruner† published his theorem of the "ideal" blast furnace, which states with the most admirable simplicity that a blast furnace operates most efficiently when a maximum proportion of the fuel is burned at the tuyères; that is, when, in present-day parlance, there is no "solution loss." The theoretical realization of Gruner's ideal requires that all reduction of iron oxide be accomplished by reaction with carbon monoxide or hydrogen to form carbon dioxide or water, as indicated below:

$$Fe_2O_3(c) + 3CO(g) \rightarrow 2Fe(c) + 3CO_2(g);$$
$$\Delta H = -4,300 \text{ cal.} \tag{26}$$
$$Fe_2O_3(c) + 3H_2(g) \rightarrow 2Fe(c) + 3H_2O(g); \quad \Delta H = +25,100 \tag{27}$$

It has long been known that in actual furnace operation a con-

---

* This mass, called the "salamander," sometimes weighs as much as 150 tons.
† M. L. Gruner, *Blast Furnace Phenomena*, H. C. Baird and Co., 1874.

siderable proportion of the carbon dioxide thus formed reacts with carbon to form carbon monoxide, thus:

$$CO_2(g) + C(c) \rightarrow 2CO(g); \quad \Delta H = +41,500 \tag{28}$$

which reaction not only "dissolves" carbon into the furnace gases but also absorbs a very large quantity of heat. It is further probable that in many furnaces considerable iron oxide is reduced directly with carbon to form carbon monoxide, thus:

$$FeO(c) + C(c) \rightarrow Fe(c) + CO(g); \quad \Delta H = +37,600 \tag{29}$$

which likewise has the effect of "dissolving" carbon and again absorbing a large quantity of heat. Reactions 28 and 29 are then the "solution loss reactions," and the degree to which they are avoided determines the closeness of approach to Gruner's theoretical ideal of maximum chemical and thermal efficiency in blast-furnace operation.

Johnson[*] pointed out in 1918 that avoidance of solution loss requires that the ore be reduced to metal as high up in the furnace shaft as possible and that the hearth, or bosh, of the furnace should not be called upon to do any chemical work or preheating that can be accomplished higher up in the shaft. Joseph,[33] in 1927, expanded the idea by showing that if the ore is reduced by carbon monoxide, with formation of carbon dioxide, at temperatures below 1000°C., the reaction of the resultant carbon dioxide with carbon is so slow and the linear velocity of the gas so great that most of the carbon dioxide formed reaches the top of the furnace without being reduced to carbon monoxide. This is merely another way of saying that, if the ore can be completely reduced before it reaches a zone where the temperature is as high as 1000°C., solution loss will be nearly, if not quite, eliminated. Of course, the same consideration applies to the carbon dioxide formed through the calcination of the limestone.

It has been established that in normal American blast-furnace practice solution loss is of the order of 300 to 400 pounds of coke per ton of pig iron, or 15 to 25 per cent of the total fuel. Moreover, since the solution loss reactions are strongly endothermic, it is clear that additional coke must be burned at the tuyères to supply the heat thus absorbed. It follows then that solution loss very seriously affects blast-furnace operation and economy and that it has the effect of forcing the blast furnace to operate as a gas producer to an extent far beyond the immediate requirements for pig-iron smelting. Al-

[*] J. E. Johnson, Jr., *Principles, Operation and Products of the Blast Furnace*, McGraw-Hill Book Co., 1918.

though in its dual role of pig-iron smelter and gas producer, the blast furnace is a remarkably satisfactory and efficient apparatus, many metallurgists and engineers have pointed out that the primary function of the blast furnace being the production of pig iron at the lowest possible cost, its function as a gas producer should be subordinated to this primary function.

189. Pressure Operation. Julian M. Avery[2] has pointed out that during the past ten years or more, improvements in blast-furnace technique and economy have been directed primarily to increasing efficiency in the use of the reducing power of the gases produced by combustion of the coke at the tuyères, to reduce iron ore within the furnace. The net overall result is a decrease in the fuel value of the top gas per unit of volume and per ton of pig iron, which is evidently more than offset in value by the corollary saving in coke and the possibility of increased furnace capacity, for otherwise there would be no point in making such improvements. He suggests that there is another approach to the problem of increasing the chemical and thermal efficiency of the blast furnace, in its primary role as a pig-iron producer, which appears to offer possibilities of improvements in overall economy of a different order of magnitude and results than thus far obtained by the use of other expedients. He believes that the efficiency and the economics of pig-iron smelting are seriously and adversely affected by solution loss and that the problem can be successfully attacked by increasing the overall pressure (top pressure) under which the furnace is operating.

So far as equilibrium is concerned, reference to reaction 29 shows that increased pressure, other conditions being equal, obviously shifts the equilibrium of this reaction toward the left; and as it is a fundamental principle of chemistry that the rate of a chemical reaction decreases as equilibrium is approached, it follows that pressure has the effect of inhibiting the solution loss reaction. The effect of pressure on rates, however, is not quite so simple, because, if pressure increases the rate of reduction of iron ore by reason of increased molecular concentration of carbon monoxide, it is to be expected that pressure will likewise increase the rate of reaction between carbon dioxide and carbon (some believe that as a consequence pressure might conceivably increase the solution loss instead of decreasing it). Let us examine the immediate result of increasing the top pressure without any change in other conditions. One immediate effect is an increase in the rate of reduction of iron ore in the upper portion of the shaft. The inevitable result is that less oxygen will reach lower zones of the furnace in the form of iron oxide and less carbon dioxide will be formed deep in the furnace. On the other hand, in the lower levels of the furnace, where the ratio of carbon monoxide to carbon dioxide is normally lower than the equilibrium ratio in contact with carbon, a larger proportion of the carbon dioxide formed will react with carbon to produce carbon monoxide. Considered as an isolated reaction, this indicates increased solution loss. It must be remembered, however, that, to the extent this reaction is increased, the reducing power of the gases in the upper portion of the stack is likewise increased, which in turn increases the rate of reduction of the ore and thereby further decreases the amount of carbon dioxide in the lower portion of the stack. It appears, then, that, regardless of the relative importance of the changes in various reaction rates, the net effect of increased pressure must be to reduce iron ore higher in the stack and to decrease solution loss by decreasing the quantity of carbon dioxide formed in high-temperature zones in the furnace. Obviously, then, for a given increase in pressure a new chemical balance will be reached within the furnace leading to decreased solution loss, smaller volume, and a leaner quantity of top gas and less coke required per ton of pig iron.

The physical effects of pressure are more apparent and favorable. Assuming that solution loss is increased by pressure operation, it is obvious that for a given rate of production the blast rate will be less, and experience with slow blowing has proved this means less channeling, less dusting, less pressure drop, and a better gas-solid contact. The work of Furnas[16] has shown that the pressure drop of gases flowing through a bed of broken solids varies, for a given mass velocity, inversely as the overall pressure. From his formula for the floating of solid particles in a stream of gas it can be shown that the tendency to dusting, other things being equal, appears to vary, roughly, inversely as the overall pressure. This decrease in channeling is also bound to improve the gas-solid contact, and this in turn to insure better heat transfer and also increase the probability of reduction of the ore high up in the stack.

Because of the large thermal effect of the solution loss reactions, it is evident that a considerable decrease in this factor must result in an important change in the internal thermal balance of the blast furnace. It is well known that in normal operation solution loss occurs principally in the bosh of the furnace, a zone whose primary function is to complete the heating of the charge and to melt metallic and non-metallic materials to form pig iron and slag. Clearly the absorption of large quantities of heat in the bosh by the solution loss reactions operates to hold down the temperature of the gases and thus prevent the bosh zone from properly carrying out its primary functions. Furthermore, since it will not usually be desirable to have such a high gas temperature at the top of the bosh, decreased solution loss should permit the use of lower blast temperatures, which has the twofold effect of conserving fuel gas for other purposes and increasing the reducing power of the furnace gases by burning more coke at the tuyères. In a sense, lowering the blast temperature is equivalent to operating the blast furnace as a gas producer, but only to the extent that such practice is justified by conditions within the furnace; and only actual trial in commercial furnaces can determine the optimum balance between the economic factors and operating conditions involved.

Pressure operation will also affect capacity and fixed charges because the ratio of ore to coke in the charge will be correspondingly increased, and, if the rate of combustion of the coke at the tuyères is maintained constant, it is clear that furnace capacity will be increased. Furthermore, increased burden also increases the effective exposure of ore, on the average, to the action of reducing gases, for at a given instant there is more ore in the furnace. This is another factor that acts in favor of pressure operation as a means of reducing solution loss, for it increases the spread between the direct effect of pressure upon the rate of the solution loss reaction and its effect upon the rate of reduction of the ore.

It is the belief of Mr. Avery[2] that very substantial benefits may be obtained by using top pressures of the order of 10 to 30 pounds gage, and even considerably higher top pressures may ultimately be found desirable; that pressures required need not seriously affect decomposition of carbon monoxide; that additional blast power required may in most cases be recovered by expanding the top gases; that furnace production may be very substantially increased, and perhaps doubled by pressure operation; and that because of increased capacity combined overall fuel economy and savings in fixed charges may ultimately be expected to exceed substantially $1.00 per ton of pig iron produced.

DIRECT PRODUCTION OF IRON AND STEEL

190. General. In view of the fact that such a small proportion of ferrous alloys is represented by cast iron, and yet over 50 per cent of steel production must first pass through this initial step, direct reduction from the ore appears enticingly simple and logical because of the ease of reduction. This reduction takes place at low temperatures and absorbs little heat. Although hardy perennials, the processes for the direct production of iron and steel from ores have acquired a bad name.

These direct processes cannot, except in special instances, be regarded as a substitute for any single operation in the present iron and steel practice but rather must be considered as one link in an entirely new chain of metallurgical processes for the manufacture of steel. Furthermore, the field for direct processes is to be found with ores that are either of high purity as mined or ones that are not of blast-furnace grade in their natural state but from which concentrates of high purity can easily be obtained. In connection with these latter ores it does appear that, if a concentration process must be employed, it will prove more profitable to go the limit and obtain all the advantages accruing thereto by the use of direct processes of reduction.

The blast furnace is essentially a concentrator just as the copper-matting furnace used to be a concentrator, but it is now more economical to concentrate copper ores in a mill so that the matting furnace is now essentially a melting furnace. It seems certain that with some iron ores the mill likewise will be found a more economical concentrator, thus eliminating blast-furnace operation. When this is done, the open hearth must go, because as it functions now it is dependent on carbon and silicon in the pig-iron charge, and these elements will not be present in direct iron. The attractive aspects of the concentration problem have already been considered in Articles 41 to 47.

191. Reduction by Natural Gas. On the Pacific Coast and in the Southwest natural gas is the cheapest reducing agent available, with the result that a pilot plant has been installed by the Mountain Copper Company in Martinez, California. This process depends on the conversion of natural gas to carbon monoxide and hydrogen by decomposition over a catalyst of nickel or alumina. The heat from this partial decomposition is sufficient to supply that necessary for the reduction of preheated ferric oxide. Utilization of this heat is obtained in a rotary kiln constructed of alloy steel, through the center of which a fire tube of the same material is provided to furnish the small extraneous heat. The vertically disposed catalytic converter is connected to the discharge end of the kiln so that the sponge iron is cooled in water-cooled cans in an atmosphere of fresh converter gas

The sponge iron so produced from high-purity hematite can be converted into wrought iron or high-grade melting stock by briquetting, compressing, and sintering at about 1400°C. The compositions of typical sponge irons made in this way are shown in Table 36.

TABLE 36

ANALYSES OF SPONGE IRON

(Per Cent)

| Product | Iron | | S | O₂ | C | P |
	Total	Metal				
No. 1	96.2	93.2	0.006	0.80	0.37	0.05
2	93.6	93.2	0.100	....	....	0.012
3	94.2	88.5	0.003	1.30	0.45	0.05

192. Reduction by Solid Fuel. Another possibility lies in the direct production of a slag-metal mixture resembling a wrought-iron ball by briquetting a mixture of fine ore and fine coal and heating, at a proper rate, through a temperature range of 1450 to 1500°C. The amount of slag produced will depend on the silica content of the ore and coal, and the puddle ball so formed can subsequently be squeezed in the usual manner for the removal of slag.

Many other attempts, embracing practically every known type of apparatus suitable for the purpose, as well as various kinds of reducing agents, have been made, but practically all these processes have been abandoned, and consequently details are not included here.

193. The Smith Process. The process of the General Reduction Corporation for the production of fine sponge iron has been under experimentation at the plant of the Ford Motor Company for a number of years. The process consists of the reduction of iron ores, roll scale, mill scale, and magnetic concentrates in vertical ovens or retorts at comparatively low temperatures and without fusion, usually in contact with solid reducing materials. The ore should be crushed to size depending on its character, usually not over ¼-inch diameter. It is mixed with carbonaceous material and charged into ovens not unlike the Kopper's oven for coking coal. There, it is preheated in the upper part of the oven by waste gases which leave the stack at about 200°C., then enters the reduction zone, where temperatures range from about 870 to 1090°C., and, after reduction, the charge is cooled by the incoming air for combustion, being discharged at less than 125°C., usually cool enough to touch. The percentage of iron oxide reduced to metal is very high, usually of the order of 95 per cent. It is an interesting fact also that this reduced iron will absorb carbon if given time. Although these results have been encouraging, up to date it has not been found feasible or possible to apply them to large-scale operation.

194. Economic Aspects of Sponge Iron. Sponge iron has certain substantial advantages over scrap. First, it contains no nickel, copper, or chromium, and these, because they are not oxidized in the open-hearth furnace, are accumulating in steel scrap and yearly are becoming a more serious problem. Sponge iron is also low in combined oxygen, and this may be an important factor in improving the quality of steel. It has been observed in both the electric furnace and the crucible processes that highly oxidized steel scrap does not give as high quality steel as does normal material or wrought iron. On the other hand, sponge iron has some serious disadvantages because of the possibility of its being only partially reduced, being non-uniform in analysis, and frequently containing objectionable impurities. The spongy condition of the material promotes oxidization, and its texture makes it difficult to handle and likely to absorb moisture during transportation.

The greatest possibilities for the success of a sponge-iron industry are when:

1. Ores are available which are either very low in phosphorus and sulfur or else very low in price.

2. A reducing agent or fuel which is cheap and low in sulfur is available.

3. A reduction process that is complete in one operation is developed.

4. A process that will give a reasonably uniform product is developed.

5. Either a near-by market for a goodly amount of high-quality steel for which high prices are paid or else an assured scarcity of steel scrap at ordinary prices in combination with a lack of fuel suitable for blast-furnace smelting exists. In this connection the reader is referred to Article 397, for a more complete discussion of the scrap situation.

BIBLIOGRAPHY

1. Austin, J. B., "Efficiency of the Blast-Furnace Process," American Institute of Mining and Metallurgical Engineers, *Transactions,* 1938.
2. Avery, J. M., "Pressure Operation of the Pig Iron Blast Furnace and the Problem of Solution Loss," American Institute of Mining and Metallurgical Engineers, *Technical Paper* 921.

3. BARKLEY, J. F., "Blast Furnace Gas Studies," Bureau of Mines, *Technical Paper* 401.

4. BOOTH, B. H., "Silvery Iron," *The Foundry*, 1941.

5. BOYLSTON, H. M., *An Introduction to the Metallurgy of Iron and Steel*. New York: John Wiley and Sons, 1936. 563 pp.

6. BOYNTON, A. J., "The Cleaning of Blast Furnace Gas," *Blast Furnace and. Steel Plant*, April, 1928.

7. BOYNTON, A. J., "Gas Washing," *Steel*, December 4, 1939.

8. BOYNTON, A. J., and S. P. KINNEY, "Some Principles of Hot Blast Stove Design," *Blast Furnace and Steel Plant*, February, 1930.

9. CONLEY, J. E., "Calcination Conditions for Limestone, Dolomite, and Magnesite," American Institute of Mining and Metallurgical Engineers, *Technical Paper* 1037, 1939.

10. COUNSELMAN, T. B., "Recovery of Blast-furnace Flue Dust from Scrubber Water," American Institute of Mining and Metallurgical Engineers, *Transactions*, 1937.

11. EDWARDS, C. L. T., "Effects of Scrap in the Blast Furnace Burden," American Institute of Mining and Metallurgical Engineers, *Technical Paper* 1270.

12. FORSYTHE, R., C. A. MEISSNER, and J. A. MOHR, *The Blast Furnace and the Manufacture of Pig Iron*. New York: U.P.C. Book Company, 1922.

13. FRANCIS, C. B., *The Making, Shaping, and Treating of Steel*. Pittsburgh: Carnegie-Illinois Steel Corporation, 1940. 1440 pp.

14. FURNAS, C. C., "Flow of Gases through Broken Solids," Bureau of Mines, *Bulletin* 307, 1930.

15. FURNAS, C. C., and T. L. JOSEPH, "Blast-furnace Filling and Size Segregation," American Institute of Mining and Metallurgical Engineers, *Technical Paper* 249, 1929.

16. FURNAS, C. C., and T. L. JOSEPH, "Stock Distribution and Gas-Solid Contact in the Blast Furnace," Bureau of Mines, *Technical Paper* 476, 1930.

17. GREENAWALT, J. E., "The Sintering Process and Some Recent Developments," American Institute of Mining and Metallurgical Engineers, *Transactions*, 1938.

18. HARMON, R. R., "Condensation Cleaning of Blast Furnace Gas," *Steel*, August 23, 1937.

19. HAVEN, W. A., "Foreign Iron Blast Furnace Practice," *Mining and Metallurgy*, April, 1940.

20. HAVEN, W. A., "Recent Developments in American Blast Furnace Design and Practice," Cleveland Institute of Engineers, Middlebrough, England, 1933-1934.

21. HAYWARD, C. R., *An Outline of Metallurgical Practice*. New York: D. Van Nostrand Company, 1940. 612 pp.

22. HERTY, C. H., and J. M. GAMES, "Desulfurizing Action of Manganese in Iron," American Institute of Mining and Metallurgical Engineers, *Transactions*, 1926.

23. HOLBROOK, W. F., and T. L. JOSEPH, "Relative Desulphurizing Powers of Blast Furnace Slags," American Institute of Mining and Metallurgical Engineers, Iron and Steel Division, *Transactions*, vol. 120, 1936.

24. HULTON, R. S., "Refractories," American Institute of Mining and Metallurgical Engineers, *Technical Paper* 817, 1937.

25. JOHNSON, H. W., "The Peripheral Distribution of Gases in the Blast Furnace," American Iron and Steel Institute, *Transactions*, 1938.

26. JOHNSON, J. E., JR., *Blast Furnace Construction in America*. New York: McGraw-Hill Book Company, 1917. 415 pp.

27. JOSEPH, T. L., "Porosity, Reducibility, and Size Preparation of Iron Ores," American Institute of Mining and Metallurgical Engineers, *Technical Paper* 688, 1936.

28. JOSEPH, T. L., "The Iron Blast Furnace," United States Bureau of Mines, *Information Circular* 6779, 1934.

29. JOSEPH, T. L., S. P. KINNEY, and C. E. WOOD, "Production of High-Alumina Slags in the Blast Furnace, American Institute of Mining and Metallurgical Engineers, *Transactions*, vol. 80, 1928.

30. KINNEY, S. P., "The Blast Furnace Stock Column," United States Bureau of Mines, *Technical Paper* 442, 1929.

31. KINNEY, S. P., "Composition of Materials from Various Elevations in an Iron Blast Furnace," United States Bureau of Mines, *Technical Paper* 397, 1936.

32. KINNEY, S. P., "Effect of Sized Ore on Blast Furnace Operation," United States Bureau of Mines, *Technical Paper* 459, 1930.

33. KINNEY, S. P., P. H. ROYSTER, and T. L. JOSEPH, "Iron Blast Furnace Reactions," United States Bureau of Mines, *Technical Paper* 391, 1927.

34. LINDGREN, R. A., "Some Observations Regarding Refractories for Iron Blast Furnaces," American Institute of Mining and Metallurgical Engineers, *Transactions*, 1937.

35. LISSMAN, M. A., "Mechanical Methods of Dust Collection," *Chemical and Metallurgical Engineering*, October, 1930.

36. McCAFFERY, R. S., "A Study of Blast Furnace Slags," American Iron and Steel Institute, *Transactions*, 1938.

37. MARTIN, A. E., G. GLOCKLER, and C. E. WOOD, "Form of Occurrence of Sulfur in Blast-Furnace Slag," Bureau of Mines, *Reports of Investigators* 3552, 1941.

38. MARTIN, P. V., "Effect of the Solution-loss Reactions on Blast-furnace Efficiency," American Institute of Mining and Metallurgical Engineers, *Technical Paper* 1107, 1939.

39. MOHR, A., and F. WILLE, "Analysis of Design and Construction of Hot Blast Stoves, *Iron Age*, July 4, 1935.

40. SHADGEN, J. F., "Graphical Balances Applied to Blast Furnace Operation," *Iron Age*, July 5, 1934.

41. SLATER, J. H., "Use of Sinter in Blast Furnace Burden," American Institute of Mining and Metallurgical Engineers, *Technical Paper* 1263, 1940.

42. STOUGHTON, B., *Metallurgy of Iron and Steel*. New York: McGraw-Hill Book Company, 1930. 441 pp.

43. TENENBAUM, M., and T. L. JOSEPH, "Reduction of Iron Ores under Pressure by Carbon Monoxide," American Institute of Mining and Metallurgical Engineers, *Technical Paper* 1134, 1939.

44. WHITING, J. T., "Microscopic and Petrographic Studies of Blast Furnace Materials," American Iron and Steel Institute, *Transactions*, 1938.

45. WILLE, F., and A. MOHR, "New Gas Cleaning System Uses Hot Washing Stage," *Steel*, May 13, 1935.

CHAPTER V

WROUGHT IRON

HISTORY

195. General. Wrought iron may be defined as "a ferrous material aggregated from a solidifying mass of particles of highly refined metallic iron with which, without subsequent fusion, is incorporated a minutely and uniformly distributed quantity of slag."* It cannot be considered as pure iron, or as the purest form of commercial iron, because the soft steel produced by the basic open-hearth process carries a smaller content of total impurities than is found in the common grades of wrought iron. As a matter of fact, one brand of open-hearth product known as "ingot iron" uniformly contains a smaller percentage of total impurities than the best grades of wrought iron. A comparison showing this is given in Table 37. The production

TABLE 37

WROUGHT IRON VS. LOW-CARBON ALLOYS

Kind of Alloy	Chemical Analysis, Per Cent						Physical Properties			
	C	Mn	S	P	Si	Oxide or Slag	Tensile Strength	Elastic Limit	Elon. 8″ per cent	Red. Area per cent
Charcoal knobbled iron	0.04	0.04	0.014	0.045	0.01	0.92	45,000	29,000	35	60
Double-refined Puddled iron	0.02	0.03	0.025	0.110	0.12	2.00	48,500	33,000	28	48
Pig iron	3.85	0.90	0.025	0.586	0.95		Weak and brittle			
Basic open-hearth ingot iron	0.02	0.05	0.030	0.010	0.01	none	41,000	28,000	36	70
Basic open-hearth dead soft ingot steel	0.08	0.35	0.035	0.015	0.01	0.002	51,000	31,000	34	62

of wrought iron reached a maximum of 1,867,000 tons in 1917, declined to 77,553, and rose again to 114,860 in 1940.

The manufacture of wrought iron is the most ancient art of the ferrous-metal industry—art because until comparatively recently suc-

* Adopted by the American Society of Testing Materials in 1930.

cess depended entirely on the skill of the operator. It is considered in some detail in this book, first because the modern blast furnace had its origin in the primitive furnaces which produced wrought iron through the ages; and second because wrought iron still has some very valuable properties peculiar to itself, and these properties cannot be reproduced except in alloy steels and at a greater cost. Another reason lies in the fact that the early methods followed the line of direct reduction from the ores, and today much discussion is given to, and much research is being done in, the production of steel directly from the ore. In connection with the history of iron and steel it should be borne in mind that much of this history antedated the blast furnace as well as the knowledge and use of cast iron and steel. It was only in attempts to get a greater output of wrought iron by the use of shaft-type furnaces that cast iron was produced in Germany about A.D. 1350 and probably in China at a much earlier date. This increased output was the result of a longer contact with the carbon of the fuel and the higher temperatures prevailing in the furnace. This first production was probably characterized at that time as an accident, because the material obtained from this furnace was cast iron, thoroughly unsatisfactory, brittle, weak, and unworkable. Early accounts of the operation of these furnaces make frequent references to "sick" iron. This period also marked the beginning of the existing two-stage operation, involving as the second step the refining of the cast iron to a malleable product, be it wrought iron or steel.

196. Catalan Forge. The earliest primitive furnaces consisted of heaps of iron ore, charcoal, and limestone in which a temperature sufficient to reduce and agglomerate the iron could be maintained. At first these were simply placed on the side of the hill facing the prevailing wind with an opening at the bottom for the necessary draft or air. Still later artificial draft was obtained by inserting fire-clay nozzles into the heap and forcing air through these nozzles by means of bellows. Still later, about A.D. 1000, the Catalan forge, shown in Figure 41, said to have originated in the province of Catalonia in Spain, came into being. The furnace proper consists of a hole or hearth lined with refractory clay in which is placed a mixture of iron ore, limestone, and charcoal. The air blast was brought to the cavity by means of a pipe or tuyère, and the air brought to this by a "trompe." This consisted of a water tank supplied with a constant stream of water and connected with a box by means of one or more vertical pipes about 20 feet long. There was an outlet at the bottom of the tank through which the water could pass to the lower box.

The tube was fitted at the top with a valve and there were holes in the tube through which air could be drawn in by the downward flow of water. The mixture of air and water fell into the lower box, and the air collected above the water and could be drawn off as needed

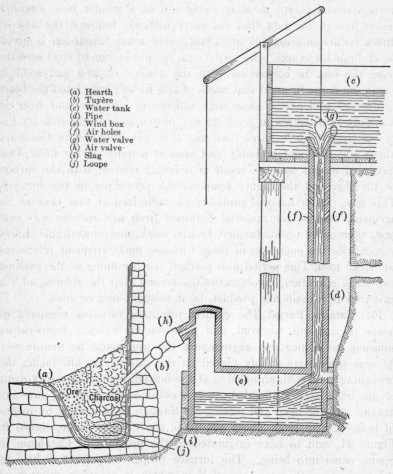

(a) Hearth
(b) Tuyère
(c) Water tank
(d) Pipe
(e) Wind box
(f) Air holes
(g) Water valve
(h) Air valve
(i) Slag
(j) Loupe

FIG. 41. Catalan Forge.

for furnace operation. In this way a fairly constant pressure of air could be maintained in the lower chamber, and the amount available was many times that used in the primitive furnaces. After about five hours of operation, the air was shut off, and there would be found in the bottom of the hearth a lump or "loupe" of iron and slag.

This material was then taken out, hammered, reheated, and hammered again until it had been brought to the desired shape and size and at the same time most of the slag eliminated to give the characteristic properties of wrought iron. From this forge developed the Stückofen or Blauofen of the thirteenth century, and finally the modern blast furnace. For the time being we shall concern ourselves only with the development of the modern puddling process.

About 1613, Rovenson invented the reverberatory furnace which, as he said, furnished a method by which "the material to be melted or rock may be kept divided from the touch of the fire." It was not employed for purifying pig iron, however, until about 1766, when the Cranege brothers took out a British patent on a process which later came to be known as puddling. By this process, using a reverberatory furnace, they were able to convert white iron, or refined iron, into good malleable iron by the use of raw coal alone. Finally, in 1784, Henry Cort hollowed out the bottom of the furnace so that it would contain the metal in the molten state. Then by agitating this "puddle" or bath of metal (hence the name puddling) with an iron bar or paddle, he was able to convert white, or refined iron into a malleable form by burning out the carbon, manganese, and silicon with the oxidizing gases of the furnace atmosphere.

This process, however, was not entirely satisfactory because the furnace bottom, made up of siliceous sand, was rapidly fluxed away by the iron oxide of the charge. Furthermore, the process consumed much time and was very wasteful of iron, the yield being frequently less than 70 per cent of the metal charged. With a view to overcoming these objectionable features, Joseph Hall, in 1830, substituted old bottom materials for the pure sand, thus introducing the oxide bottom which was adapted to the production of any iron, shortened the time of the heat, and increased the yield to about 90 per cent. On account of the boiling action of the bath brought about by the rapid oxidation of the carbon by the oxides of iron, Hall's process came to be known as the "pig boiling" process. Still later, when this process became the leading method for the production of wrought iron, the original method came to be known as "dry puddling" because of the small quantity of slag produced as contrasted to the "wet puddling" in which much larger quantities were involved. Hall, or some of his associates, also introduced the use of air-cooled iron plates for supporting the bottom and sides, thus materially increasing the life of the furnace.

PUDDLING

197. The American Bloomery. This, shown in Figure 42, was a hearth about 2 feet deep and 3 feet wide, provided with water-cooled sides and a hot blast obtained by heating the air in cast-iron pipes by means of the furnace flue gases. These hearths were open in the front, with a tuyère placed either at one side or the back, about 20 inches above the bottom. Charcoal was placed on the hearth, ignited, and,

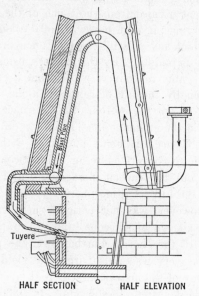

HALF SECTION　　　　HALF ELEVATION

Fig. 42. American Bloomery. (*Courtesy of American Iron and Steel Institute.*)

when burning well, covered with iron ore. This was followed by alternate layers of charcoal and ore until sufficient iron had collected on the hearth.

198. Modern Puddling Furnace. The puddling furnace is a small reverberatory-type furnace, coal-fired and with a capacity of about 600 pounds of wrought iron per heat. From the sketch of a single* furnace shown in Figure 43[9] it will be noted that the furnace is made up of three parts, the grate or fireplace located at one end of the furnace, the neck or flue at the opposite end, and the hearth or puddling

* A double furnace consists of two single furnaces placed back to back, with the dividing wall removed and with a single, enlarged hearth taking a double charge. It is worked from both sides with a four-man crew.

basin located centrally between the grate and the neck. The furnace
is constructed entirely of brick and cased on the sides by a shell of
iron plates, held in place by means of tie rods. The roof is built of
fire brick over the fireplace but usually of silica brick over the hearth
and neck and is about 9 inches thick. At the base of the uptake is an
opening, or door, called the floss hole, provided primarily for the

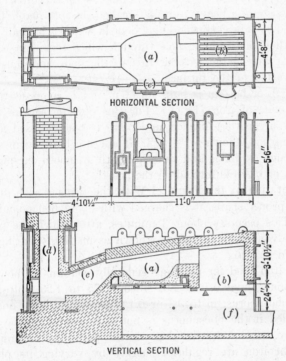

FIG. 43. Puddling Furnace. (*Courtesy of Carnegie-Illinois Steel Corp.*)

(a) Hearth   (c) Neck   (e) Charging door
(b) Grate   (d) Stack   (f) Ash pit

removal of the cinder that overflows from the puddling basin. The
hearth, or puddling basin, the most vital part of the furnace, consists
of three iron plates, one inch thick, which are supported upon four
heavy barrier bars laid transversely across the space between the
side walls of the furnace. This construction permits the use of air
for cooling of the refractories. A low brick wall laid across the furnace
and known as the bridge separates the hearth from the fireplace and
also serves as a backing for one end of the basin. At the opposite end
of the hearth, a somewhat lighter and lower wall, known as the breast

wall or altar, separates the basin from the neck. Imbedded in these walls are hollow. iron castings called "chills" through which air or water is circulated for cooling purposes. The other two sides of the basin are supported by the walls of the furnace itself and are similarly air-cooled. The back wall is built up solid to the roof, but the front wall contains the arched opening for the hearth. The sides to this opening, known as the "jams," are built of silica brick while the bottom consists of a heavy iron plate called the fore plate. This opening is closed by a brick-lined sliding door in which is a small U-shaped opening called the rabbling hole through which tools can be inserted for working the charge without raising the door and thus lowering the temperature of the furnace.

The hearth or bottom is built up of materials composed mainly of magnetic oxide of iron (Fe_3O_4). For this purpose certain grades of iron ore or of heating-furnace cinder are frequently used as well as fine iron cuttings known as "swarf." These are built up in successive layers through oxidizing and sintering until a smooth one-piece working bottom or basin is formed on the hearth.

199. Operation of the Furnace. With the furnace at heat and the bottom in proper shape, it is charged with about 600 pounds of cold pig iron. This occupies about 3 minutes, after which the process of puddling advances by the stages known as melting, clearing, boiling, balling, and drawing.

The pig iron used for puddling generally contains carbon 3.5 to 4 per cent, manganese 0.5 to 1.0, silicon 0.75 to 1.25, sulfur 0.04 to 0.08, and phosphorus up to 0.3 or 0.4. Frequently, basic open-hearth slag is added if the phosphorus is not high enough in the pig iron. Incidentally, aside from the slag content, the physical properties of the wrought iron are regulated largely by varying its phosphorus content. Being fairly high in carbon, the pig iron has a low melting point (about 1150°C.); but the melting rate is slow (because of the small surface of the pigs), and during this period, as indicated in Table 38, some of the silicon is oxidized. This forms a slag with the iron oxide of the lining material and tends to cover the pig iron that is still solid. The operator therefore raises the pigs from the bottom with an iron bar and thus keeps them exposed to the furnace gases until the whole of the iron is melted, which normally requires about 20 minutes.

During the next 8 or 10 minutes the operator continues to stir the metal until it has "cleared." This occurs when the silicon has been removed and markedly changes the character of the iron so that a

TABLE 38
Chemical Changes in Puddling

Product	Per Cent				
	Total Carbon	Mn	P	S	Si
Pig iron	4.12	0.70	0.764	0.028	1.55
After melting and clearing	3.43	0.22	0.425	0.033	0.40
Muck bar	0.05	0.08	0.230	0.025	0.18
Merchant bar—single-rolled	0.05	0.06	0.182	0.020	0.24

fracture test will show it to have a "white" fracture no matter whether the original pig was gray, mottled, or white.

Roll scale is then introduced through the charging door; and the heat in the furnace is raised to carry on the boil, which is divided into low boil and high boil. As a matter of fact, in the first part of the boil the temperature is actually reduced in order to speed up the elimination of phosphorus. The oxidizing action of the roll scale now begins, the temperature gradually rises, and, in 8 to 12 minutes after clearing has occurred, the slag begins to boil. This period is known as the "low boil," for some carbon is gradually oxidized to carbon monoxide, and this gas caught in the viscous slag causes a slow bubbling or foaming which may cause it to overflow through the charging door. As the temperature rises, with the oncoming of the "high boil," more carbon monoxide is formed, the slag becomes less viscous, and the bubbles of gas now break through the slag cover and burn with a bluish flame known as "puddler's candles." In about 20 minutes the carbon is nearly all removed, the bubbling dies down, and the slag ceases to flow from the door. As this frothy slag subsides, the stirring is kept up constantly, and the heat is now said to be "dropping." Finally, little particles of decarburized iron begin to crystallize out in the slag, for the melting point of pure iron (1530°C.) is about 100°C. above the temperature of the furnace. Finally, the mixture of slag and iron becomes thick and pasty and agglomerates, and the iron is said to have "come to nature."

When all the iron has "come to nature," the temperature of the furnace is raised to a welding heat and the particles of iron so manipulated that they form one large mass or "ball." Then, depending somewhat on local preference and equipment, this mass is separated into two or three smaller units which are stored in different parts of the furnace until the time comes to remove them. When the operator is ready, these balls of iron are removed, one at a time, and conveyed by means of an overhead trolley track to a squeezer, in which the ball is compressed to a bloom. Much of the still partly liquid slag is squeezed out and the ball made ready for the subsequent rolling operation to produce bars or sections for market.

200. **Busheling, Piling, Rolling.** After squeezing, a variety of operations in rolling the ball may be carried out, depending upon the speci-

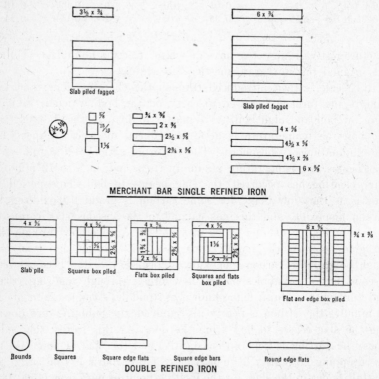

FIG. 44. Busheling, Piling, and Rolling. (*Courtesy of Carnegie-Illinois Steel Corp.*)

fications to be met. Such variables are shown in Figure 44. For ordinary muck bar No. 1 the balls are rolled out, in five to nine passes, to one 0.75-inch thick and 2.5 to 8 inches wide (this with the initial heat). To refine the bar further, the next step is "busheling," in which the muck bar (180 to 600 pounds in weight), cut into small pieces, is charged into a reheating (balling) furnace, brought to welding temperature, and rolled out into the desired section. This is obviously very costly but does yield iron of the highest quality. The more common practice, therefore, is to cut the original muck bar in lengths of 2 to 3 feet and bind them in bundles with wire or bands. They are reheated, rolled into merchant bar, single-rolled iron, single-refined iron, or No. 2 iron. Because such a bar would still lack uniformity, this bar is in turn cut into short lengths, fagoted, reheated, and rolled to produce double-rolled iron, double-refined iron, best bar, or No. 3 bar.

201. Swedish Charcoal Iron. Whereas this name will probably bring into the memory of many old consumers an extremely tough and ductile iron which was formerly used in considerable quantities for blacksmith purposes, it is today merely a specialty chosen whenever its remarkable properties can be utilized. It is also known in the United States as Norway iron from the fact that in the earlier days it was generally brought to the United States by Norwegian ships. The foundation of the process is high-grade iron ore and charcoal, from which a very pure pig iron is made containing carbon, about 4 per cent; manganese, 0.15 per cent; silicon, 0.35 to 0.50 per cent; phosphorus, 0.070 per cent; and sulfur, 0.015 per cent. From this, in special charcoal-iron puddling furnaces, and with some modifications of the conventional process, a very high-grade wrought iron is made, for which the following may be considered a representative analysis:

	Per Cent
Carbon	0.02 –0.06
Manganese	Trace–0.01
Silicon	0.02 –0.04
Phosphorus	0.04 –0.07
Sulfur	0.005–0.01

The most remarkable fact about the analysis, besides the low amount of carbon, is the very small percentage of manganese. As a matter of fact, in this respect Swedish charcoal iron is surpassed only by electrolytic iron.

Great ductility is characteristic of Swedish charcoal iron, its toughness being higher than that of puddled iron. Another remarkable property, as compared with ordinary mild steel, is its comparatively high toughness at temperatures below –10°F. An impact test on mild steel at –4°F. shows a loss of about 85 per cent, whereas under the same conditions wrought iron loses only about 40 per cent of its strength. Swedish charcoal iron melting bars furnish a good base charge for electric furnaces and the crucible steel melting on account of their purity. It is used by many tool makers for axes and machine knives where a piece of hard steel must be welded to iron, for welded chains, hollow and solid stay bolts, and for gates and fences, where a very fine finish and resistance to corrosion are desired.

202. Losses. Apart from the high labor and fuel cost referred to, there is a slight loss in the process. In spite of the fact that considerable iron oxide is reduced from the slag and hearth, this loss is ordinarily 3 to 6 per cent up to the muck bar stage. Any further reheating and rolling will increase this by 10 to 20 per cent each time the bar is reworked. In general, apart from crop losses, these are due to oxidation and expulsion of the slag.

203. Chemistry of Puddling. The composition of the bath in the middle of the boil is shown in Table 39. The changes in composition of the bath, shown in Table 38, indicate that the order of elimination is silicon, manganese, phosphorus, and carbon. This is quite in keeping with theory, for the reactions involved are:

$$2FeO(c) + Si(c) \rightarrow SiO_2(c) + 2Fe(c); \quad \Delta H = -70,200 \text{ cal.} \quad (30)$$
$$FeO(c) + SiO_2(c) \rightarrow FeO \cdot SiO_2(c); \quad \Delta H = -6,600 \text{ cal.} \quad (31)$$
$$FeO(c) + Mn(c) \rightarrow MnO(c) + Fe(c); \quad \Delta H = -32,200 \text{ cal.} \quad (32)$$
$$MnO(c) + SiO_2(c) \rightarrow (MnO)(c) \cdot SiO_2(c); \quad \Delta H = -2,200 \quad (33)$$
$$5FeO(c) + 2Fe_3P(c) \rightarrow P_2O_5(c) + 11Fe(c); \quad \Delta H = +51,300 \quad (34)$$
$$P_2O_5(c) + 3FeO(c) \rightarrow (FeO)_3 \cdot P_2O_5(c) \quad (35)$$
$$FeO(c) + Fe_3C(c) \rightarrow CO(g) + 4Fe(c) \quad (36)$$
$$FeO(c) + C(c) \rightarrow CO(g) + Fe(c); \quad \Delta H = +37,600 \quad (37)$$

It is probable that the chief oxidizing agent is ferrous oxide, because ferric oxide is decomposed at about 1100°C. to form Fe_3O_4, and that in turn is converted into ferrous oxide at higher temperatures. In this connection it is also significant to note that roll scale is always used because when hematite is employed it is found that the boil comes more slowly and is much less vigorous. Most of the silicon, and a part of the manganese, are eliminated during melting, the rest by the end of the clearing stage. Some of the phosphorus is also oxidized; and, since the slag has a limited ability to retain this phosphorus in solution, a part of this element must be removed by skimming off some of the slag. Incidentally, it has been found that in order to remove phosphorus the slag must be highly basic and oxidizing (usually containing at least 80 per cent ferrous oxide). It is evident from these reactions that if such conditions do not prevail, silica will replace phosphorus pentoxide in the slag and the phosphorus will then be reduced by silicon or carbon in the bath. Note that the slag given in Table 39 is the one characteristic of the middle of the

TABLE 39

ANALYSIS OF SLAG FROM PUDDLING FURNACE

(Sample taken near middle of the boil)

	Per Cent
SiO₂:	14.80
FeO	63.85
Fe₂O₃	8.72
MnO	2.22
P₂O₅	3.82
Al₂O₃	2.62
MgO	1.30

Resultant muck bar—0.05 per cent C, 0.06 Mn, 0.182 P, 0.02 S, 0.24 Si.

boil when carbon is the main element being eliminated. On the other hand, if it is desired to retain a part of this phosphorus (to produce a high-phosphorus wrought iron), the puddler holds more of this run-off slag in the furnace or throws coal on the bath to help in the reduction. The carbon reaction is strongly endothermic and consequently will take place only at higher temperatures. It will go nearly to completion because bubbles of carbon monoxide gas can escape. On the other hand carbon monoxide being a reducing gas, it alters, in its escape, the composition of the slag. For this reason, as well as the control of phosphorus, there must be a large and constant excess of ferrous oxide in the slag at all times. A little sulfur may be eliminated as manganese sulfide, but this is purely incidental; any great regulation of the sulfur content must be accomplished by varying the character of the pig charge.

204. Mechanical Puddling. It is at once apparent that the conventional puddling process is bound to be a very expensive one. A single heat of wrought iron requires an hour and fifty minutes to two hours and thirty minutes, the services of two highly trained men, and 500 to 600 pounds of coal. Up to the introduction of the new Aston process for the production of wrought iron, rolled bars and shapes were selling at about five cents per pound as contrasted to a similar section in low-carbon steel selling at about two cents per pound. Just as the puddling process virtually eliminated the more primitive direct reduction methods for the production of iron, so the Bessemer and open-hearth methods for the production of steel have threatened the life of the wrought-iron industry. Much attention has been given to improving this wasteful, costly, and arduous process through the use of double furnaces with enlarged hearths, making heats up to 1000 pounds in weight, the application of regenerative and recuperative furnaces, the installation of waste-heat boilers and of monorail transportation to cut down the labor costs. From 1880 to 1925 various furnaces[24] such as the Roe[15] and the Ely[8] were developed. Some of these attempted to simulate the puddling process by oscillating a rectangular furnace about a horizontal axis, by revolving a circular furnace about an axis slightly inclined to the vertical, or by rotating a cylindrical furnace about a more or less horizontal axis. None of these was very successful; eventually all were given up, and it remained for the A. M. Byers Company of Pittsburgh, Pennsylvania, to develop an entirely different process devised by Dr. James Aston.

THE ASTON PROCESS

205. General. Dr. Aston recognized the basic handicaps in the way of any mechanical puddling process, handicaps so serious as to make outstanding success difficult of attainment. He attacked the problem from an entirely different standpoint, reasoning that, since wrought iron was essentially a mechanical mixture of a pure iron base and a slag, it should be possible to make up these from the raw materials, in separate furnaces, and then, under proper thermal and mechanical conditions, combine them to give the required mixture of iron and slag, approximating the ball after it has "come to nature." Many delicate and difficult physical chemical problems were involved in the carrying out of this simple idea, and yet from it was evolved a new and highly successful process.[4]

Literally hundreds of samples of ancient and modern wrought iron in which the attractive properties of this metal were well developed, particularly resistance to corrosion, were collected and subjected to chemical and microscopical analysis. From these data the investigators were able to conclude that, if it were possible to prepare a pure iron base and a slag of definite compositions and mix these so as to obtain a uniform and finely divided* slag throughout the iron mass, one would have superior wrought iron. Analyses of a few of these wrought irons are given in Table 40. The process as finally developed consists of refining the base metal in any established steel furnace, Bessemer, open hearth, or electric, melting the slag, using iron ore, roll scale, and sand in an open-hearth furnace, and then disintegrating or granulating the metal by a "shotting process" which is based

---

* There should be 250,000 or more of these slag fibers per square inch, 0.002 to 0.001 inch apart.

TABLE 40

ANALYSES OF OLD WROUGHT IRONS[6]

Description	Years of Service	Chemical Analysis, Per Cent							Use
		C	Mn	P	S	Si	Cu	Slag	
Normal phosphorus and no copper	108	0.042	0.015	0.181	0.010	0.030		1.36	Chain link suspension bridge, Lehigh Gap, Pa.
Normal phosphorus and no copper	44	0.050	0.026	0.170	0.025	0.150		3.32	8" water pipe, Santa Cruz, Calif.
Normal phosphorus and varying copper	66	0.026	0.033	0.158	0.025	0.329	0.176	4.30	Roof, Pittsburgh, Pa.
Normal phosphorus and varying copper	59	0.040	0.026	0.138	0.020	0,150	0.170	2.60	Smoke stack, Puget Sound, reclaimed, still in use.
High phosphorus, no copper	71	0.032	0.063	0.370	0.018	0.254		3.68	Tugboat hull, Baltimore, Md.
High phosphorus and varying copper	63	0.024	0.035	0.284	0.021	0.235	0.237	3.57	Water pipe, Rochester, N. Y.

upon sound, natural principles. The molten metal, at a temperature of about 1500°C., is poured into a bath of slag which is held at a temperature of about 1300°C. The liquid metal carries large amounts of gases in solution which are liberated upon solidification, at a rate proportional to the speed of freezing, and this gas liberation may be of sufficient force to comminute thoroughly, or granulate, the metal. The particles of metal, because of their higher specific gravity, settle and collect in the bottom of the slag bath in the form of a spongy, porous ball, quite similar to a well-worked puddle ball. In the heat interchange, the slag not only remains liquid but also actually gains heat and permeates all the interstices of the metallic mass.

206. Operation of the Aston Process. Pig iron is melted in cupolas and refined to a low metalloid content by being blown full in a Bessemer converter. The metal is then desulfurized to below 0.03 per cent sulfur by treatment with soda ash in the ladle. Ordinarily, Bessemer pig iron containing about 1.5 per cent silicon, 1.0 manganese, 0.05 sulfur, and 0.08 phosphorus is used. The iron silicate slag required for the shotting operation is made up in a basic-lined open-hearth furnace, from roll mill scale, iron ore, and silica sand.* Pouring or shotting is carried out by pouring a steady stream of the metal, at a temperature of about 1510°C., into a bath of slag directly below

* Before shotting, this slag will contain, approximately: silica, 10.0 per cent; ferrous oxide, 70.3; ferric oxide, 13.5. And, after shotting: silica, 10.5 per cent; manganese, 1.0; phosphorus, 0.38; ferrous oxide, 73.7; and ferric oxide, 9.4.

the metal ladle in which slag is maintained at about 1320°C. Ordinarily no special means are employed to maintain these temperatures, for the temperature difference is automatically taken care of by the relative melting points of the two materials. The crux in all cases is to have plenty of slag volume so that, in the heat rise, the temperature of the slag will remain safely below the freezing point of the metal. Approximately three volumes of slag to one of metal is a theoretical ratio, but it may be much higher. The shotting pot, containing the mixture, automatically oscillates about a vertical axis and moves forward and backward in order to insure a uniform distribution of the metal throughout the slag and as a result a much more uniform wrought iron. The slag must be of sufficient volume to maintain a temperature well below the freezing point of the refined metal so that continuous solidification of the metal can take place and accompanying this the liberation of all the dissolved gases with sufficient force to disintegrate the metal and produce a spongy ball of iron thoroughly impregnated with the liquid slag. When the shotting process is completed, the excess slag is poured off into the next shotting cup and a ball of iron about 2500 pounds in weight is turned out onto a table and transported to a large squeezer, similar to those employed in densifying tin cans and light scrap. This squeezer then ejects a major portion of the excess slag, which operation is completed by rolling in the conventional manner in rolling mills. The chief advantages of this process are:

1. It will produce, for the first time, very high-quality wrought iron as well as iron closely conforming to certain specifications. Hitherto the puddling process has been pretty much dependent on the personality and ability of the individual operator; now the process can be very closely controlled chemically and microscopically.

2. The aggregate output or unit size of bloom is entirely a matter of engineering expediency and judgment. At present the blooms vary from 6000 to 8000 pounds; some weighing 10 tons have been turned out without any difficulty. The weight is now regulated by rolling requirements.

207. Uses of Wrought Iron. Although still a relatively high-cost material as compared to plain-carbon steel, wrought iron does possess at least three properties—resistance to corrosion, resistance to shock and fatigue, and machining properties—which make it attractive to the user of ferrous products. It finds its widest use in the manufacture of pipe (both industrial and domestic), chains and hooks, stay bolts, engine bolts, draw bars, blacksmith iron, and crucible steel.

208. Chemical Analysis. In interpreting the chemical analysis of wrought iron one must bear in mind that the customary metalloids may be in a greater or less degree alloyed with the base metal or associated as oxidized constituents with the contained slag. The commonly reported analysis of wrought iron lists the carbon, silicon, sulfur, phosphorus, and manganese of the composite. The ideal determination should separate the metal from the slag and note the metalloid distribution between the two. While this procedure is quantitatively feasible, as yet it has not been adapted to general laboratory practice.

Carbon is usually of the order of 0.02 to 0.03 per cent, although in some cases it may rise as high as 0.10 per cent. These high amounts should arouse suspicion of adulteration by steel scrap or of poor refining practice. Silicon is usually between 0.10 and 0.20 per cent. The variations here are usually due to variations in slag quantity and degree of silication. Sulfur is always undesirable and in well-made wrought iron should be under 0.05 per cent; a specification of 0.03 is quite common, and even lower sulfur may be attained by special precautions and to suit special requirements. Phosphorus is almost invariably higher in wrought iron than in steel. It must be borne in mind that it is in part alloyed with the base metal and in part associated with the slag. Good wrought iron may have 0.10 per cent or less, up to as much as 0.30 per cent, according to the manufacturer's preference, the nature of the raw materials, and the service conditions which it must withstand. The lower phosphorus is advisable for materials subject to shock, high temperature, or requiring higher ductility, whereas the higher is used to obtain increased tensile strength. As a matter of fact, phosphorus is the element commonly used for varying the tensile strength of wrought irons within narrow limits (41,280 to 54,870 pounds per square inch). Manganese is usually under 0.05 per cent, and this characteristic has caused a manganese content of 0.10 or more to be taken as indicative of steel-scrap adulteration. Conversely, low manganese in wrought iron has usually been an earmark of quality.

In view of the fact that wrought iron consists essentially of a relatively pure ferrite base through which are interspersed threadlike stringers of slag, it is obvious that this quality will be affected by the nature of the association of the base metal and slag. Because of its well-recognized fibrous structure, wrought iron responds readily to the nick-bend or fracture test, and macroscopic etching will reveal methods of piling and adulteration; but it is to the metallographic microscope that the wrought iron metallurgist is most deeply in-debted. It has given us our present-day understanding of wrought iron and may be considered as the court of last resort in quality determinations. Important disclosures of the microscope are:

1. Grain size. Coarse grain, distortion, or lack of uniformity have a very important bearing upon quality in its relation to mill history and the use of the product.

2. Pearlitic areas. The quantity of carbon (generally negligible or small in amount) and nature of its distribution (irregular or banded pearlite coupled with an absence of slag) are good evidence of steel adulteration.

3. Slag characteristics as to type and distribution. Coarse, pocketed slag is very undesirable. The finer textures result from progressive rolling reductions and are responsible for some of the better physical properties, especially ductility. Absence of slag in banded zones excites suspicion of steel adulteration.

4. Abnormalities such as grain distortion, high-phosphorus ghost lines.

BIBLIOGRAPHY

1. American Society for Testing Materials, "Qualitative Standards for Wrought Iron," *Proceedings,* Part 1, 1934.
2. Aston, J., "The Problem of Wrought Iron Manufacture and a New Process for Its Production," American Iron and Steel Institute, *Yearbook,* 1925.
3. Aston, J., "Trend of Development in the Wrought Iron Industry," American Institute of Mining and Metallurgical Engineers, *Transactions,* 1926.
4. Aston, J., "Wrought Iron in Today's Industrial Picture," American Institute of Mining and Metallurgical Engineers, *Technical Paper* 632, 1935.
5. Boylston, H. M., *An Introduction to the Metallurgy of Iron and Steel.* New York: John Wiley and Sons, 1936. 563 pp.
6. Byers, A. M., Company, *Wrought Iron,* Pittsburgh, 1936.
7. Dean, R. S., E. P. Barrett, and C. Pierson, "Some Observations on Sponge Iron and the Properties of the Direct Steel Made from It," American Institute of Mining and Metallurgical Engineers, *Technical Paper* 592.
8. Dechant, F. H., "The Ely Process of Mechanical Puddling for the Production of Wrought Iron," American Iron and Steel Institute, *Yearbook,* 1925.
9. Francis, C. B., *The Making, Shaping, and Treating of Steel.* Pittsburgh: Carnegie-Illinois Steel Corporation, 1940. 1440 pp.
10. Goodale, S. C., and J. R. Speer, *Chronology of Iron and Steel.* Cleveland: The Penton Publishing Company, 1931. 332 pp.
11. Hayward, C., *An Outline of Metallurgical Practice.* New York: D. Van Nostrand Company, 1940. 612 pp.
12. *Journal of the Iron and Steel Institute,* "Wrought Iron," 1901, II; 1903, I; 1905, II; 1906, II-IV; 1907, I; 1908, I; 1909, I; 1915, I; 1916, I-II; 1917, II; 1919, I; 1920, I; 1921, I.
13. *Journal of the Iron and Steel Institute,* "Puddling Furnaces," 1901, III; 1902, II; 1904, I; 1905, II; 1906, III; 1907, III; 1908, I; 1914, I; 1918, I; 1919, II.
14. *Journal of the Iron and Steel Institute,* "Puddling," 1901, I; 1902, II; 1904, I; 1905, II; 1906, I; 1913, I-II; 1914, I; 1917, I; 1918, I; 1919, I; 1920, I.

15. Roe, J. P., "The Roe Puddling Machine," American Iron and Steel Institute, *Yearbook*, 1925.

16. Smith, H. E., The Manufacture and Use of Wrought Iron," American Iron and Steel Institute, *Yearbook*, 1925.

17. Stoughton, B., *Metallurgy of Iron and Steel*. New York: McGraw-Hill Book Company, 1934. 519 pp.

18. Stoughton, B., and A. Butts, *Engineering Metallurgy*. New York: McGraw-Hill Book Company, 1930. 441 pp.

19. Tholand, N. K. G., "Sponge Iron as a Melting Base," *Iron Age*, May 17, 1921.

20. Tiemann, H. P., *Iron and Steel*. New York: McGraw-Hill Book Company, 1919. 514 pp.

21. Turner, T., *The Metallurgy of Iron and Steel*. London: Griffith, 1895. 367 pp.

22. Williams, C. E., E. P. Barrett, and B. M. Larsen, "Production of Sponge Iron," Bureau of Mines, *Bulletin* 270, 1927.

23. Williams, J. I., "The Danks Puddling Furnace," Engineers Society of Western Pennsylvania, *Proceedings*, Part I, September, 1886.

24. Wrought Iron Company of America, "Making Wrought Iron in 700 Pound Balls," *Iron Age*, June, 1930.

CHAPTER VI

CEMENTATION AND CRUCIBLE PROCESSES

CEMENTATION PROCESS

209. General. Although the first mention of steel was during the thirteenth century, it is probable that it was known to, and its manufacture practiced by, the ancients. The Wootz steel of India, the famous swords of Damascus, Syria, and the Toledo steels of Spain were famous the world over. The incentive for this development was without doubt the inadequate properties of wrought iron, which is soft and ductile for many of the purposes for which it is most desirable, especially tools and weapons. It seems equally certain that only two processes of manufacture were available to these ancient metallurgists, namely, the cementation and crucible processes.

210. Cementation Process. The earliest steel was made by heating wrought or puddled iron in stone boxes, with charcoal, for long periods of time (about two weeks) until some of the carbon had been absorbed by the iron, thus converting it or at least its surface into a kind of steel. This was called converted or "blister" steel because of the condition of the surface which was always covered with blisters produced by the gases formed within the metal by the combination of some of the charcoal with the oxygen present in the steel. This steel could then be worked, just as iron had previously been, with hammers or rolls into a bar called shear steel. This cementation process depends upon the fact that when a low-carbon ferrous product, such as wrought iron, is heated to a red heat (above the critical range) in contact with some carbonaceous material, the metal absorbs carbon up to the saturation point, which is about 1.7 per cent.

The iron, in the form of bar stock 2 to 3 inches wide, $\frac{5}{8}$ to $\frac{3}{4}$ inch thick, and 6 to 12 feet in length, is charged into pots, on a bed of charcoal 2 to 3 inches thick. When the first layer is completed another is started with charcoal of about $\frac{1}{4}$-inch mesh placed between and over the bars until the pots are full. These pots are then closed, made as nearly airtight as possible, transferred to a suitable furnace, and during the next 3 to 4 days gradually heated to a temperature of

800 to 1100°C., and then maintained at this temperature for 7 to 12 days, the time depending upon the size of the bars used, the carbon content desired in the finished steel, as-well as the temperature attained and maintained. The progress of the carburization can be judged by withdrawing small test bars through small openings in the pot, from time to time, and testing these by fracture. When the desired degree of carburization has been reached, the fire is drawn, the furnace allowed to cool, and the bars removed from the pot. Because of these variables, as well as other uncertainties of the process, many grades or tempers were produced. These varied from 0.5 to 1.5 per cent carbon; and, furthermore, the carbon content of a bar progressively decreased to the center. Although generally referred to as converted, cement, or blister steel, the surfaces of certain bars would be almost decarburized when air had been allowed to get into the pot, and such bars became known as aired bars. Certain varieties were known as spring plate or bar steel when it was used for springs; and, if cut up into smaller pieces as raw material for the manufacture of crucible steel, it was known as shear steel or, as in the manufacture of wrought iron, the bars might be broken or sheared into short lengths, fagoted, reheated to a welding temperature, and hammered into a bar known as single-shear. For certain special purposes requiring an exceptionally high-grade, uniform steel this process might be repeated for a third time to form double-shear steel. The name shear comes from the fact that this variety of steel was formerly used extensively in the manufacture of cutlery.

CRUCIBLE PROCESS

211. Crucible Process. Although it is certain that the ancients practiced the manufacture of steel by cementation, the evidence that they used the crucible process is not so conclusive. However, it is not reasonable to suppose that they were able to make steel as homogeneous as the fine steels already referred to by simple cementation. Presumably during the turmoil of the Middle Ages both these methods were lost to civilization. The cementation process was not revived until about 1500, and the crucible process was not rediscovered until 1742 by Benjamin Huntsman. This English clockmaker, who had experienced considerable difficulty in making clock springs from shear steel because of its lack of homogeneity, conceived the idea of producing a homogeneous alloy by melting the steel in a crucible and, while it was fluid, skimming off the slag from the top and with it, of course, many of the impurities, then casting it in the form of a block or ingot which could be worked into the desired shape or form, thus further enhancing its valuable properties. In common with other pioneers, Huntsman experienced many difficulties with the refractory crucibles as well as with reactions which took place in the molten metal; and, although he was able to rid the steel of its slag and some of its impurities, the metal was porous and brittle when cold. Heath found a way to avoid this by adding manganese oxide, and Mushet further improved the process by adding ferromanganese.

This short account of the crucible process is given largely for historical reasons but also because, for certain special purposes, high-grade tool steel is still made in this way. On the whole it is now being replaced by the electric furnace, which is cheaper, capable of giving as good steel, and possesses many metallurgical advantages over the crucible method (see Chapter X).

A cross section of a typical American crucible melting furnace is shown in Figure 45. A common type in use today is a thirty-pot one, consisting of five charging holes with six pots to each hole. The fuel is usually natural or producer gas, and regenerative chambers or checker work similar to those employed in blast-furnace stoves are used to maintain the very high temperatures necessary. During the melting period the gas is reversed every 20 to 30 minutes, and after melting the reversals may be twice as often.

A crucible furnace will make six heats every 34 hours or thirty-three heats per week, the remainder of the time being spent on repairs and the general conditioning of the furnace and its accessories; the average recovery of steel ingots will be about 2800 pounds. Traditionally pots were made of a clay-coke or charcoal mixture, kneaded by bare feet and dried into a fragile container holding about 60 pounds. Today this has given way to a mixture of natural flake graphite (about 50 per cent by weight), ball clay, and silica sand, which are thoroughly mixed, ground, spun into shape, and baked. These pots, 18 inches high, 13 at the bilge, and with a 1.5-inch wall, hold about 100 pounds of metal with the first charge and last for seven to ten heats, depending upon the care exercised in their use and the temperature attained. The thin layer of slag fluxes the crucible at the slag level; consequently, it is necessary to lower the metal level in each succeeding charge in order to avoid undue weakening of the crucible wall. Practically all crucible charges are based on puddled or charcoal iron.

Particular attention must be given to sulfur and phosphorus in selecting the raw materials, inasmuch as they cannot be removed in the process. Fluxes, chiefly silica sand, are also added to form the necessary slag with the iron oxide of the charge, all of these materials being accurately weighed for each individual pot. Charcoal, to adjust the carbon content of the steel, should be of the hard-wood variety, the size about that of a pea, with a high fixed carbon content, and screened to remove dust. Ferromanganese should be of the low-carbon grade, in clean lumps, and uniformly small. The charcoal

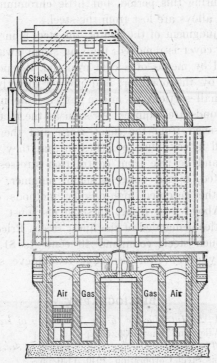

FIG. 45. Crucible Furnace. (*Courtesy of Carnegie-Illinois Steel Corp.*)

(in bags), fluxes, and ferromanganese are placed on the bottom of the pot followed by all of the iron base; steel scrap, if it is used, is added near the top of the pot. Mechanically operated shaking devices are used to pack the charge thoroughly so that the covers will fit tightly on the crucibles and thus avoid oxidation as much as possible.

Before the furnace is charged, the old bottom is cleaned out through a 6-inch opening in the bottom of the furnace, this opening sealed, and the furnace bottom covered with an 8-inch layer of coke breeze, which not only serves as a cushion when lowering the pot but also keeps the pots off the brick floor in a zone of more uniform heat. The charge will melt in approximately 3 hours after firing has begun, after which each individual pot is inspected by the melter by removing the cover; and if no further additions are required, the charge is held in the liquid state for about 45 minutes for final "killing" or liquating, during which period the last traces of rust and oxides formed during melting are eliminated. Some silicon and carbon will be picked up during this period, but little chromium, vanadium, or other oxidizable alloys are lost from the steel.

When, in the judgment of the melter, the steel is in proper condition for pouring, the cover is removed, the slag swept away from the surface of the steel by means of a cold iron rod, the pot "pulled out"* of the furnace by the operator, and poured directly into an ingot mold for the small sections or into a larger ladle in case ingots of 1000 to 2000 pounds are required. As soon as the metal solidifies, the wedges are loosened from the ingot rings and the hot ingots immediately buried in coke dust or ashes so that they will cool slowly and uniformly and be free from contraction stresses. Each ingot is analyzed, reheated, forged under a steam hammer, and reduced to billet bars by the accepted high-quality methods of modern tool steel practice. Above everything, these steels must possess "body," hardness—qualities demanded of the finest steels. Price is a secondary consideration (such steels command 40 cents to $1.25 per pound), and consequently every effort is made to achieve satisfactory and uniform results.

BIBLIOGRAPHY

1. BOYLSTON, H. M., *An Introduction to the Metallurgy of Iron and Steel*. New York: John Wiley and Sons, 1936. 563 pp.
2. FRANCIS, C. B., *The Making, Shaping, and Treating of Steel*. Pittsburgh: The Carnegie-Illinois Steel Corporation, 1940. 1440 pp.
3. *Metal Progress*, "Crucible Steel Made in America," May, 1940.
4. PARMITER, O. K., "Crucible Tool Steel Melting," *Metal Progress*, July, 1931.
5. STOUGHTON, B., *Metallurgy of Iron and Steel*. New York: McGraw-Hill Book Company, 1934. 519 pp.

* The difficulty of the work is attested by the fact that one pull consists of the crucible, 40 pounds; charge, 100 pounds; cap, 5 pounds; tongs, 20 pounds; a total of 160.

CHAPTER VII

THE BESSEMER PROCESS

HISTORY

212. General. No other invention, save possibly the telephone, automobile, or airplane, has had such an effect upon the civilized world as did the Bessemer process. The invention and patenting of this process, in 1855, because of its rapidity and cheapness made possible the production of the first really low-cost steel the world had ever known. Heretofore only wrought iron made directly from ore or pig iron by the puddling process, or the more expensive crucible steel, was available; consequently, this discovery marks a turning point in our industry as well as in our civilization. With the western movement of our people and with industrialization making such rapid advances there came a demand for new tools, new structures, and for the binding together of all parts of our country by railroads, all of which expansions could be satisfied only with low-cost steel. Certainly the statement can be made that the invention of the Bessemer process was the greatest single factor contributing to our spectacular material development in the period between the Civil War and the beginning of the present century.

213. History. The Bessemer process furnishes an excellent example of the manner in which new processes frequently develop and also emphasizes the fact that the perfecting of such a process is seldom accomplished by one mind alone but rather by many minds striving toward the same goal, because the method was almost concurrently but entirely independently originated by two men—one an American named William Kelly of Eddyville, Kentucky, the other an Englishman, the illustrious inventor, Henry Bessemer. Although Kelly did not apply for patents until 1857, almost two years after Bessemer's English patent was granted, his application was allowed on grounds of priority because he was able to prove that he had worked out the idea as early as 1847.

The facts appear to be that William Kelly and his brother purchased ore land in Kentucky about 1846, and using charcoal they made a wrought iron by the conventional bloomery process, which product was then manufactured into tools, plows, bars, and the various implements sold up and down the river and in the neighborhood. It is related that Kelly noticed that blowing a stream of air directly on molten pig iron caused it to glow and appear to become hotter (actually it did become hotter). Bessemer's patent covered a crucible full of liquid iron into which a refractory tuyère was lowered and the blow started. Starting with this experimental fact, Kelly built a semicommercial unit and soon found that his steel could be made in considerably less time; but his customers, learning that he had abandoned the conventional process, insisted that he adhere to the old rather than the "new fangled" method. Perhaps he did, but he also experimented with the new method for a number of years. Having insufficient capital, he went into partnership with a Daniel J. Morrow, who gave him a place in his Cambria plant, where Kelly built a small tilting converter (his first had been stationary ones). Out of all this, after many disappointments and failures, came a new process, known locally as "Kelly's Air Boiling Process," and the Kelly Pneumatic Process Company was formed to exploit the new invention. Thus, it seems, the Bessemer process, for which credit is usually given to Sir Henry Bessemer, was invented in this country. There are conflicting stories and claims that Bessemer had visited Eddyville and learned of Kelly's process before his own was developed. (See Boucher[2] for an excellent account of the course of events.)

Finally, after many other disappointments and negotiations in England to obtain the right to use the Mushet patents involving spiegeleisen and recarburization, the first successful blow was made in the United States at the Wyandotte plant in Michigan. The ingots cast from this steel were shipped to the North Chicago Rolling Mills, where, on May 24, 1865, they were rolled into the first steel rails produced in this country. However, this was still experimental, for it was not until 1867 that steel rails were rolled commercially at the Cambria Iron Company from Bessemer steel blown at the plant of the Pennsylvania Steel Company of Steelton, Pennsylvania. Bessemer steel plants began to spring up all over the country during the next few years until in 1875 there were nearly fifteen in operation; but it was not until 1880 that the Bessemer process in point of tonnage exceeded wrought iron. In that year 852,000 tons of Bessemer steel were made and only 441,000 tons of wrought iron. The victory was short-lived, for in 1908 the basic open-hearth process gained the ascendancy and has held it ever since; the tonnages by decades are given in Figure 46.

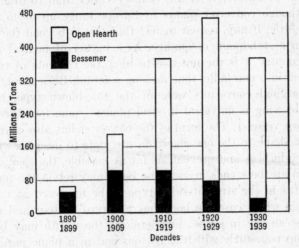

FIG. 46. Bessemer and Open-Hearth Tonnages. (*Courtesy of American Institute of Metallurgical Engineers.*)

THE BESSEMER CONVERTER

214. Bessemer Converter. An American Bessemer converter is shown in Figure 47. It consists of three separate parts, known as the nose, the body, and the bottom. All of these are made of heavy steel plates. The nose section is bolted to the body, but the bottom is held in place against the body by linked key bolts, making it easy to key the two parts firmly together and just as easy to replace an old bottom by quickly knocking out the wedges and removing it. The whole converter body is carried on two trunnions, which in turn rest on heavy bearings. On the end of one of the trunnions, both of which are hollow, an air connection is made through a packed joint to the air lines. From this a copper gooseneck leads down to the bottom of the vessel, forming a continuous passage for the blast from the air main, which is stationary, to the wind box on the converter. The converter must change its position as the blast progresses for charging of molten metal and addition agents and for skimming of slag. To the other trunnion is attached a pinion which meshes with the two racks that slide horizontally, actuated by a double-acting hydraulic piston. By this means the vessel may be easily rotated through an arc of 270 degrees, the pinion and rack being geared so that the vessel can be completely inverted for dumping slag or for relining, if necessary.

The size of converters in this country varies from 10 to 25 tons per heat, although converter plants in Europe range up to 45 tons, and there is little, if any, reason to feel that this is beyond the optimum size from a standpoint of quality. As a matter of fact, at one plant in this country it is the practice to blow the contents of two 25-ton converters into one ladle, thus making a 50-ton Bessemer heat.

The original converters were of the side-blown type, but today bottom blowing is universal in steel plants (some foundries still use side-blown vessels). The form of the converter has also changed from a potlike shape to the one shown in attempts to design a vessel that would retain heat and prevent, as far as possible, the ejection of materials. With these ends in view the body may retain the form of the cylinder as in the straight-sided type or be narrowed at the bottom as well, in which case the body has a curved contour and somewhat resembles an egg in shape. Furthermore, the mouth may be located at the top concentric with the bottom and in a plane parallel to it, or it may be placed to one side, in which case the opening lies in a plane at an angle to the bottom—the eccentric type.

215. Lining of the Converter. In this country, for reasons which will appear presently in connection with the comparison of the Bessemer process with the open-hearth, only the acid Bessemer process has been developed, with the result that the linings used are universally acid, at most plants a highly siliceous sandstone known as "firestone" or a mica schist. This lining varies in thickness from 10 to 16 inches, being thickest where the parts are subjected to the greatest erosion. The linings are built up of carefully dressed blocks of this firestone, cemented together with a mixture composed of about five parts of crushed ganister and one part of the best-quality fire clay.

Except at the slag line, this lining will not be attacked by the slag or heat but with careful patching may last for several weeks or even months of continuous running (of the order of 800 heats).

216. The Bottom. The construction of the bottom and its lining is quite another problem and merits special attention, for it is rapidly eroded by the metal and even in good practice will not last for more than twenty-five to forty heats,* after which the whole bottom must be removed and another put in its place. The shell part of the bottom is made up of heavy steel plates riveted or welded together in the form shown in Figure 47 or in the form of a shallow bowl with an

* A basic bottom may have a life of 80 to 120 blows.

open bottom. Closing this opening from within the bowl is a false bottom, a flat circular casting with openings through which the tuyères may be inserted. It is a little larger in diameter than the opening which it closes, thus making it unnecessary to fasten it in any way. It supports the bottom stuff (a moist mixture composed of crushed ganister, blue fire clay, ground brickbats, old bottom stuff, and coke dust) in which the tuyères are packed. Covering this same opening

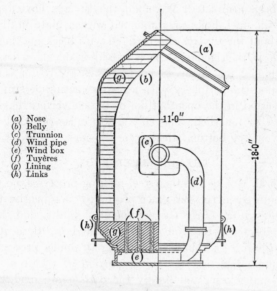

(a) Nose
(b) Belly
(c) Trunnion
(d) Wind pipe
(e) Wind box
(f) Tuyères
(g) Lining
(h) Links

Fig. 47. Bessemer Converter.

from without is the tuyère plate, a similar casting into which the tuyères fit when in place. This plate is prevented from making a tight joint with the bottom by means of the splice plates that hold the riveted plates together. Thus an open space about one inch in depth, connected to the outside of the converter, is left between the tuyère plates and the false bottom and serves the purpose of giving warning of a defective tuyère and through this lessens the danger of filling the wind box with molten metal. The plate forms the top of the wind box, the two being firmly bolted to each other and to the bottom with the same bolt. The side of this wind box is a large casting, oval in shape, and about 12 inches in depth. The bottom of the box is a steel plate which is firmly keyed to the casting to make it an almost air-tight joint when the vessel is blowing. Connecting the wind box with the interior of the bowl are nineteen to twenty-one circular, beveled holes through which the tuyères are inserted. The tuyères are cylindrical bricks, flared for a distance of about 6 inches from one end, about 30 inches long, 7 inches in diameter, and each having about twelve ½-inch holes extending longitudinally along the tuyère block. When a tuyère is placed the flare is covered with mortar composed of fire clay and Portland cement, and the tuyère is inserted through the opening in the bottom, where it is held in place with clamps until the filling has been completed. When all the tuyères have been placed in position, the open holes are protected with a plate until the space remaining about the tuyères can be filled with brick and bottom stuff. This bottom is then removed to a gas-fired drying oven, carefully dried, and baked for about 48 hours. When ready for service it is covered around the periphery with a heavy coating of stiff clay mixture and inserted in the open bottom of the converter, thus forming a tight joint with the shell. The clay mixture is sprinkled with coke dust to prevent the bottom sticking to the sides.

THE BESSEMER BLOW

217. General. Unlike all other steel-making processes, no extraneous fuels are required in the Bessemer process; consequently, the charge must be held within fairly narrow chemical limits, and the blowing time for a 10- to 25-ton converter is limited to 10 to 20 minutes. Essentially the process consists of blowing air, under pressure, through a bath of molten metal, whereby a portion of the iron, all of the silicon and manganese, and finally the carbon are oxidized. In this

TABLE 41

COMPOSITION OF BESSEMER SLAGS*

Slag	Per Cent								
	SiO_2	Al_2O_3	FeO	Fe_2O_3	MnO	CaO	MgO	P	S
Acid Bessemer	67.6	2.12	16.3	2.9	10.0	1.05	tr	0.01	0.01
Acid Bessemer (ladle)	50.3	1.33	18.8	3.0	24.1	2.45	tr	"	"
Acid Bessemer	63.2	2.8	16.4	1.9	14.7	0.7	0.3	"	"
Basic Bessemer	16.6	2.1	9.2	0.5	6.4	44.1	4.5	16.5	

* Private communications.

country there are not sufficient reserves of high-phosphorus ore to employ the basic process, and consequently only the acid is used, employing slags similar to those shown in Table 41, containing about 65 per cent silica (contrast these with the basic slags shown in Table 52). There are, therefore, two definite metallurgical limitations to the use of Bessemer steel: (1) the physical properties conferred by nitrogen and phosphorus and (2) the variability from blow to blow.

218. Character of the Charge. There is a diversity of opinion among metallurgists regarding the most suitable iron analysis for Bessemer metal, but the following chemical ranges closely approximate present-day specifications:

	Per Cent
Carbon	4 to 4.5
Manganese	0.70 maximum
Phosphorus	0.08 to 0.10
Sulfur	0.05 maximum
Silicon	1.0 to 1.75

Since phosphorus and sulfur are not affected by this process, except to increase slightly in amount owing to the loss of iron and the oxidation of silicon, manganese, and carbon, phosphorus should not run much over 0.09 per cent and sulfur should be as low as possible.

The other two metalloids, manganese and silicon, will vary considerably at individual plants and with the grade of steel desired. Iron with normal silicon (1.10 to 1.50 per cent) but with 0.45 to 0.50 per cent manganese results in a fairly liquid slag, but with manganese much above this range there is a considerable loss of metal owing to slopping; also the ladle reaction is inefficient, generally resulting in poor quality in the finished steel. A study recently made in one of the large steel plants indicates that there is a definite penalty attached to using iron with manganese over 0.45 per cent and also a resultant poorer quality steel. Iron with a manganese content of about 0.50 per cent is apparently the critical point (the point at which watery slags and slopping are encountered) in blowing quality Bessemer iron.

High-silicon iron or iron that is physically hot from the mixer or blast furnace will induce high temperature during blowing and may result in poor surface and excessive tendency towards piping. The opposite of this condition is represented by physically cold iron or iron with a low silicon content, and this metal is likely to be sluggish and dirty, producing dirty steel with tendencies towards scabbiness and generally poor rolling quality.

219. Function of the Mixer. Mixers, shown in Figure 48, are large cylindrical vessels constructed of heavy steel plates and lined with

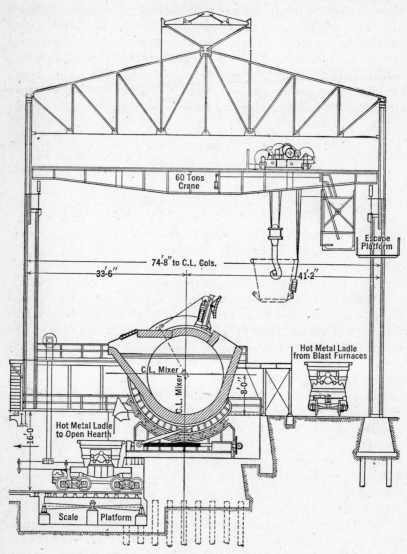

FIG. 48. Mixer. (*Courtesy of Carnegie-Illinois Steel Corp.*)

silica brick or a good grade of fire brick. They serve as a reservoir or surge tank between the blast furnace and the Bessemer converter or open-hearth furnace. These mixers are usually provided with a gas burner at one end, but very little heat above that held by the metal is ever required to keep the contents molten under normal conditions. Although molten iron could be sent directly from the blast furnace or from a cupola to the Bessemer converter, it is usually much more advantageous to utilize to the fullest extent the desirable operating and quality benefits of this piece of apparatus. The benefits derived from its use are:

1. Conservation of the heat in the pig iron.
2. Delivery to the converter of iron more nearly uniform, both chemically and physically, than in separate furnace casts.
3. Minimizing of off-casts, in that casts slightly higher or lower in a certain element, or in temperature, may be mixed with other iron of more nearly correct analysis and temperature, thus making available a larger tonnage suitable for blowing in both analysis and temperature.
4. Reduction in sulfur because the iron in the mixer is usually held at temperatures of 1200 to 1320°C.

THE BESSEMER PROCESS

220. Charging. The charge will consist of molten pig iron and cold pig iron or steel scrap in amounts sufficient to furnish the heat requirements of the blow. This is a matter of great importance, for since there is no extraneous heat applied in this process the character of the charge and its temperature are the main factors in determining the quality of the finished steel, as well as the supply of heat. In the course of the blow the only source of heat (apart from the intrinsic heat of the molten iron) is the oxidation of iron, silicon, manganese, carbon, and the formation of the ferrous silicate slag; consequently, the composition of the pig iron is extremely important. Usually the amount of heat generated by the oxidation of these elements is more than sufficient to keep the contents of the converter at a proper temperature if the charge consists entirely of molten metal from the mixer. The temperature is kept under control by charging steel scrap which may be added at any time during the blow or by injecting steam through the tuyères. In making steel of a high sulfur content, such as screw stock, the required amount of this element will be added in the form of pyrites or stick sulfur along with the molten metal; and in some plants, in order to cut down the loss of iron through oxidation, iron oxide in some form is sometimes added to the converter, but this is not common practice. The charge, weighing 15 to 18 tons, will be weighed at the mixer as it is poured into the ladle, covered with a thin layer of coke breeze in order to reduce oxidation, brought to the converter, where the latter is turned down to a horizontal position so as to bring the tuyères well above the bath. The molten iron is then poured into the mouth of the vessel by tipping the ladle with a crane. The molten metal will collect in the belly of the converter, and before the vessel is turned up the required amount of scrap will be added.

221. **Blowing.** This is the crux of the operation, for the point at which oxidation, or blowing, ceases is vital to the whole process and must be determined within seconds, not minutes. Some operators seek to blow "young"; that is, to cease blowing very early after the removal of the metalloids in order to reduce oxidation. Others, in an effort to induce a greater ladle reaction, blow "full"; that is, oxidize more of the carbon and increase the ferrous oxide content of the blown metal. The proper practice must be dictated by local conditions and the grade of steel desired.

When the charge is in the converter, the air blast is turned on, the vessel brought to an upright position, and the blow started. The silicon and manganese, along with some iron (actually ferrous oxide serves as a vehicle for the oxygen), are oxidized in the early part of the blow and a slag composed of silicates of iron and manganese formed (these too contribute a small amount of heat). The gases which pass out of the throat of the converter during this stage of the blow are, apart from the dense, brown fumes (see Article 230), mostly nitrogen, with some carbon dioxide, and oxygen and hydrogen from the moisture in the air. The bath temperature during this stage increases rather rapidly, the greater part of the heat being furnished by the oxidation of the silicon to silica, although the oxidation of iron and manganese also furnishes heat. There is relatively little carbon burned during this first stage.

When the elimination of silicon and manganese is almost complete, the carbon begins to oxidize very actively, producing carbon monoxide (the "boil"), which forms a long yellow flame as it burns to carbon dioxide (and is wasted) at the throat of the converter. The carbon in oxidizing to carbon monoxide during the carbon blow does not increase the bath temperature so rapidly as during the silicon blow. Practically, the temperature at the end of the blow is dependent on the silicon content and the initial temperature of the molten metal as regulated by the cold metal addition. Furthermore, the carbon content of the iron is about constant because of lack of control over the carbon in the blast furnace, and the heat addition from burning this constant carbon content does not vary very much from blow to blow. If the addition of the cold metal is correctly made, the silicon content and the initial temperature of the blow determine the finishing temperature and thus avoid the necessity of introducing steam toward the end of the blow in order to lower the temperature of the bath or of blowing with the converter tilted in order to expose some tuyères above the bath and thus raise the temperature through the oxidation of carbon monoxide to carbon dioxide just above the bath.

In general the steaming of the converter blow is considered to be poor practice because when it is done it involves the addition of an

TABLE 42

REMOVAL OF METALLOIDS

Element	Initial Charge, Per Cent	Time of Blowing				
		2'-0"	3'-30"	6'-0"	8'-10"	10'-0"
C	4.30	3.90	3.75	2.10	0.60	0.03
Si	1.25	0.70	0.38	0.03	0.03	0.005
Mn	0.40	0.10	0.04	0.03	0.01	0.01
P	0.085	0.088	0.090	0.092	0.094	0.096
S	0.035	0.035	0.036	0.037	0.038	0.039

uncontrolled amount of a new chemical reagent and also the uncontrolled lowering of the converter temperature. Experience indicates that iron with less than 0.95 per cent silicon will result in a cold blow, and, with more than 1.60, a hot one. Although the hot blow can be cooled by adding scrap or blowing with steam, all indications are that, from a quality standpoint, the cold blow is preferable. Moreover, the conversion of scrap into merchantable steel is a great economic advantage, particularly when scrap is cheap. The proper finishing temperature consistent with good quality and little ladle skull* appears to be 1540 to 1600°C.

The order and magnitude of the elimination of the elements may be followed by the naked eye (it is shown in tabular form in Table 42) but still better through colored glasses. The stream of dense, brown fumes which pours forth as soon as the converter is tilted in an upright direction is succeeded shortly by a dull, red, short, pointed

* Metal and slag left in the ladle.

flame, which action occupies some 5 or 6 minutes, after which this flame is gradually replaced by a short, luminous one. This soon begins to increase, both in length and luminosity, until it reaches a maximum length of more than 30 feet. During this period, the boil, there is a very violent agitation of the bath and a rapid generation of carbon monoxide. Just before the end of the blow the flame begins to drop or "die" and suddenly becomes less luminous. If this change is observed through the colored (blue) glasses, purple streaks are visible, and by the character and magnitude of these streaks the blower determines the end of the blow. If it should be continued beyond this point the flame would eventually disappear, but in the course of the oxidation of the last bit of carbon the molten iron would be very much overoxidized. The entire time required to convert the 15 to 18 tons of pig iron and scrap to steel is only about 15 minutes.

222. The End of the Blow. In a process as short as the Bessemer it is obviously impossible to stop the reaction and determine the composition of the metal; this is one of the serious shortcomings of the process. As a result, in this process more than in any other, the success of the operation and the character of the steel are almost entirely dependent upon the judgment and skill of the operator. Although it is possible to blow a heat down to an approximate carbon content, it has been found that a product much more uniform in chemical composition can be obtained by blowing the contents of the converter to the drop of the flame and then adding the requisite carbon and manganese in the

TABLE 43

LOSSES IN THE BESSEMER BLOW

	Per Cent
Carbon oxidized	4.30
Silicon oxidized	1.25
Manganese oxidized	0.40
Iron in slag and pellets	1.50
Ejected and volatilized	1.00
Total	8.45

form of ferromanganese or spiegeleisen. The blow may be turned down "young" or carried to "full" blow, but in either case the silicon will be completely eliminated and only small amounts of manganese and carbon retained. This residual manganese may be as high as 0.06 to 0.08 per cent, depending upon the amount present in the original metal as well as the character of the blow and slag. On the other hand, the percentage of carbon will vary from 0.08 to 0.10 per cent if the blow is turned down young up to 0.01 to 0.04 per cent if a full blow is carried out.* Phosphorus and sulfur are not affected chemically by the blow but will be slightly higher than in the original charge, owing to a loss in weight due to oxidation and elimination of silicon, carbon, and manganese as well as a loss of iron through oxidation and ejection from the vessel (see Table 43). Converter yields of 91 to 92 per cent are considered satisfactory.

223. Deoxidation and Recarburization. As soon as the blow proper has been finished, in the judgment of the operator, deoxidation and recarburization of the bath must be carried out immediately with these objects in view:

1. To adjust the carbon content of the steel, for it will be uniformly low at this point in the blow, and sufficient metalloid must be added to meet the specifications of the consumer.

2. To deoxidize the steel thoroughly, by the addition of manganese and silicon, because there will be considerable excess ferrous oxide dissolved in the bath to carry out the chemical reactions referred to.

3. To introduce certain alloying elements such as manganese, copper, silicon, and sulfur.

4. To "kill" or liquate metal in order to rid it of slag and oxides which become intimately mixed with it during the blowing period.

A large part of the Bessemer tonnage produced today is in the low-carbon grade (under 0.20 per cent); consequently, very little recarburization is carried out in the Bessemer process except that which is accomplished through the deoxidation additions (ferromanganese and spiegeleisen both contain considerable carbon). If steel is being made requiring more than 0.15 per cent carbon, this is introduced by the addition of molten pig iron rather than with crushed anthracite coal or coke dust. Actually the method of adding the ferromanganese to the bath will vary from plant to plant, especially where the minimum manganese specifications to be met are above 0.5 per cent. Sometimes the practice is to wet the ferromanganese so that the steam generated, when it comes into contact with the molten bath, will blow the slag away, thus reducing the possibility of entrapping the manganese in the slag and losing it. In some other plants a furnace is provided for heating the ferromanganese to 540 to 820°C., and in

---

* The extreme ranges in blown metal are: carbon, 0.02 to 0.10 per cent; manganese, 0.02 to 0.06; phosphorus, 0.08 to 0.11; sulfur, 0.04 to 0.06; silicon, 0.003 to 0.15; ferrous oxide, 0.35 to 0.65; and nitrogen, 0.02 to 0.03. The extreme range of nitrogen is 0.010 to 0.03 per cent.

most cases the manganese is screened to a maximum size of about 1.5 inches.

TABLE 44
DEOXIDIZERS AND RECARBURIZERS

Material	Per Cent											
	Fe	C	Mn	P	S	Si	V	Cr	Ni	Cu	Ti	Al
Ferromanganese	13.0	6.8	79.4	0.16		0.7						
Ferrophosphorus	80.0	1.1	0.2	18.0	0.65	0.10						
Ferrosilicon (electric)	49.4	0.55	0.02	0.08	0.02	49.9						
" (blast furnace)	87.5	1.5	0.4	0.08	0.02	10.5						
Ferrochrome	22.1	6.4	0.4	0.003	0.08	0.5		70.0				
Ferrovanadium	42.7	1.6	6.3	0.1	0.11	10.5	38.0					
Spiegel	75.7	4.4	19.1	0.05	0.03	0.7						
Pig nickel									97			
Pig copper										99		
Stick sulfur					100							
Pig iron	94.0	3.8	1.0	0.2	0.03	1.0						
Silicomanganese		2.0	67			18						
Ferrocarbon Titanium	69.5	7.8	0.1	0.003	0.03	2.7		0.2			17.4	1.6

A simple example of recarburization may serve to illustrate the methods employed. Let us suppose a heat of skelp steel is being blown to meet specifications of carbon, maximum 0.08 per cent; manganese, 0.3 to 0.6; phosphorus, 0.11 maximum; and sulfur 0.07 maximum. The converter is given a full blow to reduce the carbon content to about 0.04 per cent, and then hot ferromanganese is added in sufficient quantity to raise the amount of this element to 0.40 per cent. In making this calculation a proper allowance must be made for the residual manganese as well as the manganese which will be lost in the slag so that a grade of ferromanganese may be selected which will raise the carbon content to the desired 0.08 per cent.

The method of adding sulfur for certain grades of steel (0.10 to 0.18 per cent sulfur) is important. A study of 50,000 tons of Bessemer screw stock showed that when sulfur was added as crude sulfur there were 3.5 per cent more billets rejected than when added as iron pyrites.

Analyses of deoxidizers and recarburizers are shown in Table 44.

224. Loss of Deoxidizers and Recarburizers. The loss of addition agents referred to above is fairly uniform, under similar conditions, and is determined mostly by experience. In view of the fact that the analysis of the final steel depends upon the success of the operator in judging the progress of the blow, this offers another important reason for maintaining conditions as nearly constant as possible. In the case of manganese this loss amounts to 32 to 38 per cent of the element added for full-blown heats in which the per cent of manganese desired does not exceed 0.6; the loss is somewhat less, usually not over 15 per cent, if the blow is stopped young (heats containing 0.30 to 0.80 per cent manganese), for there will be less ferrous oxide with which the manganese can react. The loss varies also with the amount of manganese added, increasing as the per cent in the steel is raised above 0.6, or lowered as it goes below 0.3 per cent. If ferrosilicon is used, the loss of silicon is usually somewhat more and with anthracite coal the loss of carbon may be 50 per cent of the total amount added.

225. Teeming. The pouring of the blown metal into the ladle is carried out in such a manner as to insure complete mixing of the manganese, silicon, and carbon, which are added during the pour; consequently it is common practice to add only a part of the calculated amount of addition agents to the molten metal in the converter itself. Usually this is done by beginning the addition of the deoxidizer or recarburizer when about a quarter of the heat has been poured into the ladle, having the addition completed when the ladle is half full, and thus securing maximum mixing effect while the last half of the heat is being poured in. For certain grades of steel the ladle is held a specified number of minutes before teeming in order to permit the reactions to go to completion as well as to allow for the mechanical liquation of the oxides from the metal. In an effort to get uniformity, so characteristic of large heats, at one plant it has become practice to pour two converters into one large ladle, thus making a 50-ton heat. The silicon and manganese are added to the first blow while it is being poured into the ladle; the second blown metal is then poured into this mixture in the ladle in order to obtain the maximum stirring and mixing effect. In any case, when all the metal is out of the converter, it is inverted and the slag which did not flow out with the metal dumped into a small car beneath the vessel, which is then ready for the next charge. The blown metal is then transferred to a large teeming ladle and this taken to the teeming train where it is cast into ingots. The operations connected with that step are covered in more detail in Chapter XII devoted to the making of ingots.

226. Basic Bessemer Process. This, the Thomas process of Europe, is carried out with pig iron containing more than 1.5 per cent phosphorus because there must be a sufficient amount of this element to provide heat for the "after blow." The slag employed will resemble that used in the basic open-hearth containing about 44 per cent lime, 17 silica, 9 ferrous oxide, and up to 20 per cent phosphorus pentoxide. The vessel is similar in size and shape to that employed in the acid process but is lined with burned dolomite. In the course of the blow silicon is eliminated more rapidly, manganese and carbon less rapidly than in the other process. After the carbon is eliminated, the phosphorus is oxidized during what is termed the after blow. No changes in flame take place, and consequently the after blow can be timed by minutes or revolutions of the blowing engine—normally it is 2 to 4 minutes. Some sulfur is removed at the same time. More care must be exercised in deoxidizing and recarburizing in order to avoid rephosphorization from the slag.

METHODS OF CONTROL

227. General. The fact that open-hearth steel has superseded Bessemer steel has tended to create an impression that Bessemer steel is inferior, whereas as a matter of fact Bessemer steel is actually superior to the open-hearth grade for many applications. Bessemer has steadily lost ground to the open-hearth process during the past twenty years owing to a number of causes, partly economic and partly metallurgical, which are discussed more fully in Article 235. Technically a metallurgical process possesses no virtue, nor is it lacking in virtue, simply because it is either fast or slow. The important points are: (1) Can the process be controlled and (2) how quickly can this control be exercised? For the time being we shall content ourselves with a discussion of only one of these factors—variability. One of the causes of this variability is the relatively small size of Bessemer heats, whereby a given shipment of Bessemer steel is much more likely than a shipment of open-hearth steel to contain the product of several heats, each with its own distinctive and slightly different characteristics; and it is less reproducible than open-hearth steel.*

A second reason for lack of uniformity lies in the fact that the refining of Bessemer steel proceeds so rapidly that the timing of the end point is limited to a matter of seconds; the finishing period in the open-hearth extends over one or two hours, in which case the timing of the end point may vary by several minutes without seriously affecting the product. Furthermore, if an error has been made in an open-hearth heat, means are available to correct it; such means are usually not available in the Bessemer process. That Bessemer steel may vary is not necessarily objectionable; as a matter of fact,

* In the sense that a crankpin, valve stem, or gear can be reproduced exactly.

it may even prove an advantage because of the added flexibility, providing a precise control is available by means of which the desired qualities for any specific application can be obtained. With this control in mind much research has been carried out during the past five years towards securing a more accurate control of the blow than is afforded by the visual observation of the operator. The results have been very encouraging, but for lack of space only two of the most successful methods can be discussed in this book.

228. Photocell Control. H. K. Work[15] has developed what is probably the most successful method for controlling Bessemer converters, involving the use of photocells for following the changes in the flame, a method capable of giving an instantaneous quantitative record of the flame behavior, something the human eye cannot do. It is a well-recognized fact in photography that accurate estimation of light values by eye is extremely difficult; and in addition the eye varies from person to person, has a limited wavelength coverage, and is affected by fatigue and by the physical condition of the individual. Furthermore, the eye produces no permanent record of what has taken place, with the result that it is difficult to pass on to another individual the experiences of an individual blower or even to compare, accurately, successive blows.

Much work has been done on the spectral characteristics of the Bessemer flame, which studies have shown that at the beginning of a blow the spectral energy is rather weak* and comprises both lines and bands. As the blow progresses and the carbon begins to burn with a luminous flame, the amount of energy increases and a continuous spectrum appears which almost completely overshadows the line spectra. Toward the end of the blow the radiant energy decreases rapidly, the rate of drop, however, varying considerably from blow to blow. These general variations in the character of the flame form the basis of photocell control.

The equipment for carrying on this method of viewing the flame is shown in Figure 49. The unit is set up about 60 feet from the converter, the exact location being controlled by local conditions in the mill, such as convenience, freedom from interference by cranes and smoke, exclusion of other Bessemer flames, the sun and sky, ease of servicing, and physical surroundings. The preferred field of view incloses substantially the whole flame at its maximum size. Naturally, this also includes areas not covered by the flames, and, although these do not interfere seriously with the flame readings, their existence must

* The product of oxidation is a solid (SiO_2), not a gas, as in the carbon blow.

be considered in locating the equipment. The curve thus obtained, its significance, together with a correlation with the composition of the waste gas and the time are shown in Figures 50 and 51.

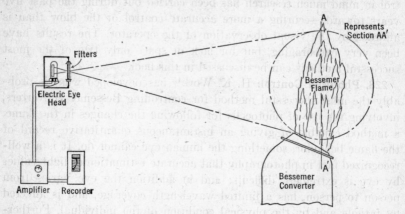

Fig. 49. Photocell Control. (*Courtesy of American Institute of Metallurgical Engineers.*)

Point *A* marks the start of the blow, and because the chart reads from right to left it is at the extreme right of the graph. The period of low-flame intensity marked *AB* is generally referred to as the silicon blow because to a large extent the silicon is oxidized during this

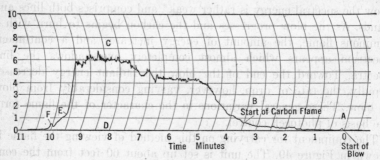

Fig. 50. Curve of Bessemer Blow. (*Courtesy of American Institute of Metallurgical Engineers.*)

period, and the *BE* is called the carbon blow for similar reasons. Experiments have shown that as the amount of silicon increases the time of the silicon blow increases, the carbon blow decreases, but the overall length of the blow increases. This indicates that the separation between the silicon blow and the carbon blow is not so clear-cut as has been assumed, but it is significant that blowers are using the relationship between the flame curve and the silicon of the iron to control the blow.

The maximum height of the curve CD furnishes information about the blown metal temperature, statistical studies having shown that the higher the maximum reading of the flame curves, the higher the blown metal temperature. In estimating this temperature, allowance must be

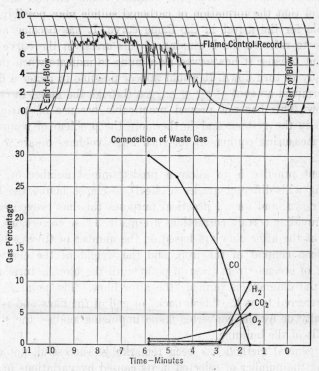

FIG. 51. Composition of Gases in Bessemer Blow. (*Courtesy of American Institute of Metallurgical Engineers.*)

made by the blower to provide for certain variables such as the condition of the nose of the converter, the number of tuyères blanked, and the air pressure. This indication of relative temperatures is one of the chief benefits from the photocell control of Bessemer steel making because of the effect of temperature on the nitrogen content of the steel and, in turn, the definite correlation between differences in physical properties, particularly hardness, brittleness, and aging, and nitrogen content.

Continuing with the blow, we find that when the flame drops at the end, an arrest (E) occurs in the curve, which may vary considerably in shape and position. It is interesting to note that one of the factors that affects the position of E is the sulfur content of the steel—high-sulfur blows containing added sulfur showing a lower end point than regular ones. On the other hand the residual sulfur, over the range 0.03 to 0.05 per cent, has no appreciable effect on the end point. This influence of sulfur, coupled with thermodynamic studies, has led to the belief that the formation of carbonyl sulfide may possibly be responsible for the arrest in the flame curve. It has become accepted practice to refer to the beginning of this arrest in the curve as the end point because it has served as a guide to indicate when the blow was ready to turn down. It would appear possible to meter a definite, predetermined amount of air or oxygen through the metal to complete the blow. This has not proved practicable because of variable air leakage in the system, and furthermore the problem of securing accurate measuring equipment for such large volumes of air would be difficult.

Present practice is to allow a predetermined number of seconds (varying with different grades of steel) to elapse before the blow is turned down, and for all practical purposes this has proved satisfactory, providing certain corrections are made. These corrections for the timing of the after blow are based on the number of tuyères blanked, the silicon content of the iron, and the weight of the charge. The number of seconds from the end point until the blow is turned down, EF in the diagram, is termed "the after blow." The point F is generally referred to as the "flash back" or end of the blow and is caused artificially or by the converter flame impinging against the shield or the walls of the building.

This general method has been remarkably successful, not only in reducing the number of rejected heats caused by variations in carbon and manganese but also in bringing about a much better control of the nitrogen content of the steel. It has been extended to many other plants than the one in which it was originally developed. The progress of the blow and the analyses of waste gases are given in Figure 51.

229. Control of the Generation and Delivery of the Blast. Another method of control and improvement has been proposed by J. S. Fulton,[6] involving changes in the generation and delivery of the blast of the Bessemer converter. In many older installations a number of blowers discharged into a common blast main which, in turn, might serve two or more converters; such conditions rendered almost impossible any regulation of pressure and volume to an individual converter. It is

significant and unfortunate that there is no accepted method of raising the capacity of a converter as there is a blast furnace. In the blast
furnace the operator knows quite accurately how much air is being
blown, its temperature, how much coke is being burned, the condition
of the tuyères, etc. In the Bessemer converter, however, there are many
variables, such as:

1. The number of tuyères may range from 16 to 30.
2. The blast pressure may range from 18 to 33 pounds per square inch.
3. The temperature of the blast may be anywhere from 15 to 180°C.
4. The heat may be blown as short a time as 5 minutes or as long as 25.

Although the "electric eye" described above has been effective, there
are five other factors: blast volume, blast pressure, blast temperature,
tuyère area, and the time of blow, any of which might be used in
controlling the Bessemer process. It is pertinent to point out, in connection with the above factors, that converter operators have always
been very "pressure" conscious. First, regulation has always been on
this basis rather than on the more reasonable one of the volume of
air being supplied. Second, they have given little thought to improving
the design of the converter and its accessory apparatus or considered
this matter from the theoretical standpoint of fluid flow. Many refinements have been carried out in blast furnace and open-hearth practice,
very few in the Bessemer process. Third, they have never realized
that the air can pick up considerable heat in passing through a bottom
which is in blast. The end of the tuyère, in contact with the metal,
may reach a temperature as high as 1540°C., and in such a rough
conduit there is bound to be turbulence which will further improve
the heat transfer from the walls.

In an effort to improve the effectiveness and efficiency of the Bessemer process, it has been suggested that:

1. The air circuit be streamlined and the joints around the vessel be made
   tighter and stronger.
2. The blast lines be insulated.
3. Hot blast stoves or heat exchangers be installed to raise the blast temperature in the wind box.
4. The humidity of the blast be maintained at a uniform level either by:
   a. Refrigeration or, preferably, by
   b. Injection of moisture to a controlled level if for no other reason
      than to decrease the nitrogen.
5. Each vessel be calibrated to determine the conditions of wind-box
   pressure, number of tuyères, and tuyère size that will give the optimum
   combination of low blowing costs and long bottom life.

6. The operator be provided with visual means of indicating the amount of wind entering the riser pipe and, if possible, the wind-box pressure, as a check on leakage.

CHEMISTRY OF THE BESSEMER PROCESS

230. General. During the course of the Bessemer blow the oxygen of the blast attacks first the iron, then both directly and indirectly (through ferrous oxide) the silicon and manganese, producing exothermic reactions which rapidly increase the temperature of the bath. The converter gases during this period produce no flame, for they are mainly nitrogen, some carbon dioxide, and traces of oxygen and hydrogen. As the temperature rises, with the elimination of these two metalloids, carbon begins to be oxidized to carbon monoxide, which burns at the mouth of the vessel to carbon dioxide and produces the characteristic flame. The escaping gases during this period consist mainly of nitrogen and carbon monoxide with small percentages of carbon dioxide and hydrogen, so that at no time during the blow, except for a short period at the beginning, do appreciable amounts of oxygen escape from the bath uncombined despite the fact that the layer of metal is only 20 inches thick and the volume of the blast more than 30,000 cubic feet per minute for a 25-ton converter. This is not surprising, for the oxygen is probably delivered from the tuyères in the form of a fine spray, and temperatures in the metal are such that these reactions go on very rapidly. Concerning the brownish fumes given off from the converter when it is first tilted into position, it has been suggested that this is manganese carbonyl; certainly it does contain volatile compounds of iron, manganese, and carbon, because analyses of the deposits of this fume indicate that they are composed roughly of about 14 per cent ferrous oxide, 28 per cent silica, and the remainder manganese oxide. It is not believed that this fume has any significance, spectacular as it may be. The reactions involved in the Bessemer blow are indicated below:

$$2Fe(c) + O_2(g) \rightarrow 2FeO(c); \quad \Delta H = -128,000 \text{ cal.} \tag{38}$$

$$2FeO(c) + Si(c) \rightarrow SiO_2(c) + 2Fe(c); \quad \Delta H = -70,200 \tag{39}$$

$$FeO(c) + Mn(c) \rightarrow MnO(c) + Fe(c); \quad \Delta H = -26,800 \tag{40}$$

$$FeO(c) + SiO_2(c) \rightarrow FeO \cdot SiO_2(c); \quad \Delta H = -6,600 \tag{41}$$

$$MnO(c) + SiO_2(c) \rightarrow MnO \cdot SiO_2(c); \quad \Delta H = -2,200 \tag{42}$$

$$2C(c) + O_2(g) \rightarrow 2CO(g); \quad \Delta H = -52,800 \tag{43}$$

$$FeO(c) + CO(g) \rightarrow Fe(c) + CO_2(g); \quad \Delta H = -3,300 \tag{44}$$

$$2CO(g) + Si(c) \rightarrow SiO_2(c) + 2C(c); \quad \Delta H = -148,900 \tag{45}$$

$$CO(g) + Mn(c) \rightarrow MnO(c) + C(c); \quad \Delta H = +69,700 \tag{46}$$

$$FeO(c) + C(c) \rightarrow Fe(c) + CO(g); \quad \Delta H = +37,500 \tag{47}$$

231. Elimination of Silicon and Manganese. Iron makes up nearly 94 per cent of the molten bath; consequently, when the air enters the tuyères, this is oxidized first, liberating considerable heat, as indicated by reaction 38. The ferrous oxide thus formed dissolves in the molten bath and serves as a vehicle to furnish oxygen for the oxidation of silicon and manganese, that of silicon taking place first, for it is strongly exothermic. With the oxidation of silicon and manganese a slag is formed which in turn liberates a small amount of heat. Incidentally, a part of the silica for reactions 41 and 42 are obtained from the bottom of the converter, which fact accounts for the rapid deterioration of the bottom. Towards the end of this period some of the carbon may be oxidized directly to carbon monoxide and then to carbon dioxide either by oxygen or ferrous oxide.

232. The Boil. With the elimination of silicon and manganese a considerable rise in temperature takes place, permitting reaction 47 to go on, and these in conjunction with reaction 43 rapidly oxidize the remaining carbon.

The phosphorus and sulfur are not affected by this process because of the acidic character of the slag and lining, so they need not be considered.

233. Recarburization and Deoxidation. The early failures of William Kelly were caused not alone by faulty technique but also because no one appreciated at that time the important role of manganese in deoxidizing the bath. It should be remembered that at the close of the Bessemer blow the bath, while perhaps not saturated with ferrous oxide, does contain appreciable quantities of this constituent, and, if allowed to remain in the metal, this oxide would detract seriously from the physical properties of the alloy. Another function of the manganese is in neutralizing or offsetting sulfur. (It does not remove sulfur from the steel.) Sulfur is normally present in steel as iron sulfide and has a tendency to segregate around the grain boundaries of the ferrite, giving rise to the phenomenon known as "hot shortness" when the metal is heated. If some manganese, slightly more than that necessary to combine directly with the sulfur, is added, the manganese sulfide is removed from the grain boundaries to appear as small inclusions within the ferrite grains, thus preventing this segregation. The reactions of deoxidation are shown in reactions 39, 40, 47, for silicon as well as carbon may serve as a deoxidizing agent. For the greatest effectiveness a considerable excess of silicon and manganese over that required by their respective reactions with ferrous oxide should be used, as neither is capable of deoxidizing the steel completely. This is one of the reasons that the manganese in most grades of steel ranges from 0.3 to 1.0 per cent. Incidentally, some manganese is lost by replacing iron in ferrous slag.

234. Problem 4. Calculate the equilibrium constants for the oxidation of carbon and silicon in the Bessemer process at 1873°K.

$$(a) \quad Si(c) + O_2(g) \rightarrow SiO_2(c); \quad \Delta F° = -213,650 + 46.61T$$
$$(b) \quad C(c) + O_2(g) \rightarrow CO_2(g); \quad \Delta F° = -90,140 - 1.93T$$
$$(c) \quad C(c) + \tfrac{1}{2}O_2(g) \rightarrow CO(g); \quad \Delta F° = -23,640 - 22.09T$$

$$\Delta F° = -RT \ln K_p.$$

From which relationship:

$$K_p \text{ for equation } a = 3.1 \times 10^{27}$$
$$K_p \text{ for equation } b = 8.5 \times 10^{10}$$
$$K_p \text{ for equation } c = 3.98 \times 10^{7}$$

Therefore one can safely say that the oxygen will be used in oxidizing silicon before any oxide of carbon will be produced.

ECONOMIC ASPECTS OF BESSEMER STEEL

235. General. It is now over thirty years since the basic open-hearth process, in point of tonnage produced, surpassed the acid Bessemer. In the succeeding years not only has the product of the Bessemer process come to be associated with inferior physical properties but also there has been an almost total lack of interest in the process itself. As a matter of fact, it is only within the last ten years that such far-seeing metallurgists as Graham, Work, Henning, and Fulton have attacked the problem in a scientific manner, have been able to show that Bessemer steel does possess some outstanding physical properties, and have awakened interest in the process as a future steel-making one.

In the years following the granting of Bessemer's patent, virtually every conceivable form of vessel, bottom arrangement, tuyère size, and location have been suggested or tried. Experiments have been carried out with the vessels of a cylindrical form supported on a long axis with the tuyères along one side submerged by a partial rotation of the vessel (similar to the Peirce-Smith type of copper converter), with stationary vessels having fixed bottoms, with vessels having two lines of tuyères, with multi-compartment vessels, with portable ones, and with various combinations of cupolas and converters in one shell. Long before the beginning of the present century, these experiments were for the most part abandoned as unfruitful and Bessemer steel accepted as a necessary but admittedly inferior product, for the following reasons:

1. With the increase in demand for steel during the latter part of the nineteenth century and the opening up of the Mesabi range, the acid Bessemer process no longer sufficed to meet our needs. The Mesabi ores were of medium phosphorus content, with the result that the basic Bessemer could not be employed any more than the acid process, but the new open-hearth process offered a very attractive method of controlling the phosphorus content of the metal. It was a more leisurely process and consequently the other metalloids were under better control than in the Bessemer. In contrast to 10 to 20 minutes of operation, during which by visual methods alone the operator had to meet specifications, the open-hearth operator had several hours—a much more attractive and effective method of control.

2. The service requirements of industry became much more severe. As the new fabricating methods, involving stamping, cold working, drawing, etc., came into vogue, the manufacturers began to demand a steel with better physical properties or with different combinations of physical properties. It was not possible to produce these consistently with the existent Bessemer process.

3. Our rapidly expanding industrial activity, during the latter part of the nineteenth century, consumed very large amounts of steel, and consequently Bessemer ores became scarce and higher in price. Furthermore, because of these conditions, producers of Bessemer steel were obliged to keep closer and closer to the limit of 0.10 per cent phosphorus, with a consequent falling off in the physical properties of the steel.

4. When the bridges, buildings, railroads, and machines produced by the early activity just mentioned became obsolete, a flood of scrap descended on the market, and, of course, only limited amounts (5 to 15 per cent) of cold metal may be charged into a Bessemer converter. The open-hearth process, on the other hand, is ideally suited to the melting of steel scrap (scrap constituting 50 to 100 per cent of the charge) and the leisurely adjustment of its metalloid content. This tonnage of scrap became very large in the early part of the twentieth century, caused more than anything else by the earlier expansions in our transportation systems, automotive and railroad.

It is well to emphasize at this point that a significant difference exists between European and American Bessemer practices. The American practice is acid, and with a siliceous lining in the converter no attempt is made to reduce the phosphorus and sulfur. The European practice, on the other hand, involves the use of a basic lining and a basic slag with an after blow which accomplishes some reduction in phosphorus and sulfur, particularly in the former. This practice is necessary with high phosphorus ores and is further sustained by the sale of high phosphorus slags which become of appreciable value as a by-product of the process. Furthermore, the quality of the steel is not greatly different from that of the American acid Bessemer process.

236. Rapid Dephosphorization of Bessemer Steel. At least one factor contributing to the superior stiffness of Bessemer steel as compared to open-hearth is the relatively high phosphorus content. The phosphorus content of basic Bessemer steel of Europe is considerably lower than the normal acid product in America. The American industry has continued the use of the acid process chiefly for the reason that the available ores are more easily adapted to this process both from a metallurgical and an economic standpoint. As these ores have become scarcer in recent years, there has been a tendency on the part of the producers of Bessemer steel to stay as close to the Bessemer limit as possible in order to use the cheaper mixtures of ores. Blast furnaces producing Bessemer iron usually operate on a mixture of three or four ores so that the finished steel will have a natural phosphorus content in the range of 0.085 to 0.10 per cent. With the demand for greatly increased tonnages, producers have considered inexpensive methods of dephosphorizing acid Bessemer steel in order to make it available for the many uses to which the normal grade of Bessemer steel is not adapted. The Wheeling Steel Corporation has developed a process, outlined below, which gives promise of successful application in a large way. Briefly this method consists of producing a special, viscous slag in the Bessemer converter, separating the blown metal from this slag, and then adding basic materials to dephosphorize the blown metal.

The first departure from regular practice has to do with the character of the slag. The physical characteristics of normal converter slags vary from very fluid ones to those which are thick and highly viscous. With the latter it is quite feasible to separate the slag and metal by the simple process of reladling. A study of slags, in an attempt to duplicate this viscous type, led to the discovery of the great importance of the silicon-manganese ratio in the iron. It was found that a silicon-manganese ratio of 2 to 1 with young blowing would produce a thick slag, but the ratio of 2.5 to 1 would fit more nearly into normal operation. At this particular plant a mixture of 40 to 50 per cent direct metal and 50 to 60 per cent cupola metal is made so that the silicon content will be about 1.4 per cent and manganese about 0.55 per cent.

Another departure from normal practice is that the dephosphorized heats are blown young; that is, the vessel is turned down from 1 to 6 seconds after the first flame change appears. After the vessel is turned down, a block of wood attached to a long rod is inserted in the nose of the converter. When the vessel is lowered to pour the blown metal into the ladle, the thick slag floats forward against the block, which prevents the slag from entering the steel ladle along with the blown metal. Converter slags produced under these conditions (containing silica, 63 to 68 per cent; ferrous oxide, 12 to 18; manganese oxide, 12 to 18; ferric oxide, 1 to 2; and alumina, 2 to 3) are uniformly thick and viscous.

Having effected the separation of the slag and metal, dephosphorization is carried out by adding the dephosphorizing material to the stream of metal as it is being poured from the converter into the steel ladle. The mixture used consists of impure lime, 50 per cent; roll scale, 30 per cent; and flux, 20 per cent. The fluxes employed for obtaining the required fluidity and melting point are bauxite, ilmenite ore, soda ash, and fluorspar.

On the other hand there are these disadvantages and limitations to the process:

1. Lower yields are obtained because of the use of iron of a higher metalloid content, and the loss in blowing the controlled iron is 9.75 per cent as against about 8.5 per cent for normal acid Bessemer operation.

2. The average scrap charge for a 6.5-ton heat of normal phosphorus metal is about 1500 pounds; when a dephosphorized heat is being made, the scrap charge must be reduced to 1000 pounds in order to provide the excess metal temperature for melting the 500 pounds of dephosphorizing mixture.

3. The method is limited to the production of soft steel. Grades of over 0.2 per cent carbon with 0.75 per cent manganese are difficult to make without introducing a reladling operation.

237. The Role of Scrap. This factor, in the acid Bessemer process, is an important one because the Bessemer process has commonly been regarded as much cheaper than the basic open-hearth, whereas the difference in cost between the two is governed largely by the relative costs of the manufacture of pig iron and the market price of steel scrap. During the recent depression years there were long periods of time during which the price of steel scrap was so low that open-hearth steel probably enjoyed lower manufacturing costs than Bessemer. Recent years have shown a marked rise in the rate of obsolescence of our industrial equipment; the critical years lying ahead of us will further accelerate this pace. From Table 45 it will be evident that a large percentage of the Bessemer steel manufactured today goes into screw steel, sheet steel, tin plate, wire, pipe, bolts, nuts, concrete reinforcing, track spikes, and many structural and special shapes; almost all of these, except concrete reinforcing, have a very high salvage value. Their life, with the possible exception of the latter item and pipe, is relatively short, with the result that a large tonnage may be returned to industry in the form of scrap. This is still good steel, differing only in form and composition from that desired by the new user; and consequently it is relatively easy to melt it in an open-hearth furnace, adjust the chemical composition to the new specifications, and return it to industry in a new form.

During the past few years we have heard much about the importance of, and superior properties conferred on steel by, the acid open-hearth, arc, high-frequency furnace, and crucible processes, but little about the acid Bessemer. As a matter of fact, the combined tonnage of these processes is not more than a fourth that of the tonnage produced by the Bessemer process. Any process that consistently produces over a million tons of ingots per year must be recognized as important and worthy of enthusiastic and extended research.

ATTRACTIVE PROPERTIES OF BESSEMER STEEL

238. General. The experience of the past thirty years, and the developments of the past ten, have shown that the Bessemer process and its products possess certain outstanding advantages which should, in the course of the next decade, increase its popularity and cause it to be regarded more favorably in the steel-making world. These advantages are:

1. The greater flexibility of the process.
2. The machinability of the product.
3. The stiffness of the product.
4. The weldability of the product.
5. The sensitivity of the product to cold work.

239. Flexibility. A Bessemer converter, with its small size and ease of handling, makes it possible to produce small tonnages of many different grades of steel—actually, three grades of steel in less than an hour. Analyses of the common grades are shown in Table 45. Furthermore, the Bessemer process, from the steel-maker's viewpoint, has certain operating advantages over the open-hearth, notably less delay in the replacement of bottoms and of repairs to the vessels themselves. If any major repair to an open-hearth furnace becomes necessary, weeks of time are involved during which the furnace must be cooled down, these repairs effected, and the whole structure reheated again. Not only is there a considerable investment of time and money in-

TABLE 45
BESSEMER STEEL COMPOSITIONS[9]

Product	Per Cent			
	C	Mn	P	S
Screw steel (standard)	0.08–0.16	0.60–0.90	0.09–0.13	0.1–0.18
" " (high-sulfur)	0.08–0.16	0.60–0.90	0.09–0.13	0.2–0.3
" " (high-carbon)	0.25–0.35	0.60–0.90	0.09–0.13	0.1–0.18
Skelp	0.08m	0.30–0.60	0.11m	0.08m
Bars, track spikes, sheet and tin plate	0.10m	0.30–0.50	0.11m	0.07m
Soft wire	0.12m	0.60m	0.11m	0.08m
Medium wire	0.10–0.20	0.70m	0.11m	0.08m
Reinforcing bars	0.15–0.35	0.70m	0.11m	0.08m
Structural soft	0.07–0.12	0.30–0.60	0.11m	0.08m
" medium	0.25–0.35	0.30–0.60	0.11m	0.08m
" high-tensile	0.35–0.45	0.30–0.60	0.11m	0.08m

m = maximum.

volved in bringing the furnace back to an operating level, but a large amount of money is idle during this period. In contrast to this, a Bessemer bottom may be replaced in a few minutes; if any major repair is necessary, the whole vessel can be removed from the trunnions and another one substituted; and the investment is much less. It is evident that flexibility is attractive in times of slack demand when quick deliveries of small tonnages are particularly desirable from the standpoint of the manufacturer, and certainly the experience of the past twenty years indicates that these times may come to be considered as normal ones.

240. **Machinability.** It is a commonly accepted fact that no grade of steel yet developed even closely approaches the high-speed-cutting quality of Bessemer screw stock, and for this reason it constitutes one of the large tonnage outlets for Bessemer steel. This advantage is measured by the fact that if low-carbon, open-hearth, low-sulfur steel is given a machinability rating of 40, high-sulfur Bessemer screw stock may have a rating of over 120. It is evident, therefore, that wherever this screw stock does possess the required physical properties, and production costs in machining are high as regards both labor and investment in machinery, the Bessemer steel possesses a tremendous

inherent advantage. As a matter of fact, a much larger tonnage would have been used in the past were it not for the fact that there were notable variations in machinability from blow to blow caused by lack of control in the process, which variability creates havoc in modern production methods by wrecking or throwing out of adjustment expensive machine tools. With the methods of control discussed earlier in this chapter now available, it seems likely that the properties referred to will not only be enhanced but also be made more subject to the control of the operator.

241. Stiffness. It is a well-known fact that Bessemer steel, both hot-rolled and cold-drawn, in general is stiffer than open-hearth steel of equivalent tensile properties. It will show considerably higher tensile strength than equivalent carbon contents in open-hearth steel; for example, a carbon Bessemer steel containing 0.10 per cent carbon has a tensile strength of about 60,000 pounds per square inch whereas an open-hearth steel of the same strength must contain at least 0.20 per cent carbon. This has been attributed by some to the higher phosphorus or ferrous oxide content, but recent work by a large producer of Bessemer steel has failed to show any correlation, especially since open-hearth heats are frequently found with oxygen contents in excess of the average oxygen content of Bessemer steel. This property of increased stiffness is of great value in certain manufacturing operations. For example, in many hot-working operations the effect of quenching can be neglected in Bessemer steel because the steel containing as little as 0.1 per cent carbon does not respond to heat treatment.

On the other hand, if one has to go much above 0.2 per cent carbon in an open-hearth grade to get this required stiffness, sudden cooling would increase the hardness of the piece and reduce the speed of machining in the subsequent operations. Another instance of the superior stiffness of Bessemer steel is illustrated by its application to the manufacture of tin cans. Under normal fabrication, handling, and packing conditions a can body made of Bessemer steel will resist distortion to a much higher degree than one made of open-hearth steel. Furthermore, Bessemer steel has some advantage in the production of tin plate because of the lesser tendency of the sheets to stick together in hot mill rolling and subsequent annealing. This advantage, of course, will be of less importance in the years to come as improvements are made in the manufacture of strip steel.

242. Weldability. The intensive research which has been carried on during the past ten years in the various welding processes has resulted in an enormous expansion in the application of this method of construction. Probably the best example of this is in ship construction. During World War I, the best record achieved in the building of a standard cargo vessel was about eight months from the laying of the keel to the launching of the ship, whereas recent records achieved are less than one. A large outlet for Bessemer steel lies in welded pipe because of the higher strength of low-carbon Bessemer steel over the open-hearth grade as well as the more attractive machining properties which speed up the cutting of the threads. In this welding, Bessemer steel appears to produce joints which are more closely knit and freer from blow holes and inclusions than open-hearth steel. In addition the Bessemer steel is distinctly superior from the standpoint of forming and rolling, producing a final tooled product which is freer from scratches and roll marks.

TABLE 46

EFFECT OF COLD WORK ON BESSEMER AND OPEN-HEARTH STEEL[9]

Property	Bessemer Steel		Open-Hearth Steel	
	Hot-rolled	Cold-drawn	Hot-rolled	Cold-drawn
Yield point, lb. per sq. in.	42,780	75,040	39,040	63,220
Tensile strength, lb. per sq. in.	64,900	88,170	65,000	77,880
Elongation, per cent in 2 in.	38.0	19.5	36.5	19.0
Reduction area, per cent	65.2	53.3	61.8	57.0

243. Sensitivity to Cold Work. This pronounced reaction of Bessemer steel has long been regarded as an unfavorable characteristic, but it is now recognized that this property may be either a favorable or an unfavorable one, depending upon the requirements of the particular application. In cold drawing, for example, desirable increases in the yield point and tensile strength can be accomplished within a fairly large range. Table 46, for example, indicates the difference in the effect of cold work upon Bessemer steel and equivalent open-hearth steel when subjected to the same cold-drawing process. While the tensile strength was about the same in the hot-rolled condition, cold drawing increased the yield point about 19 per cent and the tensile strength 13 per cent more than was accomplished on the open-hearth grade. This is considered a favorable factor for obtaining maximum physical properties for many applications. When this sharp response to cold work is not desired, it is easily possible to modify this characteristic by means of special deoxidation.

244. Conclusions. The Bessemer process has been a major factor in our remarkable industrial development. The author believes that any steel-making process that possesses the unique quality characteristics in addition to operating flexibility and speed such as are embodied in the Bessemer process deserves study and development. Especially is this true in view of the progress that has been made in the past five years. It is particularly worthy of attention in our war effort, because large tonnages can be added to our productive capacity very cheaply by utilizing this process. In improving the control of the process as well as the quality of Bessemer steel, it seems reasonable to predict that other desirable inherent quality characteristics of the Bessemer process can be developed and improved so that further commercial applications may be possible, and this process, in a measure, regain an important position in the steel-making industry.

BIBLIOGRAPHY

1. American Society for Testing Materials, "Metals," *American Society for Testing Materials Standards,* Part I, 1936.
2. BOUCHER, J. N., *William Kelly, a True History of the So-Called Bessemer Process.* Greensburgh, Pa.: Published by the author, 1924.
3. BOYLSTON, H. M., *An Introduction to the Metallurgy of Iron and Steel.* New York: John Wiley and Sons, 1936. 563 pp.
4. CLARK, C. W. E., "The Utilization of Waste Heat in the Steel Industry," American Iron and Steel Institute, *Transactions,* May, 1930.
5. FRANCIS, C. B., *The Making, Shaping, and Treating of Steel.* Pittsburgh: Carnegie-Illinois Steel Corporation, 1940. 1440 pp.
6. FULTON, J. S., "Analysis of the Generation and Delivery of the Blast to the Metal in a Bessemer Converter," American Institute of Mining and Metallurgical Engineers, *Technical Paper* 1344, 1941.
7. GRAHAM, H. W., "The Acid Bessemer Process of 1940," American Institute of Mining and Metallurgical Engineers, *Technical Paper* 1232, 1941.
8. HAYWARD, C. R., *An Outline of Metallurgical Practice.* New York: D. Van Nostrand Company, 1940. 612 pp.
9. HENNING, C. E., "Manufacture and Properties of Bessemer Steel," American Institute of Mining and Metallurgical Engineers, Iron and Steel Division, *Technical Paper* 623, 1935.
10. *Iron Age, The,* "Numerous Uses for Bessemer Steel," Vol. 122 (13), September, 1928.
11. McCAFFEREY, R. S., "The Bessemer Process," *Blast Furnace and Steel Plant,* November, 1931.
12. SPRING, L. W., and L. E. GILMORE, "Beginnings of Bessemer Steel," *Metals and Alloys,* April, 1932.

13. STOUGHTON, B., *Metallurgy of Iron and Steel*. New York: McGraw-Hill Book Company, 1934. 519 pp.

14. STOUGHTON, B., and A. BUTTS, *Engineering Metallurgy*. New York: McGraw-Hill Book Company, 1930. 441 pp.

15. WORK, H. K., "Photocell Control of Bessemer Steelmaking," American Institute of Mining and Metallurgical Engineers, *Technical Paper* 1300½, 1941.

16. YOCOM, G. M., "A Method of Rapid Dephosphorization of Bessemer Steel," American Institute of Mining and Metallurgical Engineers, *Technical Paper* 1265, 1941.

CHAPTER VIII

THE BASIC OPEN-HEARTH PROCESS

HISTORY

245. General. The basic open-hearth process is, and probably will be for many years, the most important American steel-making process. Our cheap fuel, large reserves of medium phosphorus ores, and supplies of scrap leave little opportunity for any other process to compete on the basis of tonnage alone, although others may successfully do so on the basis of superior or peculiar products. This process for the manufacture of steel may be regarded as one that is the result of a series of developments rather than a single isolated invention. The development of so simple an implement as an axe is a case in point. The axe began as a stone in the hands of prehistoric man, and then by reason of the ingenuity and observation of the man's descendants passed through the various stages of a sharp-edged stone, the provision of a groove for the hands, the provision of a handle for this groove, improvements in balance, the drilling of a hole for the handle, the substitution of meteoric iron for stone, then wrought iron, steel, and finally the duplex structure now characteristic of such an implement. Similarly, the present basic open-hearth process was due to the cumulative efforts of Réaumur, Siemens, the Martin brothers, Wellman, Hewitt, and many less famous individuals.

246. Development in Europe. The idea of making steel by melting together cast and wrought iron on an open-hearth or a reverberatory furnace was proposed as early as 1722 by the French philosopher, Réaumur. We have records of this process being tried many times by different persons during the eighteenth and the first half of the nineteenth century; it is recorded that a commission appointed by the French, under Louis Napoleon, spent a large amount of money on experiments with such a process. As a matter of fact, they succeeded in reaching the necessary temperature and achieving some purification, but all these early experiments failed to be commercially successful on account of the destructive action of the heat and slag on the lining of the furnace (only fire clay or siliceous material was available). The

252

heat could not be obtained except by the rapid combustion of coal or coke, which created such an intense, cutting action on the brickwork of the furnace that it burned out in a very short time, and, furthermore, the quantity of fuel used per ton of metal was so large that the process could not compete from a commercial standpoint.

The next important contribution was made by Sir Francis William Siemens. He was a graduate of the Polytechnical School at Magdeburg, Germany, and in the years following his graduation in 1846 made notable contributions to the engineering profession in the form of the air pump, water meter, boilers, and steam engines. In 1857, Siemens' brilliant mind was attracted to achieving greater fuel economy in the manufacture of glass. Up to this time most of the glass-melting furnaces were heated by fuel beds which were a part of the furnace. These beds, of course, really acted as gas producers, and Siemens discovered that by separating the gas producer from the furnace and then adding a regenerator he got better results and greater economy of heat. Immediately there was a demand from the crucible steel makers to apply the Siemens regenerative principle to furnaces used in the melting of crucible steel, because it seemed a simple step to increase the capacity of these furnaces by substituting an open-hearth of larger dimensions for these small crucibles; but local prejudices and superstitions resisted, for a time, such an improvement. Finally, in 1865, Siemens attacked the problem himself, and during the next few years experimented with a furnace capable of melting a 2400-pound charge each 6 hours on a hearth lined with siliceous materials. In 1868 he was able to patent his pig-and-ore process for the making of open-hearth steel. This consisted of melting sand-cast pig iron on a siliceous hearth and, when it was melted, adding clean iron ore to the molten pig iron in amounts large enough to produce a violent evolution of gas, caused by the union of the oxygen of the ore with the carbon of the pig iron, thus rapidly oxidizing the carbon out of the pig iron down to a content low enough to fall within the steel range. After the evolution of gas has subsided, ferromanganese and spiegeleisen are added to the molten metal on the hearth and the steel poured into ingots.

It has been pointed out in Chapter VII how the Bessemer process was discovered and developed independently by two men. A somewhat similar situation now arose in the open-hearth process because priority of this steel-making method was claimed by the Martin brothers of the Sireuil Steel Company of Sireuil, France. It seems that as early as April 17, 1863, a regenerative furnace was installed for Emil Martin and his brother at this plant, and they immediately conceived the idea of melting steel directly on the hearth of this regenerative furnace. After many experiments the Martin brothers discovered that they could melt mixtures of pig iron and steel scrap together on this hearth and obtain various grades of steel from low to high carbon, depending upon the amount of pig iron charged with the steel scrap, but no ore was used in this process. They took out a patent on August 15, 1865, thus gaining priority over Siemens by patenting their pig-scrap process prior to his pig-ore one; the pig-scrap process is, of course, the one commonly used today in the production of open-hearth steel. It seems, therefore, that Siemens should be credited with the design of the regenerative type of open-hearth furnace and the Martin brothers be given the credit for the melting of steel directly on the hearth instead of placing it in crucibles. As a tribute to these three pioneers, the process is known today as the Siemens-Martin process.

247. Developments in the United States. The process was brought to the United States in 1868 when Abraham S. Hewitt purchased the American rights. The first furnace, of about four tons' capacity, was erected at the plant of Cooper-Hewitt and Company at Trenton, New Jersey, but after a year or so of operation was abandoned because it was not a commercial success from the start. In part this failure was due to lack of ability to reach and maintain the proper temperature, in part to the failure of the refractories, and in part to poor operating technique. The second American furnace to make open-hearth steel was built at the plant of the Bay State Iron Works at South Boston, Massachusetts, where, under the supervision, first of R. Cooper and later of S. J. Wellman, satisfactory steel was turned out. So successful were they that for a number of years afterward this company ran day and night in the manufacture of the highest class of ingots for boiler and firebox plates. Although the steel makers of the seventies were able to render their steel fairly malleable by deoxidation with ferromanganese, they could not overcome the difficulties of high phosphorus and sulfur because in this country ores which would yield steel below 0.09 per cent phosphorus were expensive and scarce.

At about this time a young man by the name of Sidney G. Thomas, educated at the Royal School of Mines in London was attracted to this unsolved problem of metallurgy—removing phosphorus by the Bessemer process.* He reasoned that, since phosphorus formed phosphoric acid in the steel process, it would need only a basic slag to absorb, neutralize, and fix it so that it could be removed. A basic slag might

---

* The English blast furnaces of this period produced a pig iron containing 1.5 to 2.3 per cent phosphorus.

also absorb sulfur as calcium sulfide. After many discouraging experiences with a miniature 8-pound converter lined with basic materials, he was able, in the fall of 1879, to present to the British industry a new process wherein he reduced the phosphorus from 1.5 or 2 per cent to 0.08 to 0.10 per cent in a basic-lined Bessemer with a 3-minute after blow. News of this process sped rapidly throughout Europe and America, and other pioneers were not long in applying these fundamental principles of the elimination of phosphorus to the open-hearth process. They soon learned that a similar basic slag was an excellent oxygen carrier for the basic open-hearth process and that both phosphorus and sulfur could be removed from the metal to contents well under 0.05 per cent.

The first basic-lined open-hearth furnace in this country was built in 1880 by Goetz and Wellman at the plant of the Otis Steel Company in Cleveland, Ohio. It was so successful that other steel plants followed in rapid succession, and by 1890 there were forty-seven plants in ten

TABLE 47

TONNAGE OF STEEL INGOTS AND CASTINGS BY DIFFERENT PROCESSES

Year	Bessemer	Open Hearth	Crucible	Electric	Per Cent Capacity
1875	335,000	8,080	35,180		
1880	1,074,000	110,850	64,660		
1890	4,131,536	574,820	79,176	4,248	60.8
1900	7,486,942	3,805,911	112,629	5,446	52.6
1907	13,067,655	12,935,704	146,982	15,764	40.6
1908	6,850,766	8,777,136	71,267	6,868	41.1
1915	9,281,679	26,520,594	127,436	79,452	77.9
1918	10,501,384	38,594,518	128,925	573,096	84.6
1921	4,497,851	17,460,578	8,527	190,897	34.5
1929	7,977,210	54,155,235	7,442	1,065,603	88.5
1932	1,715,925	13,336,210	722	270,044	19.5
1940	3,708,573	61,573,083	1,024	1,700,006	82.1
....	....	....	....	....	....

states producing 574,800 net tons of open-hearth steel, both acid and basic, and yet the largest proportion of this tonnage was tapped from acid-lined furnaces, there being only 15 basic open hearths in the country. All these were of small size (15 to 30 tons per heat) as compared to the modern furnace. Statistics covering the rapid growth of this process are given in Table 47. Suffice it to say that ten years later, in 1901, about 13 million tons of steel were produced by the open-hearth process, and by 1940 this had risen to 60,882,840 net tons.*

248. Reasons for Growth. The unusually rapid growth of the basic open-hearth process is due to certain outstanding metallurgical and chemical advantages, which are:

1. The process makes it possible to remove phosphorus and sulfur and by so doing to open up vast tonnages of ores and large tonnages of steel scrap which ordinarily would not be available for the acid open-hearth process.

2. It permits the use of all types of steel scrap, light and bulky, heavy and dense, dirty and clean, to produce high-grade steel.

3. It is a much more flexible process, permitting furnace operators to vary the proportion of steel scrap to pig iron to suit local and economic conditions. This flexibility of charging makes it a very popular process. For example, the shortage of scrap beginning in 1941 made necessary a change to high percentages of liquid iron (usually not blown) and the use of much greater amounts of iron ore (see Article 293).

4. A wide range of fuels and a greater range of sulfur content in these fuels are permissible.

5. There is a wide range permissible in chemical composition and physical characteristics of the lining materials and of the slag and base metal.

6. The process is a leisurely one, giving the operator ample time in which to make slag and metal adjustments.

7. Steels of a wide range of carbon content can be made, from as low as 0.03 to as high as 1.10 per cent.

8. A wide range of quality may also be obtained by this process from the open or rimmed steel, up to specially finished, deoxidized, grain control, forging, and alloy grades of steel.

9. Great improvements have been made by increasing the size of the furnaces, perfecting heating equipment to meet increased size of charge, greater use of insulation to increase the heat economy of the process, instrumentation for better control of furnace atmospheres and slag, and in the deoxidation process.

CONSTRUCTION OF THE BASIC OPEN-HEARTH FURNACE

249. General. The basic open-hearth furnace is a reverberatory taking the form of a rectangular brick structure whose sides and ends are supported by steel buck stays in the form of channels or slabs and bound together at the top, both longitudinally and crosswise, by stays and tie rods. Although these furnaces are built in sizes ranging from 15 to 350 tons, the standard furnace (100 tons capacity) is approxi-

---

* In 1944 there were over 1,000 open-hearth furnaces in the U. S. In the same year over 30 per cent of the alloy steel made was produced in open-hearth furnaces.

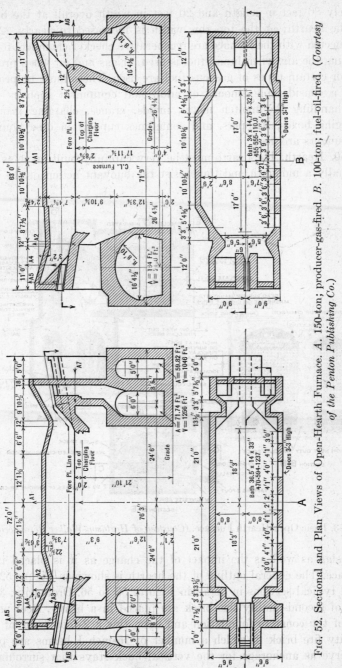

Fig. 52. Sectional and Plan Views of Open-Hearth Furnace. A. 150-ton; producer-gas-fired. B. 100-ton; fuel-oil-fired. (*Courtesy of the Penton Publishing Co.*)

mately 80 feet in length and 20 feet in width overall at the bottom
of the hearth; at the top this width is increased to nearly 22 feet.
Connected with the furnace are regenerative checker chambers for preheating the air, when liquid fuel is used, or gas and air when producer
gas or certain types of gaseous fuel are used. There must be provided
also a considerable amount of additional equipment such as ladles
for handling the molten metal, molds, cranes, charging machines,
charging boxes, strippers, and sometimes cupolas in case liquid recarburizers are used.

250. Hearth. The hearth must be very carefully built up so as to be
virtually a monolith and thus resist the buoyant action of the metal

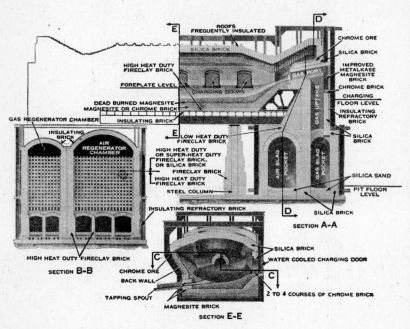

FIG. 53. Basic Open-Hearth Furnace. (*Courtesy of Harbison-Walker Refractories Co.*)

and slag as well as the impact of the charge as it is placed in the
furnace. The general outline of the hearth is shown in Figure 52, and
some typical sections in detail in Figures 53 to 56. Ordinarily, 3 or 4
feet of second-quality fire brick are placed in a heavy, steel pan on
top of the concrete foundation and upon this a 2-foot layer of first-
quality fire brick in which a number of 15-inch I beams are placed
to serve as anchorage for the vertical buck stays that surround the

furnace. On top of the fire brick is laid a 9-inch layer of magnesite brick, and frequently one or both of these layers are set back at intervals to form roughly the basin or cup-shaped hearth. On top of the

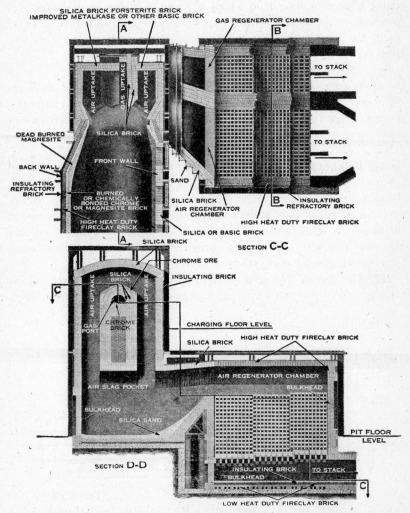

FIG. 54. Basic Open-Hearth Furnace. (*Courtesy of Harbison-Walker Refractories Co.*)

magnesite brick is sintered, about one inch at a time, 12 inches of a mixture of burned magnesite and ground basic slag. Dolomite, which is cheaper, may be substituted for magnesite, but to the extent that it is substituted the bottom must be made thicker. When the operation is completed, the hearth will take the form of a shallow dish, 2 to 3 feet deep, extending up to the level of the charging doors where the silica brick walls begin. The back wall of the furnace is pierced at its exact center with a tapping hole which is about 8 inches in diameter and provided on the outside with a removable cast-iron lip called the steel spout, the function of which is to conduct the molten slag and steel from the furnace into the steel ladle at the time of tapping. The slag hole, if provided, is placed about 15 feet from the tap hole and near the upper edge of the hearth; but in modern furnace practice, with the high percentage of scrap, relatively low phosphorus contents, and consequently less volume of slag, it was formerly seldom necessary to tap out slag during the heat; that is, the heat is finished under the original slag.

251. Bulkheads. These are formed by the ends of the hearth below the ports, although the back walls of the up- and downtakes, opposite the port, are also known as bulkheads. Exposed to much erosion by the hot furnace gases, they have been a source of much trouble. In recent furnaces the solid brickwork has been replaced by a large, hollow, cast-steel box with open ends to provide for air cooling, and in some furnaces water-cooled inserts have been experimented with.

252. The Ports. The number and disposition of the ports, which are the orifices through which air and gas are supplied to the furnace,

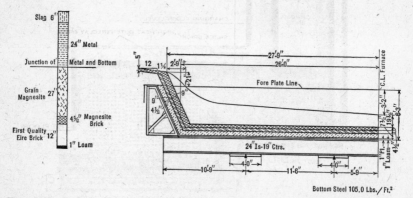

Fig. 55. Basic Open-Hearth Furnace Bottom. (*Courtesy of the Penton Publishing Co.*)

will vary with the kind of fuel used. Up to about 20 years ago open-hearth furnaces were almost universally fired with producer gas,* and

---

* With the present demands for petroleum and coal-tar products, the next few years may witness a return to producer gas firing.

in order to attain the required temperature, as well as to have the necessary flexibility, it was necessary to heat both gas and air (there were two ports at each end of the furnace, one for gas and one for air). Present practice requires that, when using any fuel but natural gas, two ports are built at an angle to the bath so that the flame may

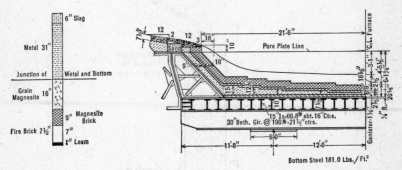

Fig. 56. Basic Open-Hearth Furnace Bottom. (*Courtesy of the Penton Publishing Co.*)

be directed against the bath and away from the roof, the air entering above the fuel stream. Where natural gas is used, at least in new furnaces, there is but one port at each end of the furnace, gas entering on each side of either end of the furnace behind the brick wall which extends across the furnace in front of the well or uptake from the checkers. This wall will be built of either magnesite brick or chrome brick. When fuel oil or coal tar are used as sources of heat (very common practice today), these fuels, usually heated, are sprayed through a nozzle located at about the center of the end of the furnace.

253. Walls. These are built nearly universally of silica brick, about 14 inches thick, begun on the course of chrome brick, placed on top of the magnesite brick that surrounds the upper edge or brim of the hearth, and extending to a distance of about 8 feet above the charging floor level. The back wall is built up solid except for the tapping hole and slag hole, but the front wall is broken by a series, usually five, of arched doorways for charging. The sills of these openings are so placed that they are about 3 inches above the slag line,* and each opening is provided with a water-cooled cast-steel frame and a water-cooled, fire-brick-lined cast-iron or steel door that is lifted vertically by power. A wicket, or keyhole, is placed on the center line near the bottom of each door through which the melter may observe conditions in the

* The capacity of a furnace can be increased considerably by building across this a magnesite dam about 6 inches high.

furnace and make the required changes in fuel, air, slag, or metal. The construction of a typical front wall is shown in Figure 57.

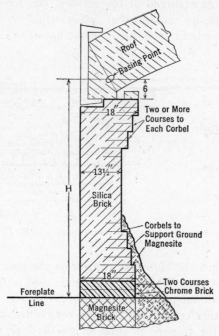

Fig. 57. Basic Open-Hearth Front Wall (section). (*Courtesy of the Penton Publishing Co.*)

254. Roofs. The roof of a conventional open hearth consists of a sprung arch and special brick and structural members (skew backs) for taking the thrust of the arch. It is built, independent of the walls, of silica brick, 13 to 18 inches thick. Sometimes it is arched longitudinally as well as transversely. Rib brick are used near the front and back walls to increase the life and permit a better skew-back brick design by allowing the roof brick to bear in their full area. Longitudinally every fourth ring of brick is ribbed about $2\frac{1}{2}$ to 6 inches to strengthen the roof. This extra depth extends above the roof, leaving the inner or hot face as a smooth surface. As the roof decreases through use the entire structure tends to weaken, but these ribs exercise a considerable strengthening effect.

The skew-back brick, usually of silica, aids first to insulate the metal skew back and second to form a properly angled surface to receive the roof arc ends, and to assure an equitable distribution of roof stresses. The skew back, of either cast or rolled steel, supports the skew-back brick against the horizontal thrust of the roof. Sometimes the skew back at the back of the furnace is water-cooled.

255. Up- and Downtakes. These are vertical flues which connect the air and fuel ports with the slag pockets and with other flues leading to respective checker chambers. The arrangement of these up- and downtakes will vary with the kind of fuel being employed. In producer-gas-fired furnaces there is a pair of up- and downtakes for air at each end of the furnace, the two in each pair being at opposite sides of the furnace. The up- and downtakes for the gas rise with their centers coincident with the center line of the furnace, usually between the air flues. If coke-oven or natural gas is employed, there need be only one uptake for air at each end of the furnace; each uptake is usually about $6\frac{1}{2}$ feet in diameter and is, therefore, called the "well."

256. Slag Pockets. These are chambers located at the bottom of the up- and downtakes serving as flues to conduct the gases to and from the checkers as well as to retain as much as possible of the dust or solid matter from the charge that is carried over with the products of combustion, thus preventing most of this material from reaching the checkers, slagging the brick, and obstructing the openings. In the conventional 100-ton furnace the slag pockets are about 3.5 feet wide and 8 feet high, large enough to last for an entire run of the furnace. The walls are built up of first-quality fire brick lined on the inside with silica. One end of each pocket merges into a short fanlike flue called a neck or "fantail" which leads to the top of the regenerator chambers.

257. Regenerators. The regenerators, or checker work, for preheating the gas or air are built out in front of the furnace and under the charging floor itself. Their size and disposition will depend upon the kind of fuel being used. If the fuel is producer gas the total space occupied by the checkers in all four chambers will be 120 to 150 cubic feet per ton of furnace capacity, the gas chamber always being smaller than the air chamber because of the larger volume of air necessary to burn this gas. For a 100-ton furnace the volume of the checkers in the air-chamber will usually be 3500 to 3600 cubic feet and the gas chamber between 2500 and 2600 cubic feet. As indicated in Figure 58, the walls of both chambers are usually built of common brick on the outside and first-quality fire brick on the inside, strongly reinforced by channel buck-stays and tie-rods. The base floor is usually of concrete covered with heavy pitch for waterproofing, and on this, another layer of concrete, followed by a layer of common brick and finally one of first-quality fire brick. On this floor are laid fire-brick rider walls which divide the gas and air chambers longitudinally into three or four flues with a height of about 4 feet, and these spaces are spanned by fire-brick tile about 3 inches by 12 inches by 31 inches. On these tiles the checker work of the regenerator, formed of the best quality fire brick, is begun and continued to within 3.5 feet of the top of the gas chamber. The common size for checker brick is 10.5 inches by 4.5 inches by 3 inches, laid to give checker openings 7.5 inches square.

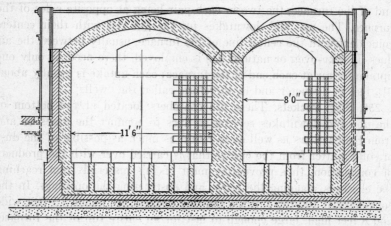

FIG. 58. Checker Chamber (cross section). (*Courtesy of Carnegie-Illinois Steel Corp.*)

When natural gas, coke-oven gas, or liquid fuel is used, the disposition is slightly different. Many old furnaces have been changed over to these fuels, in which case the gas chamber, in addition to the regular air chamber, is utilized for preheating the air. Actually, it has been found that when two checkers at each end of the furnace are thus employed, better results are obtained than when only one large chamber is used. In furnaces where only one large checker chamber has been provided, it is found that the air and stack gases, instead of flowing equally through all parts of the chamber, tend to take a direct course from inlet to outlet, reducing considerably the efficiency of the heat transfer.

258. Flues and Valves. The openings for the ingress and egress of gases from the checker work, at the bottom of the chamber, take the form of small flues formed by the rider walls, opening into a large one which leads to the stack flue, when liquid fuel is used, or to a three-way valve when gaseous fuel must be heated. This valve must be constructed to withstand rather high temperatures, as well as sudden

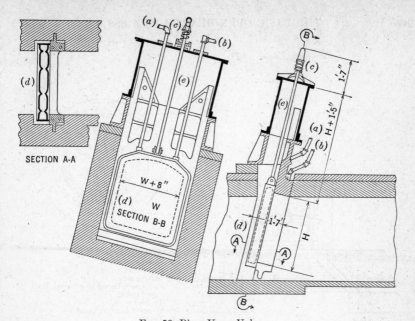

SECTION A-A

FIG. 59. Blaw-Knox Valve.

(a) Outlet   (c) Spring   (e) Valve stem
(b) Inlet   (d) Valve

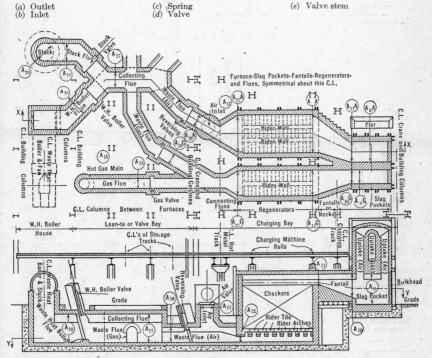

FIG. 60. Auxiliary System of Open-Hearth Furnace (producer-gas-fired). (*Courtesy of the Penton Publishing Co.*)

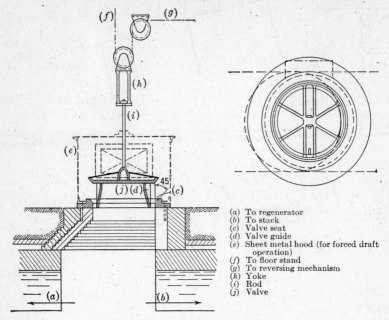

(a) To regenerator
(b) To stack
(c) Valve seat
(d) Valve guide
(e) Sheet metal hood (for forced draft
       operation)
(f) To floor stand
(g) To reversing mechanism
(h) Yoke
(i) Rod
(j) Valve

FIG. 61. Air Inlet Valve.

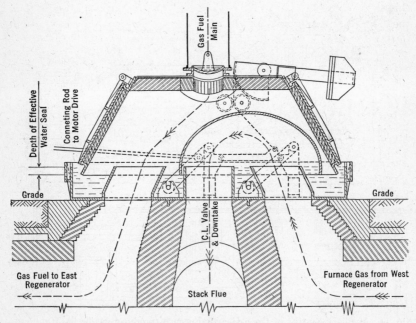

FIG. 62. Wellman Valve. (*Courtesy of the Penton Publishing Co.*)

changes, and still form a perfect seal from the stack, to avoid waste of fuel. Another branch of this valve leads to the stack and a third to the gas main. These valves (shown in Figures 59 to 62), together with the dampers and mushroom valves in the flues from the air chamber, supply the means by which reversals of the flame are made. The Blaw-Knox valve unit (see Figure 59) consists of a heavy-type, water-cooled, cast-iron valve seat with the pipes cast integral with the casting; pressed and welded steel-plate water-cooled valve damper (valve and seat being finished on contacting faces to insure gas tightness); cast-iron hood base; steel-plate hood; lifting stem assembly, including shock springs and sealing washers; inlet and outlet water connections extending from the top of the valve damper through the cover plate of the hood. All valves and dampers are controlled from the charging floor and means provided so that the reversal of the air and gas currents may take place simultaneously.

259. Stack. Except in the newer forms of controlled-draft systems, the stack is usually 5 feet inside diameter with a height of 140 to 160 feet above the charging door and lined with first-quality fire brick. The outside shell is made of boiler plate resting on a heavy concrete foundation, on the same level as the floor of the checker chambers. At this level, openings are provided for connections with the flues from the gas and air chambers. For controlling the draft, a damper is placed in the flue at its entrance to the stack.

260. Suspended Roofs. Reference has already been made to the fundamental weakness of an open-hearth roof made of silica brick.

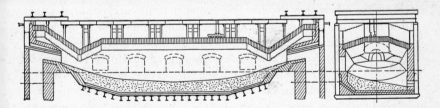

Fig. 63. Open-Hearth Suspended Roof. (*Courtesy of Metals and Alloys.*)

Not only is such material fundamentally weak at the elevated temperatures employed, but with the sprung-arch type of roof a failure in one spot endangers the whole roof structure. With a view to overcoming this serious defect of a sprung-arch roof, the suspended type shown in Figure 63, based on experience with copper matting furnaces, is meeting with increasing favor. The buck-stays or other suitable supports carry the entire load of the suspended roof; longitudinal members are joined to the top of the vertical supports, and from them a series of cross members span the furnace on 4-foot centers. The roof brick are hung from these cross members, in small groups, by means of suspension rod castings. The roof has a thickness of about 15 inches, and the contour can be made practically the same as that of the sprung-arch type without the use of specially shaped brick because the sloping portions can be formed by the use of rods of various lengths. A steel plate, 1/32 inch thick, is provided in every joint between the roof bricks (in case magnesite brick is employed). For ease in assembling, one-half the brick are provided with a steel plate covering each of its four principal faces; when assembled they can be placed so that each joint has a single thickness of metal. While this facilitates greatly the erection of the roof, the use of steel plates is not necessary, and ordinary unplated brick can be used throughout. The arrangement for supporting the brick is very flexible; skew backs are eliminated and no side thrust is necessary to maintain the arch in position. The roof is free from the shifting, compressive forces which are present in a sprung arch, for the bricks are really hung like a pendulum and are free to move, without harm, when the refractory expands and contracts. Proper expansion joints, about ¾ inch wide, are provided every 3 feet in both directions. Furthermore, a liberal joint is allowed around the periphery of the roof where it laps into the front, back, and end walls.

With these ample provisions there is no possibility of strain being set up on the brick because of thermal expansion or the swelling of the steel plates when they oxidize. No wooden forms are required either in the initial installations or in making replacements such as are necessary in erecting a conventional roof. The steel cross members that support the roof form a convenient staging or platform for periodic inspection and for repairs, and when the latter become necessary, small units of brick can be removed through the top of the arch and replaced with new ones. These repairs can be confined to the immediate area that requires replacement with no danger of the adjacent brick falling into the furnace. This is an important feature of the suspended roof as it permits more continuous operation and shortens the time lost for roof repairs.

261. The Completely Basic Furnace. The performance of basic brick in roof shoulders has suggested the elimination of silica brick from the remaining sections of the roof so that a completely basic open-hearth furnace would result. As a matter of fact a complete sprung-

roof section using magnesite brick instead of silica was installed in a
furnace several years ago, but the life obtained was less than that for
silica. Meanwhile, experience in the use of suspended basic arches in
copper reverberatory smelting furnaces has been very satisfactory.
Much work has been done in England, particularly with the chrome-
magnesite refractories, which have had considerable success without
the suspended-roof modifications. The first installations had relatively
short lives, but recently a life of 700 heats has become relatively common while one furnace has been in operation for 99 weeks (94 in production), and when last reported it was still in operation after making
1335 casts. True, these English furnaces are much smaller than ours
(this furnace has averaged 14.2 casts, 792 tons per week, and in its
best week did 1094 tons or 18 casts), but there seems to be no reason
why this technique could not be adapted to our larger furnaces. The
original type of vertical back wall (see Article 253), similar to and
generally symmetrical with the front wall, is frequently referred to as
"straight" in that the wall was practically vertical.

262. Sloping Back Wall. One of the great difficulties experienced
with the back wall of the basic open-hearth furnace has been that of

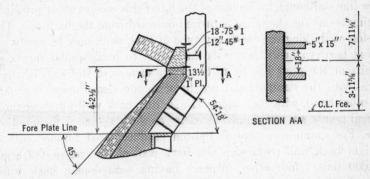

FIG. 64. Open-Hearth Sloping Back Wall. (*Courtesy of the Penton Publishing Co.*)

protecting or renewing the lower portion of it with ground magnesite
or dolomite. In 1925 S. Naismith devised and patented (U. S. Patent
1,563,038) the full sloping back walls, hereinafter referred to as
"sloping," as distinguished from the straight or semi-sloping walls.
This modification of the open-hearth construction, shown in Figure 64,
consists of a wall sloping outwardly from the bottom to top and consisting of a corbeled refractory wall upon which ground magnesite or
dolomite will lie when thrown thereon. Thus, the inner finished surface of this type of back wall is angled to that of the repose of the

material used, the actual angle being of the order of 45 to 50 degrees from the horizontal. This modification has greatly increased the life of the wall itself, the skew-back brick, and the rear portion of the roof, which, when employed with a straight-wall construction, receives severe punishment and requires frequent renewal. Its use also permits the maintenance of a much wider hearth than is possible with the conventional straight type.

This sloping back wall has proved of such value that many older furnaces have been rebuilt or modified to include it; however, in the rebuilding of these or in the addition of new furnaces to existing plants, it has not always been possible to incorporate the full sloping back wall on account of building, crane, or other physical limitations. Accordingly, there has come into use a modified form of sloping back wall known as "semi-sloping," in which the back wall is angled outward from the foreplate line as far as possible and is continued from the top of the angle portion as a vertical wall to the line of the skew-back brick.

In any back wall there are two areas that are subject to severe and continuous erosion effects from heat or bath—the slag line and the roof skew line—although in the case of the latter this erosive effect probably diminishes as the skew line is carried outward from the bath line. The erosion at the slag line, with any type of back wall, may be easily repaired between heats, but it is impossible to make replacements or repairs at the skew line or to the plain surface of the wall between them, with the straight, and usually with the semi-sloping type. On the other hand, with the sloping (Naismith) back wall all these three critical points are maintained as easily as the slag line is in the other type. For example, a typical 100-ton producer-fired furnace with a straight back wall required a new back wall at the end of 182 heats (19,000 tons); four other furnaces having semi-sloping back walls have reached 152 heats (18,000 tons); and another group of furnaces, tar-fired, 169 heats (20,000 tons). In contrast to this, properly designed, installed, and maintained sloping back walls have lasted as long as 2000 heats; and as the skew area may be maintained in a condition to protect the roof skews at all times, the roof life also is notably increased.

263. Flow Diagrams in Critical Areas. Flow diagrams, such as those shown in Figure 65, are commonly used nowadays because the weakness of certain points, such as those of excessive velocity or "bottlenecks" which will develop abnormal upkeep and limit operating rate, stand out clearly in the diagram. Having been located, these shortcomings may be reduced or remedied. When a furnace develops points of unusual upkeep, when the operating time of heat appears excessive, when a furnace must be forced in order to accomplish a reasonable time of heat, or when fuel rates are unduly high, a flow diagram presents a picture of furnace operation in such a manner as to permit a correct diagnosis, to locate the trouble and its cause, and in addition

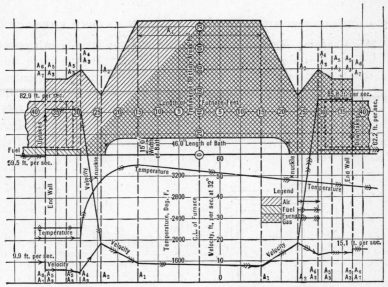

Fig. 65. Open-Hearth Flow Diagram. (*Courtesy of the Penton Publishing Co.*)

to direct the method of its abatement, if under the direction of a competent operator.

264. Critical Areas. In the proper design of a furnace much attention must be given to the development of several cross-sectional areas of great importance to operation because they are among the principal factors that later will have a great bearing on the success or quality of this operation. It is a fact that the most carefully designed refractory and furnace structure cannot overcome the handicap of poorly conceived and developed controlling areas. Such critical areas are, for example: (1) the free transverse area of the furnace hearth above the foreplate line at the furnace center line, (2) in gas-fired furnaces the area of the gas port or nozzle at its least dimension, (3) the free vertical transverse area immediately over the downtake, (4) the combined horizontal cross-sectional area of the air uptake, and (5) the combined minimum area of the ducts through which the furnace gases pass in

transit from the hearth to the slag pocket. It is obvious that the speed
of the flow of the gases across the hearth, the transfer of heat to the
bath, and the direction of the flow of the gases are in a major degree
regulated by the contour development of the various cross sections and
their areas. Appropriate cross sections are, therefore, of the utmost
importance in the design and economical operation of open-hearth
furnaces.

ACCESSORY EQUIPMENT FOR THE OPEN-HEARTH FURNACE

265 Charging Machines. In the early days of open-hearth operation the furnaces were charged entirely by hand. Iron or other solid
materials in a small box were balanced on one end of a long iron rod,
and at the other end were eight to ten men who manipulated this
contrivance to place a solid charge in the furnace. Even with the small
furnaces then used, charging sometimes occupied 4 hours, involving
not only this considerable loss in time but also the cooling off of the
furnaces from the long-opened doors; and the men were unable to

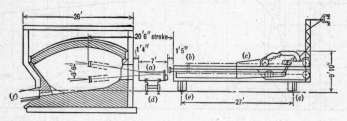

FIG. 66. Charging Machine (low type).

(a) Charging box	(c) Carriage	(e) Rails for charging machine
(b) Charging arm	(d) Rails for charging boxes	(f) Tapping hole

handle very heavy pieces. As a matter of fact, these difficulties, along
with labor troubles incident to working the men on hot floors in sum-
mer weather, were a strong deterrent against the expansion of the steel
industry at a time when railway and industrial growth was making
strong demands on steel production. It is estimated that the first four
charging machines installed at the Homestead Steel Works resulted
in the saving of over $4,000,000 in operating costs in 22 years of service.

Three different types of open-hearth charging machines—the high-
type floor, the low-type floor, and the crane type—have been designed
and used, but the one most generally employed at the present time
is the low-type. It consists of two main parts, as shown in Figure
66. First, there is the heavy-bottom truck traveling on a very wide
gage track laid in front of the open-hearth furnaces; second, there

is the charging carriage which travels on a track laid on the frame of the first truck and moving at right angles to it; third, on this carriage is mounted a lever or long arm, known as the charging bar, which extends toward and into the furnace. This bar is hollow, to provide space and bearings for the locking bar about which it can be made to revolve, and is suitably formed on the end to fit into the socket of the charging box. By this arrangement the charging box can be given eight primary motions, or any number of resultants of these motions, permitting very flexible operation in the charging of the furnace.

In charging a furnace a long line of charging boxes, made of cast-steel or boiler plate, are lined up, on trucks, in front of the furnace. One end of the box is provided with a socket opening so that the key section on the end of the charging machine arm, a T-sction, may be inserted readily into it and held in place by a heavy pin. These boxes have a capacity of about 16 cubic feet, and into them all solid materials of the furnace charge are placed. When the time comes to charge the furnace, the truck of the charging machine is moved up so that the charging bar is directly opposite the first charging box to be emptied, and the carriage is moved forward to bring into position the end of the charging bar, which is then dropped into the socket on the end of the charging box and locked in position by advancing the locking bar until its front end projects into a hole provided for this purpose. Next, by means of the broad gage trucks, the whole machine moves the entire train of boxes along the tracks until the box engaged is directly opposite the desired furnace door. The charging box is then raised by the bar, and by a forward movement of the carriage the box is passed into the furnace, rotated by the charging bar, turned upside down, and its contents deposited on the hearth. By reversing these motions, the box is then placed upon the buggy again. An expert charger will pick up and empty a box in less than a minute; and since the capacity of the box is more than a ton for the lightest materials of the charge, it is possible to charge large furnaces in less than an hour.

266. Steel Ladles. These are made of heavy boiler plate, formerly riveted but now of welded construction, lined with two courses of fire-clay "ladle" brick, each about 2½ inches thick. The cross section is circular, the general shape somewhat thimblelike, and of a capacity dependent on the amount of steel to be handled in each heat. Standard ladles must be of such a size as to contain 125 tons of metal and still leave space for about a foot of slag on top. Attached to the shell are heavy trunnions by means of which it may be lifted by the crane.

There is an opening (about 2 inches in diameter) provided at the bottom of the ladle, closed by a refractory stopper, so that the flow of metal into the ingot mold can be controlled at will. The stopper is made of clay-bonded graphite, mounted on a rod protected by a fire-clay sleeve brick which reaches to the top of the ladle. Both stopper and nozzle must usually be replaced after each heat; and great care must be exercised in placing these, for a bad fit results' in a "running stopper" which may cause a great loss of metal.

267. The Stripper. The stripper is a device whereby the standard molds can be pulled or stripped from the ingots after the metal has cooled sufficiently to form a solid shell on the outside. Such a stripper takes the form of a strong overhead crane from which is suspended a vertical arm provided with two jaws that fit over lugs cast on either side, and near the top, of the mold. Operating between the jaws is a ram or punch capable of exerting considerable pressure on the top of the ingot, while it is being stripped, sufficient to balance the pull of the jaws. In the operation of stripping, the jaws engage the lugs and exert a powerful pull upward while the ram holds the ingot on the stool until the mold is loosened, when it can be raised high enough to clear the ingot and be placed upon an empty car standing near ready to receive it. When the heat is stripped, these ingots are taken to soaking pits and brought back to the proper temperature for the rolling operation, unless they are to be shipped as ingots, in which case they are allowed to cool slowly.

268. Cupolas. In many plants, especially those manufacturing medium-carbon, high-carbon, or high-manganese steels, cupolas are employed for melting the large amounts of deoxidizers and recarburizers used. These cupolas are similar in construction to those used in the gray-iron foundries and may be up to 8 feet in diameter by 20 feet in height. Sometimes, to secure even greater uniformity and provide an ever-ready supply of molten recarburizer, the cupolas attached to modern plants are provided with a small mixer.

269. Ingot Mold Cars. The conventional ingot mold car formerly had four wheels, two axles with simple journal boxes and brass bearings, four springs, and a cast-steel car body covering the wheel and axle assemblies. The ingot car tracks in most plants have many short curves, are narrow gage, and without proper road bed; consequently, derailment is a common occurrence. Another source of trouble is the dropping of ingots on the car or extra loading from the stripper itself. The new type of ingot mold car is made with a rolled-steel top, welded construction, especially heavy, and with limiting springs in the assembly, preventing excessive strain. The truck is arranged to give the car a low center of gravity, and, to prevent derailment, it is of the compensating type that allows the wheels the necessary free vertical movement without distorting the frames.

BASIC OPEN-HEARTH REFRACTORIES

270. General. In fifty years of commercial steel production by the basic open-hearth process the design and operation of the furnaces

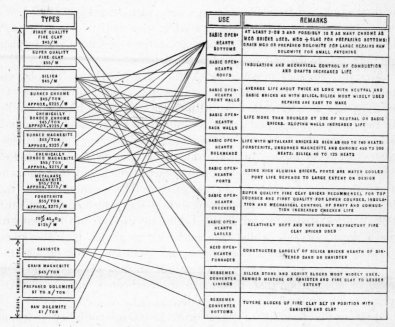

FIG. 67. Open-Hearth Refractories. (*Courtesy of the American Institute of Metallurgical Engineers.*)

have shown continuous improvement. The size of the charge has been increased from 5 to over 300 tons and the handling of materials to and from the furnace almost completely mechanized. Reference to Article 286 will reveal the fact that various types of fuels have been introduced in order to obtain improved combustion control, faster melting, and better fuel economy. Furthermore, the metallurgy of the refining operation has been brought under strict supervision, using the fundamentals of modern physical chemistry. A discussion of the performance and life of open-hearth furnaces is best introduced by reference to

.Figure 67, which shows the most important types of refractories going into various parts of the furnace, together with their cost and certain remarks as to their use. It has been estimated that one-half of the refractory makers' market comes from the iron and steel industry, and something like one-third of all refractory brick used finds its way into the construction of open-hearth furnaces.

271. Silica Brick. It should be recalled that the original open-hearth furnaces were built entirely of siliceous material. This choice was made because silica bricks were relatively inexpensive and capable of withstanding somewhat basic conditions with surprisingly good results; basic bricks, at first not available, were until a few years ago expensive and incapable of proper applications because of their poor thermal resistance and other physical defects.

The shortcomings of silica brick for open-hearth use can be attributed chiefly to the relatively low melting point of silica (1710° C. or 3110° F.) as well as the ease with which it is fluxed by basic oxides in the furnace charge and gases. An important constituent of the dust in a furnace atmosphere is "fume," composed of very fine particles, almost colloidal in size, of iron oxide. This fume probably originates from the bases given off by the molten metal which condense to form small droplets of oxides in the gas stream. These combine with the silica of the roof and side walls to form a slag which soaks into the porous brick structure and finally begins to drip off into the bath or wash down the side walls. One authority estimates that the silica brick in a roof are worn away, in normal operation, a few hundredths of an inch per heat or perhaps a tenth of an inch per day; and it is common observation that, if furnaces are overheated, "dripping" takes place at a very much accelerated rate.

Another shortcoming of silica brick is its susceptibility to rapid thermal change. The raw material consists essentially of a quartzite plus a small amount of bonding material. The aim in firing is to produce a brick consisting essentially of cristobalite or of cristobalite plus tridymite. The density of quartz at room temperature is 2.65, whereas that of cristobalite is 2.32 and tridymite 2.26. In firing silica bricks the expansion may be as much as one inch per foot; consequently, one can readily see what would happen to an open-hearth roof if the quartzite were not properly inverted in the firing operation before the brick came to the steel plant.

The question naturally arises why silica brick last as long as they do when operated at temperatures so much higher than the melting point of mixtures of iron oxide and silica. The answer is found partly in the large percentages of iron oxide which can be absorbed by silica without appreciably decreasing its melting point, and partly in the fact that much of the iron oxide present may be there as magnetic iron oxide because the atmosphere next to the roof where such fluxing would go on is essentially oxidizing, and this oxide does not react with silica.

272. Grain Magnesite. The use of dead-burned magnesite in basic open-hearth furnace bottoms dates back to late in the nineteenth century when brunnerite, a natural magnesium carbonate rock containing desirable amounts of iron carbonate, was found in the province of Styria (Austria). Prior to that, dolomite had been used as a bottom-making material, but magnesite is much more refractory and stands the most severe working conditions better. Ordinarily, the burning-in of the bottom is expedited by mixing with the burned magnesite a certain amount of basic open-hearth slag, usually up to 20 per cent by weight. The effect of the slag is to cause the highly refractory magnesite grains to sinter together into a well-bonded mass under the high temperature of the burning-in operation. This results in a furnace bottom high in magnesia and low in lime, and therefore less subject to fluxing and loss of lime from the bottom by the slag-forming elements present in the furnace charge. Typical analyses of grain magnesite are:

	Per Cent					
	SiO_2	Fe_2O_3	Al_2O_3	CaO	MgO	MnO
Austrian	2.42	6.80	0.35	2.15	88.25	
Chewelah (Wash.)	6.16	4.45	2.02	5.11	82.07	
Synthetic	1.88	7.14		54.22	34.58	0.74
		(FeO)				

The use of grain of lower magnesia and higher lime content to cut down the time for burning-in is not recommended. There are, however, certain furnace-operating conditions, notably the necessity of a quick patching repair, when the use of such high-lime materials is warranted. The result of this has been the appearance on the market of a large number of synthetic refractories made up of magnesite and various proportions of silica, iron oxide, alumina, and lime to give the desired properties. The analysis of one such synthetic material is given in the last column.

273. Basic Brick. With all its shortcomings, silica brick continues to be widely used in the basic open-hearth furnaces because, up to date, magnesite bricks, although they have a very much higher melting point (300° C. or more in excess of silica brick), have not been by any means the answer to the steel maker's prayer. Such bricks have spalled very badly when used in place of silica brick, and furthermore they lack sufficient strength at high temperatures. As a result of extensive research, very much improved basic brick have been produced to overcome at least some of these difficulties. Such research has been aimed at better grain sizing of the mixtures, better binding agents, and the use of unburned brick.

274. Bottom Refractories. Up to about ten years ago magnesite brick was used almost exclusively in building up new bottoms, but today, because of the high cost of magnesite, it is being replaced by chrome brick. It is still general practice to use magnesite brick around tap holes, and a few companies still use all-magnesite bottoms. Grain chrome is often placed on the chrome brick and a thinner grain-magnesite hearth used. Some of the more recent furnaces employ insulation between the metal shell and fire-clay bricks. Deep holes in the hearth are ordinarily packed with dead burned grain magnesite or prepared refractory dolomite (see Article 298), and smaller holes with raw or calcined dolomite. The hearth must withstand shock during charging, be dense enough to prevent soaking up of the slag, resistant to attack by the slag, and thoroughly sintered to avoid formation of holes by the loosening of part of the bottom material.

The Crespi method, involving the use of powdered dolomite, is attracting attention. This material, of proper composition and controlled particle size, may be fused into a homogeneous bottom without the use of tar or other fluxing agent. It is said to have an insulating value nearly three times that of sintered magnesite and a high resistance to slag penetration.

275. Roofs. Open-hearth roofs must withstand not only high temperatures, approaching 1680° C. and the chemical attack of fumes and corrosive gases laden with solid particles but also sudden temperature changes. They must be able to resist considerable pressure in the sprung-arch type of roof without softening, crushing, or distorting. On the whole, silica brick is the only satisfactory refractory, and when failure occurs it is usually due to attack by iron oxide rising from the bath. Formerly, many roofs were burned out by careless melters who allowed the flame to attack, thermally, the roof; but mechanical control of combustion and flame reversals, by balanced draft, has markedly lengthened the life of the roofs. Insulation is now generally adopted, and this has reduced heat loss through the roof so that equivalent heat transfer in the bath can be maintained with less fuel consumption or with lower flame temperatures. The maintenance of a more uniform temperature throughout the brick also tends to decrease its tendency to spall.

276. Insulation of Open-Hearth Furnaces. Because of the large amount of heat lost through the inclosing brickwork of open-hearth furnaces (see Table 48), their insulation has been suggested by tech-

TABLE 48

HEAT BALANCE OF A BASIC OPEN-HEARTH FURNACE

	Millions B.t.u.
Calorific and sensible heat in fuel	397.456
Sensible heat in air for combustion	90.885
Heat added by chemical reactions	58.384
Infiltrated air:	
(a) In checkers	.195
(b) Flues	.744
Total	547.664

	Millions B.t.u.	Per Cent Based on Total Heat	Per Cent Based on Heat in Fuel Only
Heat absorbed by steel	110.673	20.21	27.84
Heat absorbed by chemical reactions	14.190	2.59	3.57
Heat absorbed by combustion of H_2 (latent)	34.647	6.33	8.72
Heat absorbed by cooling water	19.660	3.59	4.95
Heat radiated from bath and port ends	81.853	14.95	20.59
Heat absorbed by air in checkers	90.008	16.43	22.65
Heat radiated from checkers	15.353	2.80	3.86
Heat radiated from flues	10.979	2.00	2.76
Heat in waste gases in stack	170.301	31.10	42.85
Total	547.664	100.00	137.79

nical writers for a number of years; but these same writers have expressed the opinion that the prevailing methods of open-hearth temperature control were not accurate enough to permit this insulation. While the economies brought about by such insulation are apparent, the ranges of temperature to which the refractory brick will be exposed are also obvious; and, if insulation is applied without recognizing the fact that the silica brick refractories are operating at a temperature close to their melting point, the life of the furnace may be materially shortened instead of being increased.

Two factors have been instrumental in bringing about a wider use of insulation during the past ten years, with the result that at the present time large basic open-hearth furnaces are almost universally insulated. The first has to do with a search for lower operating costs.

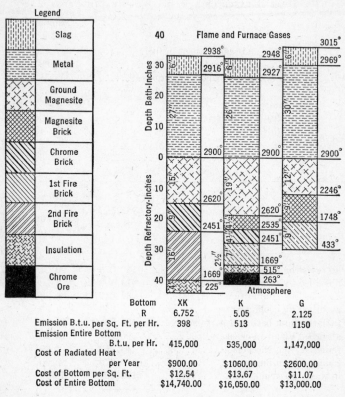

Bottom	XK	K	G
R	6.752	5.05	2.125
Emission B.t.u. per Sq. Ft. per Hr.	398	513	1150
Emission Entire Bottom B.t.u. per Hr.	415,000	535,000	1,147,000
Cost of Radiated Heat per Year	$900.00	$1060.00	$2600.00
Cost of Bottom per Sq. Ft.	$12.54	$13.67	$11.07
Cost of Entire Bottom	$14,740.00	$16,050.00	$13,000.00

Fig. 68. Insulated vs. Uninsulated Bottom. (*Courtesy of the Penton Publishing Co.*)

Heating expense has always been one of the largest single items in open-hearth costs; and, with this item becoming more important with the irregular rates of operation prevailing during the depression years, operators began to give serious attention to the heat thus lost and to seek means for saving this large amount of money. The second factor at work has been the development of new materials and new methods of insulation. The insulation of the furnace, therefore, will result in:

1. Maintenance of the same temperature with less fuel input per unit of time, or

2. Maintenance of higher temperatures with the same fuel input per unit of time.

Until some economical refractory is developed whose safe working temperature is greater than that of silica brick, the inner brick surface temperature cannot exceed 2950° F., and consequently the prob-

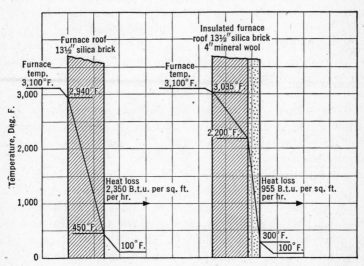

FIG. 69. Effect of Insulation on Roof. (*Courtesy of the Penton Publishing Co.*)

lems involved in the insulation of an open-hearth furnace above the floor line are those connected with Item 1. The effect of insulation is shown graphically in Figures 68 and 69.

277. Character of Roof Brick Deterioration. Examination of silica brick taken from a conventional roof shows four distinct zones. The inner zone is $\frac{1}{4}$ to $\frac{5}{8}$ inch in depth, and from this the calcium-aluminum silicates of the bond have been driven. It is mostly finely divided tridymite interspersed in the fused mass of the brick, highly glazed, and the most refractory part of the brick. The second zone, usually $\frac{3}{4}$ to $1\frac{1}{4}$ inch in depth, is practically all cristobalite and contains the iron oxide taken into the brick by capillary attraction and some tridymite. The iron is in the form of the magnetic oxide, in which condition it is stable and does not react with silica even at the high temperatures prevailing. The fusion point of this zone is 10-20° C. lower than zone 1. The third zone, usually $\frac{1}{2}$ to $1\frac{1}{2}$ inches in depth contains the calcium-aluminum silicates driven back from zone 1 and is the weakest and least refractory portion of the brick. Its fusion point is 50 to 60° C. lower than zone 1. The fourth zone constitutes the remainder of the brick, out to its outer surface, and is substantially the same as that produced in the original burning operation.

Examination of a brick taken from the roof of an insulated furnace shows only three zones and infrequently a fourth. The first zone, in structure, is the same as the first zone of the uninsulated brick but three to four times as deep. Behind this zone, the boundary of which is distinct, the second and third zones and the fourth, if it actually exists, are much less definitely outlined. The iron oxide penetrates all the way to the cool end of the brick. The third zone is dispersed gradually to the end of the brick, and the definitely weak, rather narrow, area which is formed in the uninsulated brick does not exist. These changes, at the high average temperature in the brick, constitute the most dangerous condition arising from insulation. The changes are caused by the penetration of high temperatures deep within the brick.

When insulation is applied to the outside surface of a silica wall or roof, the outer temperature rises to an amount dependent on the quantity and quality of the insulating materials. Usually the cool end of the brick rises to a temperature well above the critical expansion temperature, which is 130 to 300° C., at which critical temperature this expansion rate is so rapid as to result in the pronounced spalling tendency of silica brick. On uninsulated roofs, particularly those over 15 inches, there is a likelihood that some portions of the brick have passed through the critical temperature many times during the furnace campaign owing to shutdowns for patching, etc., and that the brick life is appreciably shortened by these temperature changes. In an insulated wall or roof, once up to temperature, it is unlikely that any part of the brick approaches the critical temperature except for shutdowns extending beyond six or seven days. During such shutdowns the furnace may be kept tightly sealed and shut off from the stacks. Laboratory tests show that silica brick should not be heated through this critical range faster than 70° C. per hour; where the heating of any portion of the brick is accomplished at a faster rate, the brick will crack. In order to bring all portions of an uninsulated 12-inch roof brick above 300° C., the hot face must be heated to a temperature of 1620° C. To accomplish this at a uniform heating rate of 70° C. per hour will require 18 hours. For an uninsulated 18-inch roof, the hot face will have to reach 1730° C., requiring 20 hours. It is evident that the outer portion of 18-inch brick does not entirely pass through the critical range until after the brick length is decreased by wear.

278. Insulating Materials. There are a number of these now on the market suitable for application to open-hearth furnaces. In selecting a material, the maximum temperature reached by the surface of the brick in contact with the insulation must be known and the insulation must be able to withstand this temperature without deterioration and without chemical or fluxing action with the brick. Its permeability must be taken into consideration as prevention of air infiltration is of extreme importance in fuel economy; and, if the insulation is not practically airtight, it must be made so by the application of some sealing medium. The amount of insulation to be applied must be based on the minimum thickness the brick finally reaches at the end of the furnace campaign as well as the physical properties of the insulating material.

279. Results of Insulation. The average open-hearth furnace of 100-ton capacity has approximately 2500 square feet of exposed surface above the floor line and 5700 square feet below the floor line and above ground level that can be insulated. Although additional surfaces are available for insulation below ground level, it is in the range of lowest temperatures, and the cost of application here would not ordinarily be justified. The total amount of heat radiated from these surfaces at temperatures that prevail during the making of a heat is approximately 9 million B.t.u. per hour. By insulation this loss can be reduced to 4 million B.t.u., often 8 to 10 per cent of the fuel input. Of this saving nearly 60 per cent is above the floor line.

Another advantage of roof insulation has to do with the longer life thus attained. This is well illustrated by a roof which was brought to the attention of the author. Patching of this roof commenced at 275 to 300 heats and extended 1 to 4 feet out from the skew backs, and 425 heats represented the end of the furnace campaign. After this roof was insulated, very little patching was done up to 350 heats, and the furnace campaign was increased to 470. At still another plant the average roof life before insulation on a 120-ton furnace was 350 heats, but after insulation as high as 550 were obtained. On the whole, operators generally report an increase of 10 to 25 per cent in roof life, after insulation. Obviously operators must be more careful in operating such insulated furnaces beyond their rated capacity.

280. Front and Back Walls. On the whole, silica front walls and back walls have shorter lives (100 to 150 heats) than the roofs. Deterioration is caused by absorption of iron oxides from the gas stream, the cutting action of a misdirected flame, and spalling, especially in the neighborhood of the door jambs of the front door walls. Chemical attack by slag splashings and roof drippings is also bad. Some furnaces have been built with chrome or magnesite front walls, and these basic and neutral bricks give at least twice the life of silica bricks. Chrome bricks are also finding more extensive use in back walls, taking the place of silica. Metalkase magnesite, unburned magnesite, and unburned chrome are also rapidly gaining favor. Introduction of sloping back walls and semi-sloping front walls has facilitated fettling, with resultant longer refractory life.

281. Ports and Bulkheads. Abrasion is the important factor here, owing to the changing direction of the gas stream, which, laden with oxide particles, has a much more severe cutting action than on the roof. The designs of ports, particularly the application of the movable ports, have been factors in lengthening the life of these parts of the furnace. Mechanical control of combustion has also been a means of increasing port life. In bulkheads silica brick gives as low as 40 and rarely over 125 heats; with Metalkase magnesite as high as 600 to 700 heats have been reported; and with unburned magnesite and unburned chrome 450 to 500 heats. High alumina (70 per cent aluminum oxide) fire bricks have also made excellent records in recent furnaces, but these are relatively expensive.

282. Checker Chambers. The requirements of checker brick are high thermal capacity, high thermal conductivity, resistance to slagging action of dust, and resistance to spalling by sudden temperature changes. Silica bricks have largely been superseded by high-grade fire-clay bricks for this purpose. Within the past few years the tendency has been to employ super-fire-clay bricks, at least for the upper course, where they are subject to extremely high temperatures. These bricks are denser, more refractory, and have less tendency to spall than high-duty fire-clay bricks. Checkers made of super-fire-clay bricks are not so readily clogged and are more easily cleaned. Because of their higher density, they have higher thermal conductivity and capacity. On the whole, basic or neutral bricks have not given satisfactory results in checker chambers, but insulation to prevent air infiltration and to conserve heat and the mechanical control of combustion have served to increase the life of checker brick.

283. Ladles. One is confronted with a considerable problem in selecting a good ladle brick, for the refractory should have a long life and yet be of such a nature that it will not contaminate the steel. On the average approximately two ladle bricks are consumed per ton of steel, and one of these actually dissolves in the metal and slag. Fire-clay bricks are almost universally used for the purpose.

284. Nozzles. These require careful attention because they should be true to shape and properly fired. They must be sufficiently refractory to resist the hot metal but still soft enough to maintain a proper seat for the stopper. They must be resistant to cutting by the stream of molten metal and should not contaminate the steel. The chief recent advance in fire-clay nozzles is an increase in refractoriness without sacrificing the slight softening needed at pouring temperatures. Magnesite nozzles and stoppers are now used to a limited extent in teeming certain quality steels.

285. Chrome-Magnesite Brick. One of the greatest obstacles to the use of an all-basic open-hearth furnace has been the physical limitations of basic refractories. The ordinary magnesite brick is very heavy, and therefore requires a much stronger roof suspension than does silica brick. It spalls rather readily, has a comparatively low refractoriness under load, and its heat conductivity is high. In the last few years a great deal of very encouraging experimental work has been done toward the development of a special chrome-magnesite brick. It has long been known that the addition of a small amount of magnesia improves the properties of chrome brick and incidentally reduces the difficulties of manufacture. The result of a systematic research, mainly carried out in the United States, Canada, and Austria, has resulted in the development of a chrome-magnesite brick possessing three very important properties:

1. High thermal shock resistance.
2. High strength under load.
3. Volume stability at high temperatures.
4. High refractoriness.

The high thermal shock resistance of special chrome-magnesite brick depends upon careful control of the grading. With fired brick this is generally obtained by keeping the chrome fraction (generally 60 to 75 per cent of the total) in the coarse section and the magnesite (40 to 25 per cent of the total) in the fine section. The high refractoriness under load depends on the conversion of the low melting point gangue material in the chrome ore to forsterite ($2MgO \cdot SiO_2$) by reaction with the added magnesia. To insure complete conversion, the amount of magnesia added is far more than is theoretically required to satisfy the silica present. Volume stability seems to be a property of this chrome-magnesite brick and has been variously attributed to the reaction between the added magnesia and the gangue, solid solution of magnesia in the chromite, and replacement of the iron oxide in the chrome by magnesia. In all probability all these factors play a part.

Chrome-magnesite brick has proved its usefulness in back walls, front walls, and ports; and experiments abroad have indicated that it will be a means of achieving the all-basic furnace. To the casual observer the much higher price of the chrome-magnesite brick, as contrasted to standard silica, might seem to demand too great an increase in furnace life to justify its use. Those who have had experience with this type of brick and then had to return to normal practice realize that it has many advantages besides long furnace life. Thus, the use of chrome-magnesite brick in the back wall and roof results in a marked decrease in the amount of fettling required and also a much lower slag bulk, and there is little doubt that all-basic furnaces may be run very much harder than the old silica ones.

OPEN-HEARTH FUELS

286. General. Open-hearth furnaces have been operated with natural gas, coke oven gas, producer gas, pulverized coal, fuel oil, tar, mixtures of coke oven and blast furnace gas, and mixtures of tar and soft pitch. The choice of the fuel will depend largely upon the kind of steel being made and local conditions of supply and price. Natural gas, on the whole, is preferable when it can be obtained because it is of uniform composition, is easily controlled, usually free of sulfur, and has a high calorific value. The present great demand for petroleum products has made fuel oil costly in many steel-producing centers while the supply of tar from the coke ovens is also limited because it may find other more attractive uses in industry.

For the above reason it may be well to consider the advantages and economies of producer gas, because we may be obliged to return to the former practice of producer gas-fired furnaces. Although each installation constitutes a separate case, it may be stated generally that:

1. The cost of conversion varies from 90 cents to $1.10 per long ton of fuel, depending upon the kind and quality of the fuel, labor costs, and other local conditions.

2. The efficiency of conversion (per cent total calorific value of the fuel recovered) is 88 to 90 per cent when raw gas is consumed hot and 69 to 72 per cent when the gas is cooled and cleaned.

3. The gas made per pound of fuel varies from 50 to 74 cubic feet at 60°F., depending upon the kind and grade of fuel used.

4. It can be regenerated or otherwise preheated for combustion.

5. Using a high-volatile, 8 per cent ash coal, the net heating value of the clean, cool gas will be about 150 B.t.u. (gross including tar, 170 to 190 B.t.u.).

6. The raw gas contains practically all the sulfur that was in the fuel.

287. Pulverized Coal. The increasing cost of liquid fuels such as fuel oil and coal tar and the very rapid advances which have been made in the application of pulverized coal to the generation of power may result, in the next few years, in a more extended application of this fuel to open-hearth furnaces. Obviously, pulverized coal will introduce a very serious difficulty in the operation of the regenerators because of the relatively large quantities of ash that will be carried over into these chambers by the products of combustion. This fume will soon clog the ordinary checkers to such an extent that they will no longer be efficient. Furthermore, the ash will fuse the brick and rapidly slag that away; as a matter of fact, many furnaces which have used pulverized coal were forced to substitute a large brick measuring about 24 inches by 9 inches by 4 inches instead of the conventional ones in order to provide larger openings for the passage of gas.

Another difficulty encountered is that the combustion of solid fuel really takes place in four steps: namely, heating and drying, gasification of the volatile matter, combustion of the gases, and finally combustion of the small particles of coke that form. This is bound to result in a less intense cutting flame than is the case with most gaseous or liquid fuels. In addition, most pulverized coal burns with a rather long flame which, along with the ash, tends to erode the roof and side walls of the furnace more rapidly than with the conventional fuels. The other disadvantages, such as drying, pulverizing, storing, conveying, and safety precautions, which were important in the past, have, by reason of the developments referred to, been largely eliminated. On the whole, with all conditions met for properly handling and burning it, pulverized coal is one of the cheapest sources of heat available. As compared with producer gas, the cost of preparing it is somewhat less than the cost of producing an equivalent amount of gas from the same grade of coal, and higher temperatures are attainable.

OPERATION OF THE BASIC OPEN-HEARTH FURNACE

288. General. Let us assume that the superintendent of an open-hearth plant has received an order for 95 tons of No. SAE 1035 steel. According to the specifications, this should contain carbon, 0.30 to 0.40 per cent; manganese, 0.60 to 0.90; phosphorus, 0.05 maximum; and sulfur, 0.055 maximum. The open-hearth receives a tapping schedule from the schedule clerk in which is included these specifications as well as any other metallurgical requirement which may be listed by the customer: grain size, soundness, degree of deoxidation, and condition of surface, for example. The melter then calculates* the charge necessary for this type of heat from the materials available in the stockyard, as well as hot metal from the mixer or Bessemer converter, if these are available.

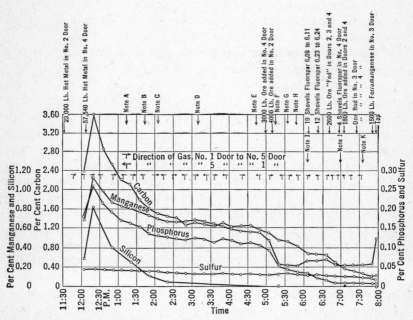

FIG. 70. Elimination of Metalloids. (*Courtesy of the American Institute of Metallurgical Engineers.*)

When the character of the charge is thus determined, order slips are sent to the scrap yard, limestone storage, pig-iron storage, and hot-metal mixer; the charging pans are loaded with steel scrap and pig iron, as well as with the required amount of limestone in the form of lumps 4 to 8 inches in diameter. All these materials are then weighed and the string of cars switched to the open-hearth floor to await charging into one of the furnaces. Charging weight sheets from the scalemen are sent to the melter as soon as the string of cars arrives on the floor.

* See Figure 71.

As soon as the previous heat has been tapped from the furnace, the second helper of the floor gang prepares the furnace to receive the above charge; he plugs up the tap hole with dolomite and loam while the floor gang makes bottom and fills in the slag line with dolomite. This is done while the furnace is still quite hot from the residual heat left in the furnace from the previous heat. The furnace is then ready to receive the charge; the heat is given a number, 921789, for example, the first digit indicating the number of furnace and the last digits the series of heat.

Incidentally, in large steel plants all records of heat numbers must be carefully recorded and carried through the mills with the greatest of care to avoid any mix-up of the ingots and billets. It is obvious that a steel plant with 15 open-hearth furnaces, tapping 2500 to 3000 tons of steel every 24 hours, which is to be rolled and sheared into over 4000 billets, has a very intricate problem of classifying each billet or group of billets, and any mis-scheduling of a billet into a wrong bar order may prove disastrous in subsequent fabrication operations. Beginning at 8:23 A.M. and continuing up to 9:20, the furnace is charged first with 2700 pounds of dolomite on the back wall, then 26,000 pounds of limestone, then 1570 pounds of dolomite on the front wall, and finally 175,000 pounds of scrap. Figure 70 and Table 49 show the progress of the heat and the elimination of the metalloids.

TABLE 49

Changes in Slag and Metal Compositions vs. Time[24]

Time	Per Cent												
	SiO$_2$	CaO	MgO	Al$_2$O$_3$	FeO	Fe$_2$O$_3$	MnO	P$_2$O$_5$	S	C	Mn	P	Si
Slag													
12.05 P.M.	19.46	40.5	3.65	2.50	9.56	3.54	15.60	1.78	0.067				
12.51	37.50	33.6	4.85	4.17	3.82	0.39	15.18	0.184	0.255				
3.50	31.95	38.72	7.74	3.60	3.15	0.42	13.32	0.382	0.064				
5.34	19.58	33.55	4.77	2.58	13.35	3.12	16.82	5.22	0.052				
7.35	15.85	46.9	5.78	2.14	11.07	2.57	9.70	3.89	0.158				
Metal													
12.05									0.046	2.88	0.70	0.18	0.28
12.51									0.043	2.72	0.87	0.19	0.39
3.50									0.035	1.30	0.61	0.12	0.005
5.34									0.035	0.92	0.22	0.048	tr
7.35									0.023	0.26	0.24	0.009	tr
2nd Ingot									0.021	0.36	0.58	0.011	0.088
21st Ingot									0.021	0.37	0.62	0.015	0.074

At 11:34 the first ladle of pig iron is poured into the furnace, and at 12:14 another ladle. At 1:15 lime begins to show up on the slag,

and by 2:05 there is an appreciable amount of lime floating over its entire surface. The metal at this time is boiling vigorously on the mounds of scrap. At 3:20 the slag begins to thicken, and the lime is boiling up over the entire bath. At 4:45 the slag is very viscous, and in both ends the lime is apparently "all up." Lime is still boiling up at the middle door. At 5:00, 3000 pounds of ore are added, and at 5:10 another 4000 pounds, whereby a vigorous action takes place, the lime begins to dissolve rapidly, and the slag becomes more fluid. As more lime is dissolved the slag thickens up somewhat and elimination of carbon and phosphorus practically ceases. Fluorspar is added at 6:08 and 2600 pounds of ore at 6:38. Rapid elimination of phosphorus begins as soon as the slag is thinned out by the spar addition, whereas the carbon is eliminated slowly until the ore addition, when the rate of elimination proceeds more rapidly. The slag being still a little heavy, more fluorspar and ore are added at 6:58 and 7:05 respectively. The slag is now frothing somewhat, and two rods are stirred through the heat to settle the frothing. Samples indicate that the carbon is dropping at the rate of about 0.15 per cent per hour and the slag is of good consistency. At 7:52, 1500 pounds of ferromanganese are charged in No. 3 door, where a slight foaming of the slag takes place. At 7:55 the metal starts flowing out of the tap hole, and 420 pounds of coal and 700 pounds of ferrosilicon are thrown into the ladle. Two slag samples are taken as the slag overflows from the ladle. At 8:06 the tap is completed and the ingots are teemed from 8:08 to 8:39. The temperature of the metal during teeming averages 1520°C. The amount of materials charged and produced is shown in Table 50.

TABLE 50

MATERIALS CHARGED AND PRODUCED[24]

Charged	Pounds	Produced	Pounds
Dolomite	4,270	Steel	248,100
Limestone	26,000	Slag	24,500
Scrap	175,000		
Hot Metal	80,540	Final Analysis of Steel	
Ore	11,400		Per Cent
Spar	716	C	0.372
Ferromanganese	1,500	Mn	0.608
Ferrosilicon	700	P	0.0138
Coal (ladle)	420	S	0.0209
Aluminum	2	Si	0.081

289. Weight of Slag. Slag weights during the heat may be calculated on the basis of manganese, phosphorus, and silicon. Such slag weights are shown in Table 51. The rapid increase in slag weight between

TABLE 51

CALCULATION OF SLAG WEIGHTS[24]

Time	Pounds Slag
12.51	2,370
1.35	4,290
2.20	6,360
3.05	7,450
3.50	7,760
4.35	8,500
4.50	10,160
5.05	11,770
5.20	14,230
5.34	15,400
5.50	18,500
6.06	19,560
6.21	20,600
6.36	21,900
6.51	25,600
7.07	26,900
7.21	26,800
7.35	27,400
7.52	28,300
Final weight	24,500

12:51 and 2:20 is the result of the elimination of silicon from the metal, the erosion of the lining, and the solution of lime into the slag. During the last half of the boil, from 2:20 to 2:35, the increase in slag weight is small, the silicon having been eliminated and the slag being too heavy to act on the banks or to dissolve the limestone to any great extent. During the remainder of the heat, the increase in slag weight between samples is fairly uniform, except for the period following the two ore additions, when it increases rapidly from the ore added, the action on the banks, and the lime dissolved by the slag after these additions. The difference between the calculated and the recorded slag weights is due to unavoidable losses of slag during and after tapping, which make the recorded slag weight low, and to the volatilization of manganese which gives a high value for the calculated weight. The true final weight, therefore, is somewhere between the two values given in the tables.

290. Erosion of the Lining. This may readily be obtained by calculation from the slag weights given in Table 51 and from the magnesium oxide content of the slag samples. The erosion of the lining will depend on five factors: (1) the amount of slag in contact with the banks, (2) the acidity of the slag, (3) the temperature of the slag, (4) the viscosity of the slag, and (5) the iron oxide content of the slag. Such a calculation indicates that the dolomite eroded, during the course of the heat, expressed in pounds of lining eroded per hour per 1000 pounds of slag, varies from 270 at the beginning of the heat to about 27 at its close. The controlling factors in this erosion are the silicon content and the fluidity of the slag, for the erosion stops completely when the slag becomes very viscous; and after each ore and fluorspar addition, which thins out the slag, the rate of erosion increases. The most rapid rate is found when the slag is most weakly basic, the slag at that time being very fluid. The total amount of lining eroded during this particular heat was 3240 pounds.

The rate at which lime is dissolved depends on the same factors which influence the rate of erosion of the lining, except that the amount of surface exposed by the lime floating on the bath must be added because surface exposed to the action of the slag is a very important factor. This surface will decrease as the heat progresses, and in comparing the beginning and the end of the heat it must be taken into consideration. Calculations show that the pounds of lime dissolved per hour per thousand pounds of slag vary from as high as 321 at about the middle of the heat to as little as 24 at its beginning and end.

291. Character of the Slag. Table 52 furnishes a comparison between the tapping slag and the ladle slag; and apart from showing the

TABLE 52

CompositIONS of Basic Open-Hearth Slags*

Slag	Per Cent								
	CaO	MgO	SiO₂	Al₂O₃	FeO	Fe₂O₃	MnO	P₂O₅	S
First	40.5	3.7	19.5	2.5	9.6	3.5	15.6	1.8	0.067
After hot metal addition	33.6	4.9	37.5	4.2	3.8	0.4	15.2	0.18	0.26
Middle of lime boil	38.7	7.7	32.0	3.6	3.2	0.4	13.3	0.38	0.064
After ore addition	33.6	4.8	19.6	2.6	13.4	3.1	16.8	5.2	0.052
After ferrosilicon addition	46.9	5.8	15.9	2.1	11.3	3.5	9.6	3.8	0.152
Final	48.0	6.0	15.6	2.1	10.7	3.3	9.7	3.7	0.16
Ladle	39.6	5.3	23.6	6.3	9.6	0.93	10.1	2.8	0.11

* Final metal: C, 0.372 per cent, Mn 0.608; P, 0.014; S, 0.021; Si, 0.08.

composition of the slag under which this particular grade of steel was finished, this analysis shows the importance of the ladle reaction. The slag, in its attack on the ladle lining, absorbs considerable quantities of silica and alumina, thus decreasing its basicity. The result of this decrease in basicity is rephosphorization of the metal accompanied by marked drops in phosphorus in the slag. The iron oxides, particularly ferric oxide, are decreased in concentration, and manganese oxide is increased by oxidation of the ferromanganese added. The remaining slag components decrease in concentration because of the dilution from the ladle lining.

292. Composition of Basic Pig Iron. A very important matter in basic open-hearth operation is the selection of the pig iron for the charge. The two important constituents which must be considered are silicon and manganese, and operators, over a period of years, have found that the silicon content of basic pig iron must be held within certain well-defined limits—between 0.80 and 1.25 per cent silicon. If the silicon is too high, more lime must be charged in order to neutralize it, and thus prevent excessive erosion of the lining; if it is high, this addition of limestone increases the volume of the slag, thus preventing rapid reactions and a satisfactory heat transfer from the furnace atmosphere to the metal. On the other hand, if the silicon is too low, the heat may melt too soft (low in carbon) in carbon. Silicon is the most readily oxidized constituent of the pig iron, and it is considered a safeguard against excessive oxidation of iron and carbon during melt-down; the higher the silicon, the higher the carbon content of the bath. Furthermore, low-silicon iron results in a cold bath because every pound of carbon eliminated absorbs 5400 B.t.u., whereas every pound of silicon oxidized gives off 4170 B.t.u. Silicon will also affect the viscosity of the slag, relatively low silicon yielding a very heavy, foamy slag that will require excessive amounts of ore or fluorspar, whereas high-silicon irons yield very thin, sloppy slags. Low silicon also forces too much ferrous oxide into the metal, reducing the carbon in the metal unduly by the time the limestone is all up from the bottom of the hearth. Such a heat is said to have melted "soft," * and extra pig iron must be charged to increase the carbon in the metal bath to a point where final shaping-up is possible. For this reason furnace men prefer not to use pig iron with a silicon content much under 0.80 per cent.

The manganese content of basic pig iron has shown an increase in recent years. Furnace operators noticed that, beginning with about 1.0 per cent, a higher manganese content in the pig iron gave rise to

* Low in carbon.

higher carbon melts and to lower sulfur than those made from lower manganese irons; consequently, manganese has been increased to the range of 1.25 to 1.50 per cent, and some operators are demanding 1.75 or even 2.0 per cent. This is in accordance with European practice where some of the basic irons contain as much as 4.0 per cent manganese. In the basic process manganese combines with sulfur forming manganese sulfide, which is absorbed by the basic slag. It also prevents excessive oxidation of the metal, although recent work has indicated that residual manganese contents of 0.30 may still be accompanied by as much as 0.17 per cent ferrous oxide.

293. Run-off Slag. It will be evident from the discussion in Article 247 that in the open-hearth process a certain excess of lime over the amount required to neutralize the silica is necessary to insure the desired elimination of phosphorus. For other reasons it has been well established that the ratio of lime to silica should be at least 2 to 1, which corresponds to the formation of a dicalcium silicate, $2CaO \cdot SiO_2$. Provided that the total silicon in the charge is known, it is a simple calculation to arrive at the total amount of limestone required to bring about this relationship. It is much more difficult to arrive at the proper slag composition when the scrap consists of both light and heavy material, which moreover varies in iron oxide (rust) content. Furthermore, with a high-iron charge, retention of the slag in the furnace may make it difficult to maintain or control the temperature of the bath through such a thick blanket of slag, which is a fairly good insulator.

Another difficulty lies in the fact, that with high-phosphorus heats, the slag may be called upon to absorb so much phosphorus that the rate of elimination will be slowed down notably; and also, if this slag were carried through to the end of the heat, there would be greater danger of reversion of phosphorus in the deoxidation period or in the ladle. All these difficulties may be overcome to some extent by removing a "run-off" slag. If it is timed correctly, between the ore boil and the lime boil, a large proportion of the silicon and a part of the phosphorus are carried out of the furnace, as shown in Table 53. The run-off slag will carry with it a considerable amount of iron and manganese oxides so that further additions of ore will be necessary in order to obtain rapid elimination of the carbon. If the charging of the furnace, the addition of hot metal, and the run-off are timed properly, the silicon remaining to be neutralized with lime can be reduced to a small and almost constant amount, irrespective of the silicon in the charge, making possible a relatively small limestone charge which is roughly pro-

TABLE 53

COMPARISONS OF FINAL AND RUN-OFF SLAGS

(Conventional Heats)

Slag	Per Cent									
	SiO₂	P₂O₅	CaO	MgO	Fe	Mn	Fe : Si Ratio	Phosphate Slag	Silicate Slag	Silicate Slag to SiO₂ Ratio
A—Final	17.80	2.21	41.79	6.50	14.86	5.96	1.79	5.70	94.30	5.29
A—Run-off	21.35	2.54	19.20	7.14	25.39	9.30	2.75	6.55	93.45	4.38
B—Final	19.03	1.85	41.10	7.30	13.50	5.58	1.52	4.77	95.23	5.00
B—Run-off	24.14	2.16	14.68	4.20	27.25	9.00	2.42	5.57	94.43	3.91
C—Final	17.05	1.51	46.85	8.00	11.68	5.65	1.47	3.90	96.10	5.64
C—Run-off	23.19	2.04	21.11	7.67	22.92	10.85	2.11	5.26	94.74	4.09

portional to the phosphorus. The chief reason for adding lime is to form this slag, and the calcination of limestone, of course, absorbs heat. Consequently, holding the limestone to a minimum not only decreases slag volume and the cost of flux, but gives increased production with a decrease in fuel consumption.

Beginning with 1941 a shortage of scrap brought about a change in practice. Formerly the pig iron made up less than 50 per cent of the charge but in 1942 it amounted to 60 and even 70 per cent. If the large amount of slag were allowed to remain in the furnace the cycle would be unduly lengthened. As a consequence, such heats must be flushed, thus removing a large part of the silicon, phosphorus, and, unfortunately, the manganese. (The dividing line for the removal of such a slag seems to be 55 per cent liquid iron.) This is a good example of the play of economic forces under pressure of increased output. Although the operator does waste manganese and iron in this way, iron ore is cheap enough so that the increase in the capacity of the furnace results in a net gain. Slag analyses from such high pig-iron heats are shown in Table 54 in order that they may be contrasted to conventional heats, given in Table 53. Reference to Figure 71, a record of such a heat, indicates that 70,000 pounds of ore was added as compared to 6000 to 15,000 pounds in a conventional heat.

294. Capacity of Furnaces. In the past the capacity of an open-hearth furnace has been commonly expressed in tons per heat, but this has not proved to be a good measure of the real production rate of a furnace. Consequently, William C. Buell, Jr., has suggested, as

TABLE 54

Comparisons of Final and Run-off Slags

(High Pig-Iron Heats)

Per Cent

Heat	Slag	Weight Slag Pounds	Slag								Fe Metal-lic	S Total	Metal					Weight Steel Tons
			SiO$_2$	CaO	FeO	Fe$_2$O$_3$	MnO	Al$_2$O$_3$	MgO	P$_2$O$_5$			C	Mn	P	S	Si	
A	Run-off	20,600	23.8	13.7	27.0	3.9	18.8	3.3	4.4	3.2	0.6	0.08						
A	Final	20,400	12.2	44.2	14.3	7.1	4.9	2.6	10.4	2.4	1.7	0.14	0.47	0.65	0.018	0.027	0.20	146
B	Run-off	21,500	24.3	14.2	24.1	3.4	20.8	3.0	5.7	3.3	0.4	0.08						
B	Final	12,200	19.6	45.1	9.2	2.6	7.2	2.7	7.4	3.3	3.7	0.05	0.36	0.17	0.018	0.025	0.016	151

1. Slag sample taken just before deoxidation.
2. Final slag weight is that actually tapped from furnace.

HARGED	3-4-42		A 1-5
DAT IN CHARGE	73.0		A 11-12

20

HEARGE	AMOUNT		
GRA ng Basic Bessemer			A 21
	12	000	↑
Ord Misc.			
Chg isc.			
Lad tal	240	000	36
Pre Pig Iron			B 30
			33
Prel .			B 52-59
			A
Res ron	252	000	
Slag tal	12	000	A 37
KINI	38	000	↑
Hare			
TAP	43	000	
Size			
High Stripper			
Misc.			
& Butts			
MEL			
1st I			
Stop sc.			
Pou			69
Floo		200	
Pit C			
MEL			
Ore in & Steel	345	200	E 57-69
TAP ORE # 2	59	000	A 18-19
eed Ore	11	000	B 22-25
Heav			
AMT ale			
Heav xides	70	000	
Activ ONS			B 34
Bath			↑
Tap			
FLUX			
Spar			
Raw con (10%)	1	500	
Chro Mn			51
Magr			54
Magr Mn	1	600	↑
Mago Mn			
Kelly licon		700	
Std. um		195	
Basit			
Stafl			
r			
hos.			
TOTA			79
dditions	3	995	
Bath TOTAL			
Ladle			

POURING DATA	E
Heat No. 2123	

KIII ☑ Semi-Rim ☐ Rim ☐ Cap ☐

MOLD ACTION		22
Active ☐1 Weak ☐2 Inactive Ⓧ3		↑

MOLD TEMP. & WASH

Hot ☐1 Warm Ⓧ2 Cold ☐3 Damp ☐4 Wet ☐5

None ☐0 Oil Ⓧ1 Tar ☐2 Graph. ☐3 Spec. ☐4

Ladle No. 67	No. Heats 12	
Nozzle Type	Long	
Nozzle Size	2"	
Type Stopper	Clay	

NOZZLE CONDITION

1st Ingot Shut-off: Good Ⓧ

Leak ☐   Spray ☐   Run ☐

Leaking	Ingots
Running	Ingots
Prickers	
Oxy- Used	
Head off	

POURING TEMPERATURES

First	Middle	Last
2921	2904	2921
Average	2915	

Mold Size	No. Poured	Poured
92" (30¼)²	18	87½"

KIND OF TOP	
No. Used	
Inset	Poured
Inches Steel in Collar	

BACKPOUR PRACTICE

CAPPED STEEL

Poured	
Metal Hit Cap in	Minutes
Al $\frac{02}{ING}$ 1 NaF $\frac{02}{ING}$ 3	
Total Additions/Heat–Lbs.	

RIMMED STEEL

Al $\frac{02}{ING}$ 1 NaF $\frac{02}{ING}$ 3	
90% Sil $\frac{02}{ING}$ 2	
How Used	
Total Additions/Heat–Lbs.	
Rimmed in Flat	
Opening At Cap	

KILLED STEEL	
Al $\frac{02}{ING}$ 1 Tot. Al Used	65

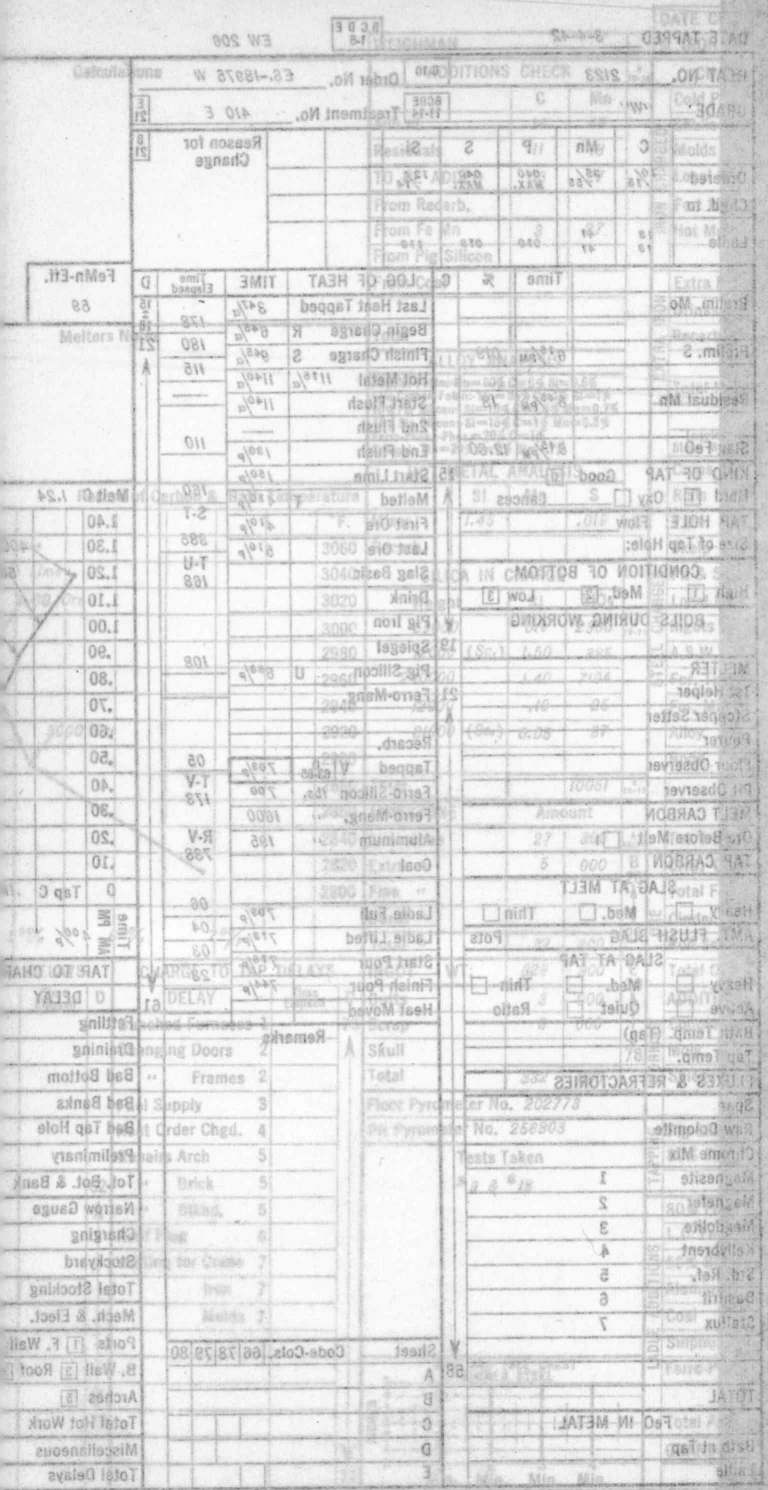

Fig. 71. Open-Hearth Heat Record.

TABLE 55. Basic Open-Hearth Data*

Plant	Type of Furnace	No. Heats Included in Data	Bath Tapping Capacity, Net Tons	Bath Metal Volume, Cu. Ft.	Metal Depth, Inches	Iron Total Charge, Per Cent	Iron Si Hot Iron Per Cent	Production Low Carbon Steel Time of Heat, Hr.	P_1	Med. Carbon Steel Time of Heat, Hr.	P_2	Fuel	Consumption, Million B.t.u. Net Ton
						Hot-Metal Practice							
A	Old	438	62.2	312.6	30	57.0	1.05	8.25	26.1	8.84	24.3	Liquid	4.820
B	"	7589	91.3	424.7	34*	38.9	1.05	9.67	22.2	9.00	23.9	"	4.420
C	"	1521	131.0	609.3	31	47.7	1.05	10.20	21.1			"	4.000
D	"	6181	142.8	664.2	36*	42.7	1.00	12.66	17.9	12.16	17.7	"	4.275
E	Rebuilt	4500	152.3	708.4	36*	35.0		12.00	17.7			Nat. and C. O. Gas	.
F	Modern	425	156.8	729.3	28	60.0		12.16	17.7			Producer	4.050
D2	"	4806	171.5	797.7	37*	41.4	1.05	12.66	16.6	12.16	17.7	C. O. Gas and Oil	4.125
G	"	375	173.6	807.4	28	58.0		12.00	17.9	12.00	17.9	Producer	4.320
H1	"	1075	190.0	883.7	28	45.0	1.10	11.00	19.5	11.50	18.7	B. F. Gas and Oil	3.274
H2	"	350	190.0	883.7	28	45.0	1.10	11.00	19.5	11.50	18.7	B.F. Gas C. O. Gas	2.900
I	Rebuilt	3748	194.3	903.7	38*	53.8	1.00	12.00	17.9	11.75	18.3	Liquid	3.380
J	"	1676	195.9	911.2	30	61.0	1.10	11.84	18.2			Producer	2.945
K	Modern	4880	198.0	920.9	28	56.9	0.75	8.16	26.3			Liquid	2.850
L	"	600	201.7	938.1	38*	55.0	1.10	11.00	19.5			"	4.018
M	Rebuilt	1856	207.2	963.7	28	53.9	1.00	11.66	18.4			"	3.125
N	Old	250	295.0	1372.0	41*	60.0		15.50	13.9			Producer	4.510
						Cold-Metal Practice							
R	Old	4854	69.6	323.7	28	23.0		9.90	21.7	11.80	18.2	Liquid	5.360
S	Rebuilt	335	114.3	531.6	24	42.5		11.80	18.2	12.00	17.9	"	5.820
I	Old		121.0	562.8	22	20.0		12.00	17.9			N. G. and Oil	
U	"	420	123.4	574.0	36*	12.0		11.50	18.7	11.50		Liquid	4.480
V	Modern		134.4	625.1	30	15.0		13.66	15.7	13.33	16.1	"	4.018

* Factors of Open Hearth Design and Practice, W. C. Buell, Iron and Steel Engineer, March, 1941.

a unit of comparative production rate and overall operating effects, the value "production of steel, net tons per hour per thousand cubic feet of metal volume," designated in the formula below as P. This has the advantage of placing the results of the operation of all furnaces, no matter what their size, in a directly comparable plane. Furthermore, as this rating is founded on the metal actually tapped into the ladle, it has as its basis the only really accurate and most easily checked value of steel-making practice. The factors involved are:

M = Volume of molten steel (base) in thousands of cubic feet.
S = Tons of steel tapped per heat.
T = Time of heat in hours.
Y = Pounds per ton (2000).
W = Weight of molten steel; pounds per cubic foot.
P = Tons of steel made per hour per thousand cubic feet of bath.

The formula suggested is:

$$P = \frac{M \times S}{S \times \left(\frac{Y}{W}\right) \times T}$$

In Table 55 are shown data for a number of furnaces studied by Mr. Buell and the production rate calculated by the above formula. Apparently, this offers an easy and simple method of making many interesting comparisons of furnace operations; for example, the productive rate of furnaces of different sizes and the effects for furnaces of like sizes, working on different fuels or on different grades of steel. The table itself is a result of a questionnaire sent out to some thirty-five companies representing almost 80 per cent of the ingot-producing capacity of the country and obviously furnishes an excellent cross section of American practice. In the great majority of hot-metal plants, steel is usually made in furnaces tapping 125 to about 200 tons, and furnaces approaching the latter capacity appear to offer the optimum economic practice. Above this capacity, the various limitations of plant and equipment, particularly as regards charging and teeming, soaking pit, and blooming mill schedules, are likely to offset the advantages of the lower processing cost of larger units.

295. Depth of Bath. The expansion in steel capacity, along about 1928, brought with it a number of furnaces built to tap more than 200 tons, and such furnaces were usually designed with baths 48 inches in depth. Since original construction, many of these baths have been reduced in depth and the tapping capacity of the furnaces lowered accordingly, with the result that today hearths are seldom found that are much more than 36 inches deep. It was found that if satisfactory steel was to be made in the deeper baths, an unduly long processing time was required. Assuming hearths of equal steel-holding volume, it is apparent that the area of metal exposed to slag action per ton of steel contained will be greater with shallow baths and less with deep baths. Inasmuch as practically all the refining action is accomplished at or near the slag-metal interface, a relatively great interface area, as found with a shallow bath, expedites the refining effects, thus saving considerable time. If a similar charge analysis is assumed, it is obvious that the total slag weight and volume must be the same to accomplish similar refining, and thus with a deeper bath the thickness of the slag covering the metal must be greater. A thicker slag blanket increases the difficulty of heat transmission from the flame to the metal because the slag resistance to heat flow is about four times that of molten steel. The result is a higher operating temperature with more fuel and greater furnace maintenance cost.

The extent to which temperature must be increased with greater slag depth is indicated by the following example. Assume in both cases that the metal at the bottom of two baths is ready for tapping at 2900°F. and the hearth refractories have like characteristics as regards thermal resistance. Then, in the first case with a temperature drop through 30 inches of metal of 32° and through 4 inches of slag of 14°, a total of 46°, it follows that the temperature of the exposed surfaces of the slag must be at least 2946°F. In the second case, if a metal bath is 48 inches deep, the temperature drop will be 43° and through 8 inches of slag 28°, a total of 71°, which develops a slag surface temperature of 2971°F. While this is only 25° higher than in the first case, it should be recalled that the average temperature of the furnace gases over the bath may be lower than 3100°F., and thus 25° represents a considerable percentage of the temperature differential or thermal head available for heat transfer to the bath. If we recall that heat transmission is of the order of the fourth power of the temperature differential, it is evident that small differences of temperature will create great differences in heat transmission. Thus, with a temperature differential in the first case of 154° the transfer of heat from flame to slag will be almost 1¼ times as rapid as with a deeper bath condition or 129° differential.

296. Temperature Measurement and Control. In recent years much work has been done in perfecting automatic temperature and combustion control. Some of these systems use forced draft, some proportion the amount of air and fuel to obtain nearly perfect combustion, and others embody a thermostatically controlled, automatic reversal of the furnace, the thermostat being placed in the checker chamber. One of these systems, the Isley, is described in more detail in Article 346. The future will undoubtedly see more strides made in the use of these automatic combustion-control systems. As a result fuel consumption per ton of steel gradually is being lowered until today 4.5 million B.t.u. per ton of steel is fairly common practice, where 6.0 B.t.u. formerly was considered good. Much attention is also being given to the more accurate measurement of bath and roof temperatures than has been possible with the conventional thermocouples or optical pyrometers. The platinum couple, when used to measure temperatures of molten cast iron, must have two protecting tubes and the inner must be gastight to protect the platinum wires from carburizing gases. The outer tube must protect the inner from thermal shock and from corrosive slag or gases. Because of the lag thus introduced, a reading cannot be made in less than 1.5 minutes. Optical pyrometers are less accurate, and it is difficult to maintain true blackbody conditions because of the presence of smoke and slag.

297. Fitterer Thermocouple.* G. R. Fitterer has devised a thermocouple utilizing the carbon-silicon carbide couple. It consists of a silicon carbide rod inserted lengthwise into a carbon tube which is closed and rounded at one end. The hot junction is prepared by tightly fitting the rod into a socket on the inside of this closed end. Calibrations can be made with an optical pyrometer and apparently such calibrations were not disturbed by prolonged immersions in liquid steel. This thermocouple has been used with success in measuring temperatures in mixers, blast furnaces, open hearths, and teeming ladles. The potential involved varies from about 364 millivolts at 1250°C. to 462 at 1575°C. and is nearly a straight line.

Another one devised by F. Holtby† consists of a tungsten-graphite thermocouple. Preliminary experiments with this seem to indicate that readings can be obtained in 7 to 10 seconds without noticeable contamination of the metal. Readings up to 1970°C. have been made.

---

* The maximum temperature to which various couples may be used are C-SiC, 1800°C.; Pt-PtRh, 1400°C.; chromel-alumel, 1100°C.; and iron-constantan, 700°C.

† *Transactions of the American Society of Metals*, December, 1941.

REPAIRS AND IRREGULARITIES

298. Repairs. After the slag and steel have flowed out of the tapping hole into the ladle, fluorspar is usually thrown in on the slag left in the bottom, to be sure that as much as possible flows out and does not build up on the bottom of the furnace. Holes will be found in the bottom owing to the replacement by steel which, boiling there, brings up a part of the basic material forming the bottom. This erosion in a standard 100-ton furnace may amount to as much as 2 tons per heat. The slag and steel found in these holes after tapping must be rabbled out so that the bottom can be repaired properly. In case these depressions are very large, drains to the tap hole can be cut with oxygen or air delivered through a small pipe, and the depressions cleaned out more thoroughly. The smaller holes can be filled up with prepared dolomite, but the larger ones are best built up with magnesite, in layers, as was the original bottom. The banks, which have been cut by the slag from the previous heat, are repaired by throwing burned dolomite into the holes, and, after the tapping hole has been sealed with a plug of clay and dolomite, the furnace is again ready for charging. After a number of heats, the bottom may be eroded so that liquid slag and metal will not drain to the tap hole, in which case it is given a thorough cleaning as just described and the whole bottom built up again with 5 to 8 inches of sintered dolomite.

299. Furnace Irregularities. The trouble and difficulties to be expected in open-hearth furnace operation are quite as varied and serious as those in a blast furnace. For example, the tap hole may break out prematurely, flood the cinder pit with molten metal and slag, and, if the metal comes in contact with water which may be lying around, violent explosions will ensue. Conversely, if it becomes impossible to open the tap hole, all the calculations and plans of the melter, concerning the final analysis of the steel, will be rendered worthless. Although every effort is made in the original burning-in of the bottom to make it as nearly monolithic as possible, sometimes sections of this bottom become detached and rise, because of the buoyant force of the metal. When this does occur, the heat must be tapped at once; otherwise, the most dreaded mishap may occur—that is, a breakout, when the slag and metal flow out of the furnace through a break in the bottom. Breakouts may also be caused by a hole near the bank which may not have been noticed or have been improperly repaired, in which case the steel works down into it, gradually making it deeper and deeper until the metal finds its way out through the wall of the furnace. The ports will require constant attention to prevent them from melting away and changing the angle and direction of the flame, which might tend to overheat some part of the furnace and, of course, would be that much less effective in transmitting heat to the bath.

Leaks may occur in any part of the furnace, but particularly in the walls of the up- and downtakes, which result in the gas being burned, in part at least, before it reaches the hearth. Ordinarily, the walls and roof wear out long before the rest of the furnace. Roofs usually last 200 to 350 heats, and the normal routine of a furnace calls for a shutdown at the end of that time for a complete repair; but if a roof caves in before the end of a heat, that is indeed a very serious mishap that may involve the loss of the heat and sometimes of other parts of the furnace. Finally, the checker work may become so badly clogged and the brickwork so badly eroded that it becomes necessary to shut down the furnace for general repairs and rebuild these.

CHEMISTRY OF THE BASIC OPEN-HEARTH PROCESS

300. General. For the purposes of this discussion the open-hearth cycle can be divided into the following periods:

1. Melting-down.
2. Ore boil.
3. Lime boil.
4. Shaping-up or working.
5. Deoxidation.

The division of time between these periods is not so sharp as one might imagine, nor are their lengths exactly the same from heat to heat. They will vary with the amount of pig iron used, whether it is cold or molten, the amount of scrap, the amount and character of the limestone, ore additions, fluorspar additions, etc. There is bound to be an overlapping of the periods; for example, the melt-down period may be considered as extending on through to the end of the lime boil because all of the limestone does not rise until the scrap covering it is completely melted, and yet the lime boil starts in all its violence before the scrap is completely melted. Frequently, for the sake of reference, the furnace man describes as a lime boil the action noted on the surface of the metal bath because this is to him a guide as to what action is taking place within the molten metal.

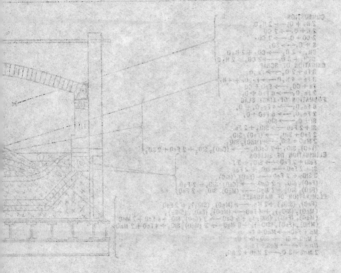

CHARGE				SLAGS				FUEL		
Limestone	Ore A	Ore B	Hot Metal	First	Flush	Final	Range of Final	Coke Oven	Producer	Tar
Fe 0.16	Fe 61.38	53.96	Fe 90.79	FeO 66.67	23.41	17.07	15-28	CO_2 1.4	5.3	H_2O
P 0.005	P 0.117	0.06	P 1.93	Fe_2O_3 6.00	4.43	4.52	3.5-8.0	O_2 0.3		V.M. 7
SiO_2 0.38	Mn 0.06	0.44	Mn 1.66	Fe(met)55.8	Fe(met) 2.65	2.06	1.1-3.9	CO 6.8	24.4	Fixed C 2
Al_2O_3 0.18	SiO_2 7.46	5.24	Si 1.02	P_2O_5 0.78	2.52	1.88	1.5-2.3	H_2 57.8	9.4	Ash
CaO 53.03	Al_2O_3 2.04	2.10	S 0.03	MnO 1.30	10.97	9.16	7-11	CH_4 26.7	2.6	S
MgO 0.91	CaO 0.42	0.19	C 4.57	SiO_2 4.72	21.81	17.11	13-20	N_2 4.0	57.5	Free C 1
S 0.085	MgO 0.53	0.36		Al_2O_3 0.53	3.73	2.40	1.7-3.5	Btu ft^3 528	144	Btu lb 15.
H_2O 2.67	S 0.018	0.004		CaO 18.00	22.04	42.66	37-45			
	H_2O 1.15	12.32		MgO 2.00	7.31	7.16	5.3-10.4			
				S 0.085						

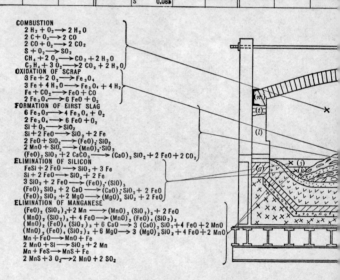

COMBUSTION

$$2 H_2 + O_2 \longrightarrow 2 H_2O$$
$$2 C + O_2 \longrightarrow 2 CO$$
$$2 CO + O_2 \longrightarrow 2 CO_2$$
$$S + O_2 \longrightarrow SO_2$$
$$CH_4 + 2 O_2 \longrightarrow CO_2 + 2 H_2O$$
$$C_2H_6 + 3 O_2 \longrightarrow 2 CO_2 + 2 H_2O$$

OXIDATION OF SCRAP

$$3 Fe + 2 O_2 \longrightarrow Fe_3O_4$$
$$3 Fe + 4 H_2O \longrightarrow Fe_3O_4 + 4 H_2$$
$$Fe + CO_2 \longrightarrow FeO + CO$$
$$2 Fe_3O_4 \longrightarrow 6 FeO + O_2$$

FORMATION OF FIRST SLAG

$$6 Fe_2O_3 \longrightarrow 4 Fe_3O_4 + O_2$$
$$2 Fe_3O_4 \longrightarrow 6 FeO + O_2$$
$$Si + O_2 \longrightarrow SiO_2$$
$$Si + 2 FeO \longrightarrow SiO_2 + 2 Fe$$
$$2 FeO + SiO_2 \longrightarrow (FeO)_2 SiO_2$$
$$2 MnO + SiO_2 \longrightarrow (MnO)_2 SiO_2$$
$$(FeO)_2 SiO_2 + 2 CaCO_3 \longrightarrow (CaO)_2 SiO_2 + 2 FeO + 2 CO_2$$

ELIMINATION OF SILICON

$$FeSi + 2 FeO \longrightarrow SiO_2 + 3 Fe$$
$$Si + 2 FeO \longrightarrow SiO_2 + 2 Fe$$
$$3 SiO_2 + 2 FeO \longrightarrow (FeO)_2 (SiO_2)_3$$
$$(FeO)_2 SiO_2 + 2 CaO \longrightarrow (CaO)_2 SiO_2 + 2 FeO$$
$$(FeO)_2 SiO_2 + 2 MgO \longrightarrow (MgO)_2 SiO_2 + 2 FeO$$

ELIMINATION OF MANGANESE

$$(FeO)_2 (SiO_2)_3 + 2 Mn \longrightarrow (MnO)_2 (SiO_2)_3 + 2 FeO$$
$$(MnO)_2 (SiO_2)_3 + 4 FeO \longrightarrow (MnO)_2 (FeO)_2 (SiO_2)_3$$
$$(MnO)_2 (FeO)_2 (SiO_2)_3 + 6 CaO \longrightarrow 3 (CaO)_2 SiO_2 + 4 FeO + 2 MnO$$
$$(MnO)_2 (FeO)_2 (SiO_2)_3 + 6 MgO \longrightarrow 3 (MgO)_2 SiO_2 + 4 FeO + 2 MnO$$
$$Mn + FeO \longrightarrow MnO + Fe$$
$$2 MnO + Si \longrightarrow SiO_2 + 2 Mn$$
$$Mn + FeS \longrightarrow MnS + Fe$$
$$2 MnS + 3 O_2 \longrightarrow 2 MnO + 2 SO_2$$

Fig. 72. The Basic O

(a) Scrap
(b) Iron ore
(c) Scrap
(d) Limestone
(e) Burned dolomite
(f) Sintered magnesite
(g) Magnesite brick

(h) Chrom
(i) Fire br
(j) Slag
(k) Metal
(l) Door
(m) Skewba
(n) Sloping

ADDITION AGENTS																
(Spiegel)	Ferro Phos.	Ferro Silicon (low)	Ferro Silicon (med)	Ferro Silicon (high)	Ferro Chromium (low)		Ferro Chromium (high)	Ferro Titanium		Fluorspar		Calcium Silicide		Alsimin	
73.21	73.20	82.88	47.18	18.00	Fe	27.56	24.00	Fe	69.20	Fe_2O_3	0.26	Fe	8.08	Fe	7.70
0.12	23.48	0.086	0.028	0.020	Mn	0.22	0.23	Mn	0.07	SiO_2	3.77	Si	60.83	Si	37.00
20.73	1.67	0.28	0.35	0.24	Si	0.49	0.86	Si	2.12	Al_2O_3	0.30	Al	1.62	Al	52.56
1.12	1.00	15.53	49.28	80.49	C	0.35	4.91	Al	1.91	$CaCO_3$	7.57	Ca	33.96	Ti	1.75
0.016	0.058	0.049	0.057	0.04	Cr	70.48	69.84	Ti	21.92	$MgCO_3$	0.27	C	0.06	C	0.88
4.80	0.09	0.61	0.13	0.04				C	4.34	CaF	86.40				
		Al 0.54	2.98	1.16						MgF	0.33				
			Cu 0.04							PbS	0.60				
										S	0.21				

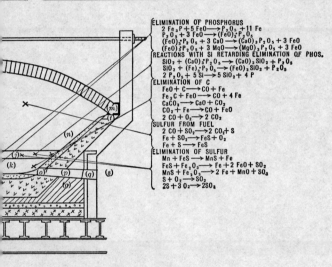

ELIMINATION OF PHOSPHORUS

$$2\,Fe_3P + 5\,FeO \longrightarrow P_2O_5 + 11\,Fe$$
$$P_2O_5 + 3\,FeO \longrightarrow (FeO)_3\,P_2O_5$$
$$(FeO)_3\,P_2O_5 + 3\,CaO \longrightarrow (CaO)_3\,P_2O_5 + 3\,FeO$$
$$(FeO)_3\,P_2O_5 + 3\,MgO \longrightarrow (MgO)_3\,P_2O_5 + 3\,FeO$$

REACTIONS WITH Si RETARDING ELIMINATION OF PHOS.

$$SiO_2 + (CaO)_3\,P_2O_5 \longrightarrow (CaO)_3\,SiO_2 + P_2O_5$$
$$SiO_2 + (Fe)_3\,P_2O_5 \longrightarrow (FeO)_3\,SiO_2 + P_2O_5$$
$$2\,P_2O_5 + 5\,Si \longrightarrow 5\,SiO_2 + 4\,P$$

ELIMINATION OF C

$$FeO + C \longrightarrow CO + Fe$$
$$Fe_3C + FeO \longrightarrow CO + 4\,Fe$$
$$CaCO_3 \longrightarrow CaO + CO_2$$
$$CO_2 + Fe \longrightarrow CO + FeO$$
$$2\,CO + O_2 \longrightarrow 2\,CO_2$$

SULFUR FROM FUEL

$$2\,CO + SO_2 \longrightarrow 2\,CO_2 + S$$
$$Fe + SO_2 \longrightarrow FeS + O_2$$
$$Fe + S \longrightarrow FeS$$

ELIMINATION OF SULFUR

$$Mn + FeS \longrightarrow MnS + Fe$$
$$FeS + Fe_2O_3 \longrightarrow Fe + 2\,FeO + SO_2$$
$$MnS + Fe_2O_3 \longrightarrow 2\,Fe + MnO + SO_2$$
$$S + O_2 \longrightarrow SO_2$$
$$2S + 3\,O_2 \longrightarrow 2SO_3$$

Process (Chemistry).

   (o) Dolomite plug
   (p) Anthracite and dolomite
   (q) Fire clay plug
   (r) Tie rod
   (s) Tap hole
   (t) Chrome brick

The following test heat[24] was made on a 100-ton stationary furnace using rail-heat butts. All materials charged, as well as the slag and metal produced, were weighed and sampled carefully.

TABLE 56

NOTES ON OPEN-HEARTH CYCLE[24]

Note A. Metal boiled vigorously around and on the outer edge of the mounds of pasty semi-molten scrap. Some lime lumps floated to the surface along the front wall. A collection of kish* still hung on the front bank at No. 4 door, remaining from the last ladle of metal which was poured in at that door.

Note B. A vigorous boiling action continued on the mound of scrap at No. 2 door.

Note C. At this time the slag had quite an appreciable amount of lime floating on its entire surface. The heat had the appearance of melting high in carbon i.e., the slag contained hard sharp-edged lumps of lime and the metal was dark in color.

Note D. Lime is boiling up over the entire bath. Several lumps of scrap still above the level of the bath. The furnace was being run at a low temperature and the lime of the slag was softening up somewhat. The fluid portion of the slag was getting thicker.

Note E. Lime was still boiling up in No. 3 door. Both ends were rather quiet, appearing as though the lime were all up in each end. The furnace and bath were quite cool and the slag was very viscous. The steam pressure was raised at this point to increase the volume of gas and thus raise the temperature, and thereby hasten the boiling up of the last of the lime.

Note F. The slag dissolved the ore at once and a vigorous action took place throughout the entire bath.

Note G. The temperature of the bath was rising; the slag was more fluid; and the general action of the bath more open.

Note H. The slag was still frothing from ore addition.

Note I. The lime was still boiling up at No. 3 door. The slag of good consistency.

Note J. Lime boil ceased and lime was apparently all up. The slag was a little heavy.

Note K. Slag still showed the effects of the two recent ore additions. The rods stirred through the heat served to settle the frothing.

* *Kish* is residue from molten pig iron.

The reactions taking place in these various periods are shown in Figures 70 and 72 and in tabular form below.

$$2Fe(c) + O_2(g) \rightarrow 2FeO(c); \quad \Delta H = -128,000 \text{ cal.} \tag{48}$$

$$Fe(c) + CO_2(g) \rightarrow FeO(c) + CO(g); \quad \Delta H = +3920 \text{ cal.} \tag{49}$$

$$Fe(c) + H_2O(g) \rightarrow FeO(c) + H_2(g); \quad \Delta H = -6210 \text{ cal.} \tag{50}$$

$$Si(c) + 2FeO(c) \rightarrow SiO_2(c) + 2Fe(c); \quad \Delta H = -70,200 \text{ cal.} \tag{51}$$

$$Mn(c) + FeO(c) \rightarrow MnO(c) + Fe(c); \quad \Delta H = -26,800 \text{ cal.} \tag{52}$$

$$2P(c) + 5FeO(c) \rightarrow P_2O_5(c) + 5Fe(c); \quad \Delta H = -45,600 \text{ cal.} \tag{53}$$

$$C(c) + FeO(c) \rightarrow CO(g) + Fe(c); \quad \Delta H = +37,600 \text{ cal.} \tag{54}$$

$$FeO(c) + SiO_2(c) \rightarrow FeO \cdot SiO_2(c); \quad \Delta H = -6,600 \text{ cal.} \tag{55}$$

$$MnO(c) + SiO_2(c) \rightarrow MnO \cdot SiO_2(c); \quad \Delta H = -2,200 \text{ cal.} \tag{56}$$

$$P_2O_5(c) + 3FeO(c) \rightarrow 3FeO \cdot P_2O_5(c); \tag{57}$$

$$CaO(c) + FeS(c) \rightarrow CaS(c) + FeO(c); \quad \Delta H = -2800 \text{ cal.} \tag{58}$$

$$CaCO_3(c) \rightarrow CaO(c) + CO_2(g); \quad \Delta H = +41,800 \tag{59}$$

$$FeO \cdot SiO_2(c) + CaO(c) \rightarrow CaO \cdot SiO_2(c) + FeO(c);$$
$$\Delta H = -23,000 \text{ cal.} \tag{60}$$

$$MnO \cdot SiO_2(c) + CaO(c) \rightarrow CaO \cdot SiO_2(c) + MnO(c);$$
$$\Delta H = -14,800 \text{ cal.} \tag{61}$$

$$3FeO \cdot P_2O_5(c) + 3CaO(c) \rightarrow 3CaO \cdot P_2O_5(c) + 3FeO(c); \tag{62}$$

$$SO_2(g) + 3Fe(c) \rightarrow 2FeO(c) + FeS(c); \quad \Delta H = -81,800 \text{ cal.} \tag{63}$$

$$6Fe_2O_3(c) \rightarrow 4Fe_3O_4(c) + O_2(g); \quad \Delta H = +123,400 \text{ cal.} \tag{64}$$

$$Fe_3O_4(c) + Fe(c) \rightarrow 4FeO(c); \quad \Delta H = +9800 \text{ cal.} \tag{65}$$

These reactions have been condensed and simplified for the purposes of instruction and discussion. They may not reach equilibrium (seldom do) and side reactions, as well as physical forces of viscosity, diffusion and agitation have a marked effect (see pages 312-320).

Notes on the progress of the heat as well as analyses of metal and slag at various periods in the heat are given in Tables 56 and 57.

The reversals (gas flowing from left to right, or vice versa) are indicated by the arrows in Fig. 70.

301. The Melting Period. In this period the object is to melt the charge and get it under a cover of slag as soon as possible during which the conditions are predominantely those of oxidation. Depending upon the character of the scrap, particularly the proportion of heavy scrap or pig iron to light scrap, reactions will go on, producing ferrous oxide that will join the slag. There will also be considerable iron oxide on the surface of the scrap that will be available at this time. Some silicon and manganese, small amounts of sulfur, and carbon may also be oxidized during this period.

TABLE 57

OPEN-HEARTH ANALYSES OF METAL AND SLAG[24]

	Charge	1 Hr. After Hot Metal Addition	At End of Lime Boil and Just Before Fluorspar Addition	After Fluorspar Addition and Just Before Ore Addition	After Addition 7000 Lb. Ore	Final Metal	Final Steel
			Metal				
C	1.96	1.75	1.04	0.73	0.32	0.09	0.09
Mn	0.92	0.27	0.38	0.46	0.16	0.17	0.35
P	0.093	0.103	0.070	0.021	0.007	0.009	0.006
S	0.038	0.050	0.043	0.035	0.036	0.025	0.045
Si	0.69	0.073					
			Slag				
FeO		6.11	3.45	4.92	11.69	11.85	
Fe_2O_3		0.13	0.94	1.17	5.81	7.10	
SiO_2		34.04	31.78	20.41		14.48	
P_2O_5		0.50	0.55			2.32	
MnO		12.38	10.66			6.63	
S		0.16	0.143			0.278	
CaO		34.25	38.95	51.83		47.45	
MgO		9.50	9.74			6.20	

Metal and slag samples were taken at 15-minute intervals at the three working doors of the furnace, starting as soon as there was enough molten material on the hearth to permit sampling. Special precautions were taken to be sure that the samples from the three doors were simultaneous.

302. The Period of Ore Boil. As soon as the liquid bath is formed and hot metal added, a rapid reaction begins between the lime and ferrous oxide of the charge and the silicon, manganese, phosphorus, and carbon of the metal. They are oxidized about in the order given. Since reactions 48 and 51 are strongly exothermic, they not only serve to increase the temperature of the iron but actually help to melt the scrap and heat up the bottom. The exact order and extent of the oxidation of these four elements will depend upon many factors, among them:

1. The viscosity of the bath.
2. The temperature.
3. The composition of the slag and metal.
4. The character of the furnace gases.

Considering only the energy liberated, we would expect that all the silicon, manganese, and phosphorus would be oxidized ahead of the carbon, but actually considerable carbon is oxidized because the product of oxidation, carbon monoxide, escapes from the bath much more readily than the other products of oxidation diffuse into it.

As soon as the silicon is oxidized, it unites with either ferrous oxide or manganese oxide, as indicated in reactions 55 and 56, to form the basic slag. The extent of the oxidation and neutralization of the phosphorus, as indicated in reactions 53, 57, and 62, will progress only to a state of equilibrium as determined by the temperature attained or the concentration of ferric oxide in the slag. It will progress toward the right at low temperatures and high concentration and toward the left at high temperatures and low concentration. The removal of sulfur will also depend upon the equilibrium attained. If the furnace gases are high in sulfur, there may actually be a slight "pick-up" of this element; on the other hand, if the slag is very basic, a small amount of sulfur may be removed and absorbed by the slag as calcium sulfide.

303. Period of Lime Boil. Sometime before the close of the ore boil, limestone will be decomposed according to reaction 59, and the carbon dioxide thus given off may, in the early stages of this period, oxidize some of the iron. As the lime boil becomes more violent, the agitation brought about by the bubbles of carbon dioxide serves to agitate the bath, remove some carbon ($CO_2 + C \rightarrow 2CO$), and cause more lime to rise to the surface. As this becomes available, the lime replaces ferrous oxide and manganese oxide in the silicates and phosphates, forming more stable compounds making up the final slag. Lime also plays a part in the oxidation of that part of the sulfur which may be eliminated at this point as calcium sulfide. The amount of iron oxide added for these reactions will depend upon the kind of scrap and pig iron used, the kind of steel to be made, and the plant and furnace conditions. If too little ore has been added, more must be added during the working period, which may not be advisable; whereas, if too much has been added, it will be not only wasteful but a great handicap during the finishing part of the heat:

304. The Working Period. During this period carbon and phosphorus are eliminated and the bath and temperature adjusted to a point suitable for finishing and tapping the steel. The temperature must be adjusted so as to bring about a proper correlation between the oxidation of carbon and phosphorus and the slag controlled as to oxidizing power and basicity so that one may be able to deliver the proper grade of steel, ranging from high carbon to low carbon and from the "dead" to the rimming steels.

305. Silicon Monoxide. Recent work, although it serves to clear up certain unexplained features of open-hearth chemistry, also complicates the situation. A recent investigation[*] led to the conclusion that silicon monoxide may play an important part in steel making. Its formation can be brought about by any of the following reactions:

$$SiO_2(c) + Fe(c) \rightarrow SiO(c) + FeO(c); \quad \Delta H = +94,500 \text{ cal.} \quad (66)$$

$$SiO_2(c) + H_2(g) \rightarrow SiO(c) + H_2O(g); \quad \Delta H = +48,000 \quad (67)$$

$$SiO_2(c) + Si(c) \rightarrow 2SiO(c); \quad \Delta H = +73,800 \quad (68)$$

$$Si(c) + FeO(c) \rightarrow SiO(c) + Fe(c); \quad \Delta H = -20,900 \quad (69)$$

$$Si(c) + H_2O(g) \rightarrow SiO(c) + H_2(g); \quad \Delta H = +25,800 \quad (70)$$

From a study of the thermodynamics of these reactions the investigators concluded that (1) silicon monoxide is present in liquid steel formed by the reduction of silica or the oxidation of silicon and (2) increasing temperature and decreasing oxygen pressure favor its formation. The existence of silicon monoxide at steel-making temperatures should occasion no more surprise than ferrous oxide or carbon monoxide.

[*] "Silicon Monoxide," Zapffe and Sims, *Iron Age,* Jan. 22, 1942.

306. Problem 5. Find the value for m in the equation $m = \dfrac{(\%C)(\%FeO)}{(CO)}$.

(a) $H_2(g) + \frac{1}{2}O_2(g) \rightarrow H_2O(g)$; $\Delta F° = -60,200 + 13.97T$
(b) $Fe(l) + H_2O(g) \rightarrow FeO(\text{in } Fe) + H_2(g)$; $\Delta F° = 46,600 - 25.17T$
Combining (a) and (b), we have
(c) $FeO(\text{in } Fe) \rightleftarrows Fe(l) + \frac{1}{2}O_2(g)$; $\Delta F° = 13,540 + 11.20T$
(d) $CO(g) + \frac{1}{2}O_2(g) \rightleftarrows CO_2(g)$; $\Delta F° = -66,500 + 20.16T$
Combining (c) and (d), we have
(e) $FeO(\text{in } Fe) + CO(g) \rightarrow Fe(l) + CO_2(g)$; $\Delta F° = -52,960 + 31.36T$
(f) $C(\text{in } Fe) + CO_2(g) \rightarrow 2CO(g)$; $\Delta F° = 41,980 - 34.45T$
Combining (e) and (f), we have
(g) $FeO(\text{in } Fe) + C(\text{in liquid } Fe) \rightarrow Fe(l) + CO(g)$; $\Delta F° = -10,980 - 3.09T$
At low carbon contents

$$\log K = \frac{\Delta F°}{-4.575T}$$

$$= \frac{2400}{T} + 0.675$$

$$m = \frac{1}{K}$$

Therefore

$$\log m = \frac{-2400}{T} - 0.675$$

$$m \text{ at } 1500°C. = 0.0094$$
$$m \text{ at } 1600°C. = 0.0111$$
$$m \text{ at } 1700°C. = 0.0129$$

307. Problem 6. What percentage of silicon will be in a heat of low-carbon steel (at 1570°C.) containing 0.1 per cent ferrous oxide?

$$2FeO(l) + Si(l) = 2Fe(l) + SiO_2(c)$$
$$\Delta F° = -200,970 + 92.59T$$
$$\Delta F_{1800°} = -34,000$$
$$= -RT \ln K$$
$$K = 12,600$$
$$K' = \frac{(\%Fe)^2}{(\%FeO)^2 \, (\%Si)}$$
$$K = \frac{1}{(\%FeO)^2 \, (\%Si)}$$

At 1800° there will be 0.008 per cent silicon in the steel.

COMPOSITION OF BASIC OPEN-HEARTH SLAGS

308. General. A normal basic open-hearth slag may be considered as a fused mixture of calcium silicate, calcium phosphate, ferrous oxide, manganese oxide, and varying proportions of the other oxides of iron, of magnesia, and alumina. These components are capable of forming numerous chemical and physical combinations so that the properties of the individual ones may be little indication of the properties of the final slag. Furthermore, slag being a mixture, the melting points of these various compounds are of little significance because they frequently form eutectic mixtures having melting points very much lower than either of the compounds.

309. Functions of Calcium Oxide. For many reasons one of the important properties of the slag is the lime: silica ratio. Among them are:

1. The oxidizing power of the normal basic open-hearth slag is probably directly proportional to this ratio.

2. Excess lime, above that required to combine with silica and ferric oxide, is available for removing sulfur from the bath.

3. Lime acts to stabilize the ferric oxide, in the formation of calcium ferrite, against the effect of high temperature, and the slightly reducing influence of carbon monoxide and metallic iron, but leaves the ferrous oxide practically free to act upon the impurities in the bath.

4. Lime is necessary to form the stable phosphates and thus fix this element in the slag.

310. Functions of Ferrous Oxide. Obviously, ferrous oxide is one of the most important constituents of the slag because, besides having a direct effect on the viscosity, melting point, and oxidizing power of the slag, it will affect the character of the steel produced, as indicated below.

1. It will affect the final analysis of the steel because the iron oxide content of the slag, together with the total manganese in the charge, affects the residual manganese in the furnace; the manganese efficiency of the final additions depends on the ferrous oxide content of the slag, its fluidity, and the time which elapses between the addition and the pouring of the heat. In rimming steel the iron oxide content and the fluidity of the ladle slag are of great importance in determining whether or not a ladle reaction will go on. Such a reaction occurs if the steel is highly oxidizing and fluid; on the other hand, if the slag is too highly oxidizing, the rate of carbon elimination may be so rapid that it will be difficult to judge properly the final additions of carbon, particularly on steels which are not dead-killed in the furnace. The addition of carbon-bearing materials in the furnace often results in a strong reaction with consequent variable loss in carbon from heat to heat. Finally, iron oxide, combined with basicity and total phosphorus in the charge, controls the phosphorus content of the metal before deoxidation, and this quantity plus any reversion in phosphorus determines the phosphorus in the

steel. For given methods of deoxidation phosphorus reversion is fairly constant, so that, for a given composition of charge and amount of lime used, the ferrous oxide content of the slag is the controlling factor in the phosphorus content of the steel.

2. Iron oxide will effect certain economies in the operation of the furnace, such as the time consumed in the working of the heat, which is mostly devoted to the elimination of carbon. This, of course, is dependent on the average iron oxide content of the slag as well as its fluidity. For example, if a slag contains much ferrous oxide immediately after the ore addition and a low amount at tap, the refining period will be just as short as if a medium iron oxide content had been carried throughout this period. The control of the speed of working is, therefore, connected with the iron oxide content of the slag. In addition the loss of deoxidizers increases as the iron oxide of the finishing slag increases, and the iron loss from the charge increases with an increase of iron oxide in the slag. By properly controlling the iron oxide at all times during the working period, it is possible to obtain the maximum efficiencies of deoxidizers and a high furnace yield at little sacrifice of speed.

3. The iron oxide content will affect the action of the steel in the ingot mold. Killed steel may be produced by properly balancing deoxidizers, pouring, and mold conditions against the iron oxide in the slag, thus producing an ingot which is free from surface blow holes and from surface defects derived from too dead a steel. This proper balance must be arrived at for each grade of steel, but for any of them iron oxide in the slag is the important factor. Semi-killed steels, in which the steel is deoxidized so that it neither pipes nor forms enough gas to give surface blow holes may be made by balancing the deoxidation with the iron oxide content of the metal, which in turn depends upon the iron oxide content of the slag. Finally, in making rimming steel the soundness of the skin and the yield from the ingot depend upon the proper evolution of the gas during solidification. The best surface and yields are obtained by carefully balancing steel oxidation with variable amounts of deoxidizers and iron content of the slag. In rimming steels the iron oxide content of the metal before deoxidation is almost directly proportional to the iron oxide content of the slag.

4. The quality of the finished steel is also dependent upon the iron oxide content of the slag. Under quality are included such items as grain size, ductility, hardenability, sensitivity to cold work, cleanliness, and many others. In all these oxidation and deoxidation are very important, and it is highly probable that variations in the oxidizing power of the slag have a pronounced effect on almost every item listed above.

311. Viscosity of the Slag. For any given basicity the fluidity of a slag increases with the temperature, being about four times as great at 1600 as at 1450°C. It is found that, below 1500°C., the fluidity of a slag decreases very rapidly because of the precipitation of the solids from the liquid solution. Apparently there is no relationship between viscosity and basicity or between foaming properties and viscosity. Ferrous oxide added to slags which are very low in this constituent causes the viscosity to fall to a minimum and then increase. Alumina up to 10 per cent does not appear to affect the fluidity or the removal of sulfur, but high percentages do affect both adversely. Fluorspar thins the slag temporarily, increases the lime content, and if added in large amounts is destructive to the banks and walls of the furnace.

312. Action of Fluorspar. Fluorspar is the commercial term for an ore containing fluorite (CaF_2) as the chief constituent. The metallurgical grade commonly contains 85 per cent or more of calcium fluorite and 5 per cent or less of silica, the remainder being mainly calcium carbonate. The principal use of fluorspar is as a flux added to slags in the basic open-hearth or electric-furnace processes for making steel and also in cupola furnace melting of iron. Its primary function is to lower the viscosity of the slag, thus aiding in the removal of sulfur and phosphorus indirectly, and directly aiding by forming compounds containing phosphorus and sulfur which may enter the slag or escape by volatilization. Fluorspar makes it possible to produce a slag having a high lime content without being excessively viscous, a fluid slag being more reactive than a viscous one.

That very little exact knowledge concerning the fluxing action of fluorspar exists becomes evident when one encounters numerous contradictory statements regarding its action, especially how and when the fluorine is driven off from the slag, and the effect of fluorspar upon viscosity, desulfurization, and dephosphorization. There seems to be general agreement that all the fluorine introduced into slag does not remain there, and it is pretty generally accepted that the loss of fluorine is due to volatilization by:

1. Formation of silicon tetrafluoride.
2. Volatilization in the form of molecular fluorine.
3. Sublimation of undecomposed fluorides.
4. Formation and evaporation of hydrogen fluoride.
5. Formation of volatile fluorides.

When silica and cobalt are present in melts, the evolution of silicon tetrafluoride is quite well established, the reaction being:

$$2CaF_2 + SiO_2 \rightarrow 2CaO + SiF_4 \tag{71}$$

Other work supports the view that sulfur fluoride is formed mainly by the reaction:

$$4CoF_3 + S \rightarrow 4CoF_2 + SF_4 \tag{72}$$

Concerning the amount of fluorine left in basic slags there is a great diversity of opinion. There are some writers who report that all the fluorine is eliminated; on the other hand, other experimenters have found up to 2.5 per cent calcium fluoride in open-hearth slags.

PHYSICAL CHEMISTRY OF THE BASIC OPEN-HEARTH PROCESS

313. General. During the past fifteen years C. H. Herty, Jr.,[20, 21] and his colleagues, subsidized by many of the large steel companies as well as by consumers of steel, have carried on a very ambitious and fruitful project in the physical chemistry of steel making. This was done under the auspices of the Carnegie Institute of Technology, and the reader is referred to a series of cooperative bulletins issued by the body which deal with many phases of the open-hearth process.

314. Carbon Equivalent of the Charge. The iron oxide removed per pound of various metalloids is given in the following table:

	Ratio $\dfrac{FeO}{Metalloid}$
C(12) + FeO(71.9)	5.99
Si(28.3) + 2FeO(143.8)	5.07
Mn(54.9) + FeO(71.9)	1.31
2P(60.6) + 5FeO(359.5)	5.92

From these data may be obtained the carbon equivalents of silicon, manganese, and phosphorus:

$$1Si = \frac{5.07}{5.99} = 0.845C$$

$$1Mn = \frac{1.31}{5.99} = 0.221C$$

$$1P = \frac{5.92}{5.99} = 0.988C$$

Having these carbon equivalents, we can calculate the carbon equivalent of pig iron and scrap and thus obtain the carbon equivalent of the charge. It will be noted that variations in the manganese of the charge are not nearly so important, as far as carbon equivalent is concerned, as variations in the other metalloids. For a given oxidation condition the higher the carbon equivalent of the charge, the higher the charge will melt in carbon. The amount of oxidation in melting is just as important as the carbon equivalent of the charge, although the composition of the furnace gases is of secondary importance except where excessively oxidizing flames are produced.

315. The Solubility of Iron Oxides in Iron. One of the first problems undertaken in the above study was the determination of the solubility of iron-oxides in iron, for obviously it was one of the most important factors in the open-hearth process. This experimental work was carried out in an induction furnace, in crucibles made of fused magnesia using slags containing ferrous oxide, ferric oxide, and lime. From these experiments the following conclusions were drawn:

1. The solubility of oxygen in pure iron is equal to 0.304 per cent at 1600°C., and 0.452 per cent at 1700°C. The solubility curve is practically straight.

2. The distribution of iron oxide between slag and metal, as determined under lime-iron oxide slags, is the same as under pure iron oxide slags.

3. Any compounds which may be formed in lime-iron oxide slags over the range 0 to 35.0 per cent lime do not affect the solubility of the iron oxide.

4. Iron oxide is dissolved in the iron as ferrous oxide.

5. From a consideration of the carbon-iron oxide equilibrium it is evident that it is of the utmost importance, in making plain carbon steel, to keep the iron oxide content of the slag as low as is consistent with economical furnace operation.

316. Oxidation by Products of Combustion. In the open-hearth furnace the metal is oxidized during melting by the furnace gases until a slag covering has been formed, and from that time on the oxidation of the heat proceeds by the oxidation of the ferrous oxide in the slag by the furnace gas or by direct additions of iron ore. During the melting-down period the two controlling factors governing oxidation are the area of scrap exposed to the gas and the time of exposure. Apparently the analysis of the gas has relatively little effect, for experiments indicated that even with high ratios of reducing to oxidizing gases the metal was still highly oxidized. After the heat is under cover a large proportion of the total oxygen transferred from slag to metal is derived from the furnace atmosphere, the amount naturally varying with the amount of ore used. The overall effect is the oxidation of ferrous to ferric oxide by the reaction of ferrous oxide with oxygen and carbon dioxide or water vapor. These reactions are necessarily balanced against the reducing action of any carbon monoxide or hydrocarbons which may be present in the gaseous phase. The equilibrium between ferrous oxide and ferric oxide and the various gases will determine whether or not ferrous oxide will be oxidized to a higher oxide and how far this oxidation will proceed. Under normal operation analyses of the furnace gases directly over the liquid slag indicate that the gases are usually so oxidizing that essentially complete oxidation of the ferrous oxide in the slag should take place.

317. Effect of Layering. In connection with the formation of ferric oxide at the gas-slag interface, it should be noted that actual contact must be established, and, inasmuch as the slag at the contact surface tends to be extremely high in ferric oxide and extremely low in ferrous oxide, there is of necessity a concentration gradient in the upper layer of slag. Inasmuch as the diffusion of ferrous oxide through the

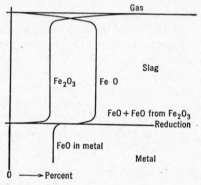

Fig. 73. Transfer of Oxygen. (*Courtesy of Carnegie Institute of Technology.*)

liquid slag would be far slower than the actual reaction of oxidation, the controlling factor in the rate of oxidation must be the diffusion of ferrous oxide through the upper layer of slag. It can be shown that the rate of diffusion and the numerical value of the diffusion constant are dependent largely on physical characteristics, such as fluidity and agitation. At the slag-metal interface the ferric oxide formed by the oxidation of ferrous oxide is constantly being reduced by contact with the iron, and the ferrous oxide thus formed distributes itself between the slag and metal with the result that the slag is continuously supplied with ferrous oxide from this source and the metal tends to approach a saturation value dependent on the iron oxide content of the slag and the temperature.

Figure 73 is a diagrammatic representation of this transfer of oxygen from gas to metal. It indicates that the concentration of ferric oxide and ferrous oxide in the body of the slag and at the slag-gas surface shows a sharp drop in concentration of ferrous oxide and an equally sharp rise in the concentration of ferric. On the other hand at the slag-metal surface ferric oxide is reduced to ferrous by iron, and the extra heavy line at the slag-metal surface shows the increase in ferrous concentration from this reduction. It is apparent then that the transfer of oxygen from the gas to the slag is controlled by the diffusion of ferrous and ferric oxide to or from the gas surface and their diffusion through the bottom layer of the slag to the metal surface.

Turbulence is of equal importance because any agitation of the slag tends to equalize the concentration of each compound in the main body of the slag. It is also obvious that if the physical characteristics

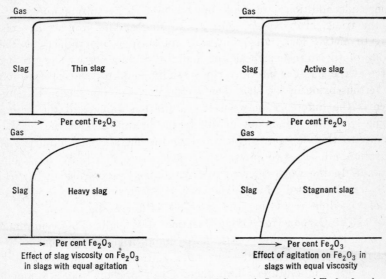

FIG. 74. Effect of Turbulence. (*Courtesy of Carnegie Institute of Technology.*)

of the top and bottom layers of the slag are the same, the overall rates of diffusion should be approximately equal. On the other hand, if either layer becomes more fluid than the other, oxidation will build up or decrease in concentration, depending upon the relative fluidities of the two layers.

Connected with this matter of turbulence is that of fluidity, as shown in Figure 74.

318. Rate of Diffusion. The diffusion of the ferrous oxide from slag to metal is governed by this general diffusion equation:

$$\frac{dv}{dt} = k\frac{d^2v}{dx^2}$$

In this equation x is the distance in the direction of which diffusion takes place; v is the degree of concentration of the diffusing material; and t is the time. The diffusion constant, k, expresses the quantity of material, in grams, which diffuses through unit area (one square centimeter) in unit time (one hour) when the difference in concentration (grams per cubic centimeter) is maintained between two sides of a layer one centimeter thick. This constant has a definite value for each pair of materials. As the temperature increases, the amplitude of thermal oscillations increases and the rate of diffusion increases.

Changes in the iron oxide content of the slag for periods when no iron oxide additions are made must be the net result of differences in the transfer of oxygen from gas to slag and of iron oxide from slag to metal. The transfer at each interface is determined by the value of the diffusion coefficient and the driving force. The driving force at the slag-gas interface is essentially equal to the concentration of ferrous oxide in the slag. The driving force of the slag-metal surface is the difference between the saturation value and the actual value from the standpoint of differences in diffusion of the ferrous oxides to the slag-gas surface and to the metal. Slag fluidity and agitation are the two physical characteristics which are most important. In the work referred to a viscosimeter, described in Article 328, was developed which gives very satisfactory results; it is commonly used in regulating the viscosity of these slags.

319. The Carbon-Iron Oxide Reaction. If a molten slag containing iron oxide is in contact with pure liquid iron, the ferrous oxide distributes itself between the slag and metal according to its solubility at various temperatures. Two factors can prevent the attainment of this equilibrium condition. First, the slag may be oxidized by the gas more rapidly than the metal can be oxidized by the slag; and second, a reaction may occur in the metal which constantly removes ferrous oxide. As a matter of fact, both of these factors are operative in the open-hearth process, and the result is that the metal is never completely saturated with ferrous oxide. The gas is constantly oxidizing the slag, and carbon in the metal constantly removing ferrous oxide from the metal until low carbon concentrations are reached or until some other deoxidizer is added which can prevent the occurrence of the carbon-iron oxide reaction, which is:

$$C(c) + FeO(c) \rightarrow CO(g) + Fe(c); \quad \Delta H = +37,600 \text{ cal.} \qquad (73)$$

The rate at which carbon is eliminated is given by the general equation:

$$\frac{-dc}{d\Theta} = k_1(C)(FeO) - k_2 PCO$$

At equilibrium the rate of elimination

$$\frac{-dc}{d\Theta} = 0$$

whence

$$k_1(C)(FeO) = k_2 PCO$$

or

$$\frac{k_1}{k_2} = K_c$$

$$= \frac{PCO}{(C)(FeO)}$$

which is the equilibrium constant for the reaction.

As the pressure of carbon monoxide is essentially constant and approximately one atmosphere,

$$K_c = \frac{1}{(C)(FeO)}$$

This may be written

$$K_c' = (C)(FeO)$$

and for convenience the equilibrium value of this product may be called m, a symbol in common use among metallurgists in this country. As $(PCO) = 1$, then

$$\frac{-dc'}{d\Theta} = k_1(C)(FeO) - k_2$$

At equilibrium

$$\frac{k_1}{k_2} = \frac{PCO}{(C)(FeO)} = \frac{1}{m}$$

whence

$$k_2 = k_1 m$$

Therefore

$$\frac{-dc}{d\Theta} = k_1(C)(FeO) - k_1 m$$

$$= k_1[(C)(FeO) - m]$$

where

$$\frac{-dc}{d\Theta} = \text{units of carbon eliminated per unit of time.}$$

k_1 = rate constant.

(C) and (FeO) = concentrations of carbon and ferrous oxide present in the metal at the time Θ.

m = the equilibrium value of the product (C)(FeO).

By plotting—$dc/d\Theta$ against the product (C) (FeO) during carbon elimination, we may obtain the value of m, as this value is the intercept on the abscissa. The slope of the line equals k_1. The results for carbons below 0.20 per cent showed the value of m to be 0.010 and k to be 0.267 for the temperature range 1570 to 1610°C. For higher carbon contents the value of m increases rapidly, and consistent results are no longer obtained. This enables the calculation of the actual ferrous oxide of the metal at low carbon contents, if the rate of carbon elimination is known and provided that the reaction proceeds as indicated above.

It appears from the experimental work carried on that the carbon-iron oxide relationship is not so simple, even at carbon contents slightly above 0.20 per cent, as would be indicated. It is well known that the insertion of a cold rod or billet into a steel bath causes a violent localized boil, showing that the normal reaction may be profoundly influenced by some external condition. Furthermore, it is the experience of melters that high carbon heats have a habit of changing their rate of carbon drop quite suddenly with little or no change in slag and metal analyses or ferrous oxide content.

The surface tension of the metal as affected by metal composition and suspended materials may well affect the release of gas to such an extent that differences in rates of carbon elimination may occur from heat to heat or from one part of a heat to another. When aluminum is added in very small quantities to rimmed steel, profound changes in the rate of gas evolution occur which cannot possibly be due to changes in the amount of iron oxide present in the steel. A change in surface tension due to the presence of alumina, which forms a fine suspension in the liquid metal, may well be the explanation of the behavior of the steel on the addition of aluminum.

Bubble formation as affected by suspended materials may also be an important factor. Heats killed and reboiled with silicon invariably showed a much more rapid rate of carbon drop when the rcboil commenced and just before the silicon was added, the increase in rate possibly being due to the presence of suspended silicates.

From the above discussion it may be concluded that in certain instances the rate of carbon elimination follows the simple kinetic law, but in many others some other factors operate which change the actual rate of elimination to a marked degree.

320. Active Iron Oxide in the Slag. Two other complications present themselves in open-hearth slags. The first of these is the unknown composition of the slag as regards the various compounds of lime and silica and other possible compounds with the other slag constituents, and the second is the uncertainty regarding the compounds of the iron oxide with lime and the question of the solid solubility of iron oxide in lime and magnesia. It has long been known that the basis of an open-hearth slag is calcium silicate, but just what silicate is formed has been the cause of considerable controversy. It can be said that the preponderance of evidence on the form of the calcium silicate in solid slags is toward the dicalcium silicate, $2CaO \cdot SiO_2$. Significantly enough, determinations of the viscosity of lime-silica slags show that there is a maximum fluidity at 48 per cent lime and 52 per cent silica, or almost the exact composition of dicalcium silicate. During the melting period of many open-hearth heats, the percentage of lime and silica in the slag is almost equal, and these slags are by far the most fluid of any slags found in open-hearth practice.

Numerous investigators have found that ferric oxide combines with lime to form calcium ferrites which are stable at steel-making temperatures. Such ferrites, ranging from $2CaO \cdot Fe_2O_3$ to $3CaO \cdot Fe_2O_3$, have been studied, and the indication is that the most stable of these is the dicalcium ferrite, $2CaO \cdot Fe_2O_3$.

321. Character of the Scrap. When the open-hearth furnace is charged with scrap, or with scrap and cold pig iron, oxidation by the furnace gases begins to take place at once. The amount of this oxidation depends primarily on the time occupied in melting and on the surface of the metal exposed, less on the character of the furnace gases, for these are almost always highly oxidizing. Thus, it has been found that with heavy scrap about 2 pounds of ferrous oxide are formed per hundred pounds of scrap, whereas with medium-sized scrap (the size equivalent to rail scrap) about 8 pounds of ferrous oxide are formed. As for length of exposure to the furnace gases, it was found, with a furnace burning fuel oil and using cold metal, that 6.5 pounds of ferrous oxide was formed per hundred pounds of charge when 5.5

hours were required to get the heat "under cover," whereas when 7.5 hours were required, 11.3 pounds of ferrous oxide were formed.

SLAG CONTROL

322. General. It is obvious, from what has gone before, that physical chemistry in the hands of patient investigators has been the means of sifting out some very important factors in open-hearth operation. Detailed records of every heat, as shown in Figure 71, are now kept in an effort to establish some correlation between slag conditions and the character of the finished steel. In a general way we know that the iron oxide content of the bath is one of its most important properties; that sulfur in the metal is lowered by increased basicity, fluidity, agitation, and high temperature; that the removal of phosphorus is favored by low temperatures, and the important role that silicon plays in the process. It is one thing to carry out these individual determinations in the laboratory, quite another to make such determinations under the pressure and conditions of steel-plant operation. Nevertheless, metallurgists have made encouraging progress, and, although the answer to their prayer, in the shape of a perfect method of control which will take into consideration all these factors, has not been found, some of the following methods have been very satisfactory from an operational standpoint.

Before we undertake a discussion of them, however, we should recapitulate by stating the ultimate objects of slag control:

1. To produce a slag in the furnace that will eliminate phosphorus and sulfur to the desired extent without excessive use of lime or excessive loss of iron as oxide.
2. To conserve as far as possible both lime and deoxidizers.
3. To prevent excessive waste of iron in the slag, particularly on grades of steel that do not have strict phosphorus requirements.
4. To shorten the melting period as much as possible through the use of as little limestone in the charge as possible.
5. To standardize the conditions of oxidation so that the deoxidizing addition will unfailingly produce the desired type of ingot.

323. Visual Observation. Up to about twenty years ago this was the only method of controlling open-hearth slags. The school of hard knocks and experience has developed melters who have an almost uncanny ability to judge the condition of the bath and metal from the appearance of a fractured surface of the metal or slag. Uncanny is probably the right word to use in describing their ability to judge the carbon content of a fractured test piece, at least in the lower brackets, within 0.03 per cent. The method is far from satisfactory, however; witness the off-heats that come along from time to time.

324. Rapid Methods of Chemical Analysis. These methods are now available, particularly with the methods of analysis developed by the chemist in his micro-methods, so that the amount of carbon can be determined fairly accurately in 3 to 15 minutes; manganese in 10 to 15 minutes; iron oxide, sulfur, and phosphorus in 20 to 30 minutes; and silicon in 30 to 40 minutes.

325. Appearance of the Slag in the Furnace. The appearance of the slag in the furnace during the melting period is indicative of its chemical composition and of its future requirements in addition agents. High-silicon slags will be thin and watery, usually low in iron oxide and with numerous lumps of lime floating around in them, apparently indifferent to the laws of solution. Incidentally, the geologist, with the petrographic microscope, has been able to show that these lumps of lime are coated with a high melting-point dicalcium silicate which can be fluxed away only by the action of fairly high concentrations of iron oxide. On the other hand, slags low in silicon are thick, stiff, and viscous, usually of a medium or high iron oxide content, but easily adjusted by additions of roll scale, sand, or fluorspar.

326. Color of the Slag. The color of the slag, when cooled in water, is a good guide to its composition. It will vary from black slags with a medium iron oxide content and a low lime-silica ratio to the light brown, which will have a medium concentration of both, down to the chocolate brown slags, which will be high in iron oxide and high in lime-silica ratio. The color of the slag as a means of control has the advantage that a review of any period of the heat may be made if samples have been taken over that period.

327. Slag Cakes. Janitsky first proposed this method of control by observing the appearance of the surface texture of slag cakes poured into standard molds. The surface of such a slag cake changes from a wrinkled, sometimes crepe-like top, in a weakly basic slag, to a shiny, smooth top in a more basic slag, and finally to a lustrous top in an extremely basic one. This method has been further refined so that surface markings, resulting from high manganese oxide and high phosphorus, give useful information as to the working of the slag with respect to the elimination of these elements. Unfortunately, changes in raw materials and changes in melters and observers influence the result, and, consequently, a given interpretation in one plant may not be applicable to some other one.

328. Slag Viscosity. Another very useful characteristic is slag viscosity, which has been long used by acid open-hearth melters as a criterion of slag conditions. The earlier methods were very rough ones consisting of pouring the slag over a slightly inclined cold plate and observing the length of run under fairly standard conditions. In the

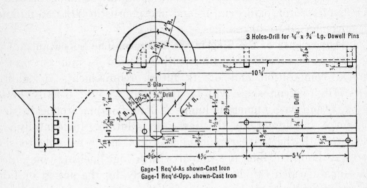

FIG. 75. Viscosimeter. (*Courtesy of Carnegie Institute of Technology.*)

investigations carried on by C. C. Herty, Jr., and his associates, a viscosimeter, shown in Figure 75, was devised which has been widely used in open-hearth plants. This viscosimeter is split along the longitudinal axis and held together by dowels. When assembled and

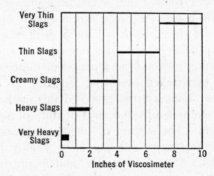

FIG. 76. Viscosimeter Relationships. (*Courtesy of Carnegie Institute of Technology.*)

in a horizontal position, it is placed as close to the wicket hole as possible. A spoon is thoroughly slagged in the bath and a sample removed and poured into the funnel as quickly as possible, making sure that the funnel is filled with slag. The distance which the slag has flowed is measured by a calibrated rod which is inserted in the quarter-inch hole in the end of the apparatus. With increased fluidity the slag flows further out the horizontal hole, and the distance of the flow is a function of slag fluidity. Unfortunately, the degree of super heat in the slag has some effect on the numerical value obtained, but variations in the temperature of the viscosimeter itself, up to the point where it can be easily handled with gloves, apparently have no effect on the results obtained. Slag relationships thus determined are shown in Figure 76.

STATISTICAL EVALUATION OF OPEN-HEARTH FACTORS

329. General. A knowledge of relationships enables one to predict and control. This is one of the major aims of science. Prediction of the weather is within our everyday experience and is made on the basis of a careful analysis of a tremendous amount of data and statistics that has been gathered over the years by the United States Weather Bureau. It is obvious that a great many factors will influence the weather, some of them being the barometric pressure, the temperature, the direction and magnitude of the wind, the configuration of the land, the presence or absence of sun spots, and the direction of ocean currents. Although it is very easy to see the relationship between a heavy rainfall and the rise of a river, the connection between the direction of water currents in the polar sea and the level of the ground water in Indiana is not quite as obvious. This study of relationships has been accelerated and simplified by the mathematics of statistics.

330. Correlation. Correlation implies reciprocal relationships, a corresponding similarity or parallelism of relation or law. There is, for example, a definite correlation between the ages of husbands and wives, although the age of one is not the cause and effect of the age of the other. There are certain, natural forces associated with age which causes the ages of husbands and wives to be associated as they are. Again, there is a definite relationship or correlation between the rate of reading and the amount comprehended. It is not the speed of reading but the ability which enables one to read fast that causes the comprehension. The numerical expression of the amount of correlation is called the coefficient of correlation and is generally expressed in hundredths.

The wheels of an automobile, if small, will make more revolutions in covering one mile than will larger wheels. Quantitatively, large wheels are associated with fewer revolutions and smaller wheels are associated with more revolutions. The quantitative relationship is, therefore, inverse; large is associated with few and small is associated with many. Such a correlation is described as a negative one.

On the other hand, values above the mean of a certain series may correspond to values above the mean of another series, and the values below a mean may be associated with the values below the mean of the related series. Such a relationship is termed a positive correlation. A partial relationship where other factors enter into the matter may be represented by the movement of the automobile and the consumption of gasoline. The relationship is obvious, but it is modified by other factors, including the roughness and grade of the road, the amount of traffic, the number of stops, the skill of the driver, the weather, and the condition and load of the automobile. Still again, the correlation between certain variables may be essentially zero; that is, there is no trend in the relationships that is apparent in either a positive or a negative correlation. No one can predict from the height of water in the Wabash River who will be elected president next year.

To return to the coefficient of correlation again: It is usually expressed as a decimal, as $0.67 \pm .32$, the latter figure indicating the quality and quantity of the probable error. It is commonly assumed that when the coefficient of correlation is greater than 0.36 and four times as great as the probable error, there is a definite relationship between the two phenomena being measured. When it is six times as great, the relationship is regarded as strong. In the case of the automobile wheels the correlation factor would be 1.00.

When there are a number of variables in the relationship under discussion, as in the prediction of weather and in the operation of an open-hearth furnace, many factors are involved. By means of a method known as multiple correlation it is sometimes possible to increase the reliability of a prediction by finding the correlation between one variable and a composite of several others.

331. Open-Hearth Data. Fetters and Chipman* attempted to work out the slag-metal relationships in the basic open-hearth furnace using the methods of simple correlation. More recently Gould and Hand have employed methods involving multiple correlation. Although this method involves a multiplicity of calculations and the use of punched tabulating cards, such as shown in Figure 77, with fully automatic calculating machines, it does permit:

* "Slag-Metal Relationships in the Basic Open-Hearth Furnace," American Institute of Mining and Metallurgical Engineers, *Transactions*, 1940.

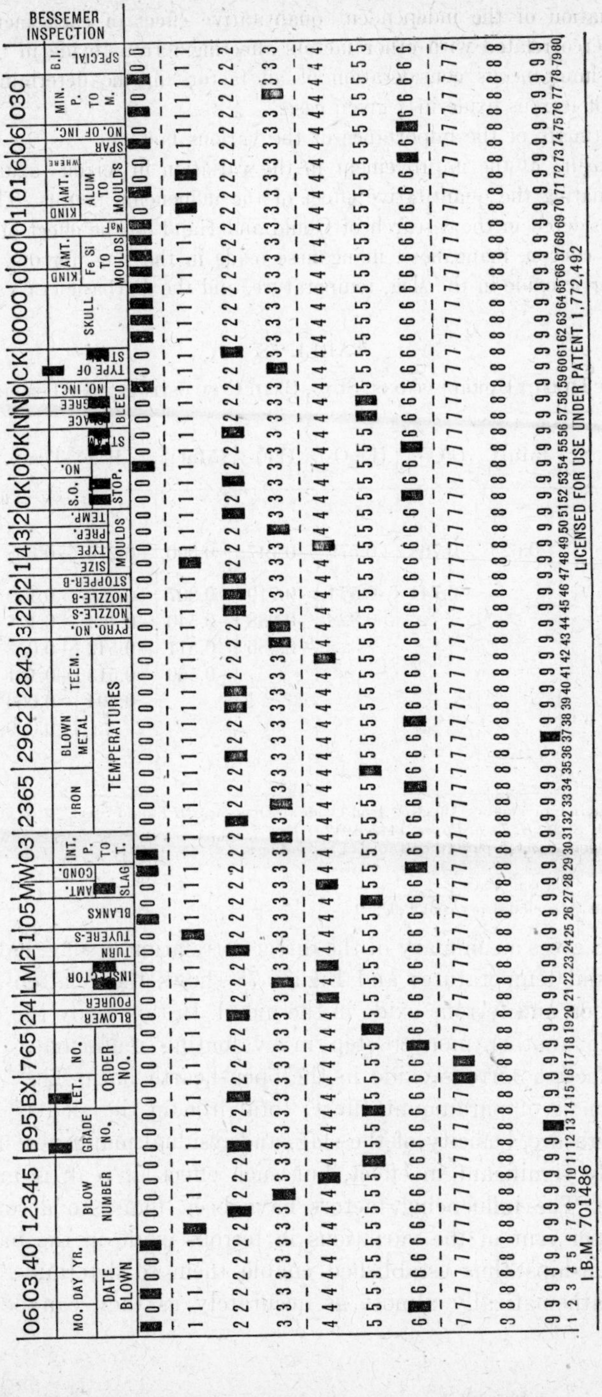

Fig. 77. Statistical Card.

1. Evaluation of the independent quantitative effect of each factor even though intercorrelated with other factors affecting ferrous oxide in the bath.

2. The simultaneous consideration of all factors in the determination of the effect of ferrous oxide in a given case.

3. An estimate of the importance of the various factors.

4. A measure of the improvement in the variation in ferrous oxide values after eliminating the quantitative effect of the influencing factors. The seven factors considered in the research of Gould and Hand on the effect on ferrous oxide were carbon, manganese, manganese oxide in the slag, ferrous oxide in the slag, ferric oxide in the slag, temperature, and the R (basicity) value.

TABLE 58

SUMMARY OF DIRECT CORRELATIONS: SLAG, BATH COMPOSITION, AND TEMPERATURE*

Factor	[Mn]†	(FeO)	(Fe₂O₃)	(Fe)	(MnO)	R	Temp.	[FeO]
$\dfrac{1}{[c]}$	−0.625	+0.764	+0.579	+0.747	−0.390	+0.216	+0.508	+0.944
[Mn]		−0.741	−0.574	−0.719	+0.807	−0.286	−0.139	−0.575
(FeO)			+0.828	+0.988	−0.540	+0.464	+0.175	+0.750
(Fe₂O₃)				+0.886	−0.511	+0.542	+0.013	+0.584
(Fe)					−0.550	+0.515	+0.161	+0.742
(MnO)						−0.494	−0.066	−0.341
R							−0.009	+0.192
Temp.								+0.497

* "An Evaluation of Factors Affecting Iron Oxide in Open-hearth Liquid Steel," J. E. Gould, and H. G. Howe, *A. S. M. E. Tech. Paper*, 1442, 1942.

† Brackets refer to metal, parantheses to slag percentages.

$n = 65$.

$$R = \frac{\text{Per cent CaO}}{\text{Per cent SiO}_2 + 0.634 \text{ per cent P}_2\text{O}_5}$$

Table 58 gives a summary of the direct correlation of slag, bath composition, and temperature; and Figure 78 shows the relationship between carbon and ferrous oxide in the metal. In this study the authors have made another pioneer step in evaluating mathematically the factors affecting ferrous oxide in the open-hearth bath. They believe that carbon is of paramount effect; total iron in the slag is second; and temperature, basicity of the slag, and residual manganese may be statistically significant in effect, but such effect, if real, is minor in magnitude. The influencing factors have been found to account for about 90 per cent of the variations in ferrous oxide in the bath and the relationships thus established enable them to determine certain factors mathematically almost as accurately as they can be determined chemically in duplicate tests. Furthermore, the carbon relationship as determined statistically from actual data has been found to fit the thermodynamic equilibrium curve with a constant supersaturation.

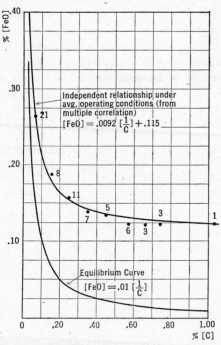

Fig. 78. Relationship between Carbon and Ferrous Oxide in the Metal. (*Courtesy of American Institute of Metallurgical Engineers.*)

DEOXIDATION OF STEELS

332. General. If the molten slag and metal reached equilibrium in the basic open-hearth furnace, the metal would contain about 0.3 per cent oxygen; but, since it never does reach equilibrium, the oxygen content must be considerably below this figure, probably never exceeding 0.15 per cent. Not only does this oxygen tend to produce blowholes, but it also has bad effects on the physical properties of the metal. It increases slightly the hardness, decreases the elastic limit, and decreases the ductility and resistance to impact; consequently, all steels must be treated after the heat is completed in the open-hearth furnace in order to remove a part or all of this oxygen. Incidentally, at the same time, carbon is also added because the practice in this country, irrespective of the kind of steel being made, is to take the carbon down to a rather low level and then add a recarburizer to meet the desired specifications. These changes are carried out by ferroalloys known as "deoxidizers" and "recarburizers." Common ones and their chemical compositions are shown in Table 44. Such additions are also made to produce the type of steel desired, such as coarse-grained or fine-grained, killed steel, rimmed steel, as well as to develop special properties in the product such as corrosion resistance, machinability, or susceptibility to aging.

333. The Reactions of Deoxidation. When silicon is added to steel, it reacts with iron oxide according to the equation

$$Si(c) + 2FeO(c) \rightarrow SiO_2(c) + 2Fe(c); \quad \Delta H = -70,200 \text{ cal.} \quad (74)$$

This equation proceeds until the silicon and iron oxide are in equilibrium with dissolved silica. If the metal is saturated with dissolved silicon, the equilibrium constant of this reaction is

$$K_{Si} = \frac{SiO_2}{(Si)(FeO)^2}$$

which may be written

$$K'_{Si} = \frac{1}{(Si)(FeO)^2}$$

or in the most convenient form for general use as

$$K''_{Si} = (Si)(FeO)^2$$

Experimental determination has indicated that the value for K''_{Si} is 1.9×10^{-5} at 1500°C.; 1.5×10^{-4} at 1400°C.; 1.0×10^{-3} at 1700°C.

Aluminum reacts with iron oxide according to the equation

$$2Al(c) + 3FeO(c) \rightarrow Al_2O_3(c) + 3Fe(c); \quad \Delta H = -207,000 \text{ cal.} \quad (75)$$

The equilibrium constant for this reaction is

$$K_{Al} = \frac{(Al_2O_3)}{(Al)^2(FeO)^3}$$

In the presence of pure alumina, as is essentially true when appreciable amounts of aluminum are added, the constant may be written

$$K''_{Al} = (Al)^2(FeO)^3$$

The experimental work of Chipman indicated that the constant for this reaction is 1.0×10^{-14} at 1500°C.; 7×10^{-13} at 1600°C.; 4×10^{-11} at 1700°C.

Manganese reacts with iron oxide according to the equation

$$FeO(c) + Mn(c) \rightarrow MnO(c) + Fe(c); \quad \Delta H = -26{,}800 \text{ cal.} \quad (76)$$

and this equilibrium constant is

$$K_{Mn} = \frac{(MnO)}{(Mn)(FeO)}$$
$$= 4.55 \text{ at } 1500°C.; \ 2.30 \text{ at } 1600°; \ 1.25 \text{ at } 1700°$$

From these and other thermochemical data it can be said that the deoxidizing powers of various elements commonly added to steel increase with the heats of formation of the oxides as follows: manganese, molybdenum, calcium, chromium, silicon, titanium, vanadium, and aluminum.

334. Other Factors in Deoxidation. The equilibrium constant for the reaction is only one of the factors involved, there being other forces at work (such as the speed of the reaction) which may affect adversely the process of deoxidation. For example, the coalescence of the non-metallic particles depends largely upon their melting points; substances formed with fusion temperatures above or near that of the metal cannot coalesce but must occur as small, widely scattered particles through the metal. Liquid substances that coalesce rise faster in the liquid metal than very small solid particles and may rise to the surface of the steel in the ladle and in the mold. The rate of the rise of solid particles varies inversely with the density and is very slow for small ones, the probable rates for particles 0.001 inch in diameter ranging from 0.35 to 0.7 centimeter per minute. The order in which additions are made in the ladle is frequently a matter of concern because, if an energetic deoxidizer of low density is added at the top of the ladle, most of it may be lost by reaction with the slag. That all these points are important ones is shown by the fact that, when silicon is used to deoxidize the steel and is added in just the right proportions, there is formed a low fusing point inclusion most likely to coalesce and rise out of the steel; but the deoxidation is not quite complete so that the steel will be of a coarse-grained type unless deoxidation is completed with some other reagent such as titanium, vanadium, or aluminum, when the steel will be of the fine-grain, abnormal type. At present, the various grades of ferromanganese and ferrosilicon and silicomanganese and ferrocarbon titanium are the most common deoxidizers used in open-hearth practice.

BASIC OPEN-HEARTH YIELDS

335. General. It is obvious from what has gone before that there is a considerable loss of iron in the basic open-hearth process. As a matter of fact, there is a distressingly large loss. Gratifying developments have taken place in recent years resulting in a better understanding of the physical chemistry of the process, the physical

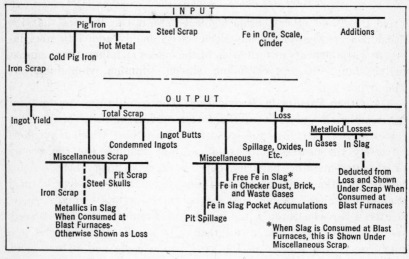

FIG. 79. Basic Open-Hearth Yields. (*Courtesy of American Institute of Metallurgical Engineers.*)

development of much larger units, decreased fuel consumption, and increased length of furnace campaigns, but there have not been comparable gains in the yield of the furnace. A basic open-hearth yield may be defined as the ingot yield obtained in the process of converting pig iron, scrap, and ore into steel. The difference between the total weight of ingots and the scrap produced and the original metal charged constitutes the loss. The character of this loss is shown in diagrammatic form in Figure 79. In standard practice yields will run as low as 87 per cent to as high as 92 per cent. Unfortunately, this discussion must be confined to only the more important losses. For a more detailed discussion, as well as a description of the methods of calculation, the reader is referred to the excellent paper by C. D. King.[25]

336. Spillage, Oxidation, Foreign Material. In handling the hot metal at the mixer, or at the open-hearth furnace, mechanical losses in the form of shots, spittings, and splashings are bound to occur, normally amounting to about 0.5 per cent per ton of hot metal.

Wherever hot metal is used, kish* is bound to form in transfer ladles, and sometimes this is difficult to remove. A part of this kish may be returned in the ladle or some of it may join the slag, and in most plants this is not taken into account, leading to fictitious low yields. For example, if the original metal contains 1 per cent of kish and no consideration is given to this, on a 50 per cent hot metal charge the yield will show an error of at least 0.5 per cent.

At most plants no allowance is usually made for losses on steel scrap due to the presence in this scrap of foreign materials such as scale, dirt, oil, and paint. Although actual losses of this nature are very difficult to determine, and will vary considerably from heat to heat and from plant to plant, a conservative figure is 0.4 per cent per ton of steel scrap.

Still another loss is caused by the silica and silicon in the steel scrap or pig iron. Such scrap may contain as much as 10 per cent of slag by weight, and dirt and sand will be found attached to many forms of light scrap, the poorer forms of market scrap, and pig iron.

The loss of manganese, silicon, carbon, vanadium, etc., through the addition of ferroalloys, varies in practice, depending upon slag conditions, presence of other oxidizable elements, temperature, the time allowed for deoxidizing action, and other factors. For manganese and silicon this can be assumed to be about a 25 per cent loss.

337. Scrap Losses. Besides the formation of iron scrap, which has been treated in the previous article, considerable pit scrap will be formed as iron skulls, steel skulls, pit scrap, etc. This loss will naturally vary with the quantity and kind of pit scrap produced and with the care with which it is handled, but a fair figure is 0.3 per cent on the total metallic charge. In addition to this there is also the production of condemned ingots and ingot butts.

338. Miscellaneous Losses. It is evident from the large amounts of materials taken out of slag pockets, when furnaces are rebuilt, and from the analyses of the same, that appreciable amounts of iron are lost in this manner. One plant showed an accumulation of about 14 pounds of slag per ton of ingots, which was the equivalent of 6.5

* A mixture of iron, graphite, and magnetic iron oxide.

pounds of iron or 0.29 per cent per net ton of ingots. Other plants
showed a range of 0.06 to 0.35 per cent per net ton of ingots.

There is another loss, and a like variation in its magnitude, in
checker-chamber dust. A test made on the production of about 16,000
tons of ingots produced about 61,000 pounds of checker dust or the

TABLE 59

CALCULATION OF BASIC OPEN-HEARTH YIELDS[25]

Materials	Percentage of Materials Used per Ton Metallic Charge	Percentage of Losses in Charge Components	Percentage of Losses per Ton of Total Metallic Charge
Iron in ore, scale, etc.	4.5	7.41	0.333
Hot metal	61.8	8.36	5.167
Steel scrap	33.3	1.40	0.466
Additions	0.4	25.00	0.100
Total metallic charge	100.0		6.066
Limestone	4.36	0.28	0.012
Dolomite	2.37	1.07	0.025
Fluorspar	0.28	0.90	0.003
Total losses			6.106
Net losses			6.11
Scrap recovered: miscellaneous scrap			3.00
Condemned ingots and butts			1.00
Total scrap			4.00
Total net loss and scrap			10.11
Ingot yield			89.89
Total			100.00

equivalent of 3.8 pounds of iron per ton of ingots, and, assuming
that it contained 50 per cent iron, this is the equivalent of 0.09
per cent iron per ton of ingots. The loss will vary with the type of
fuel used, being lowest when natural gas and highest when tar is
employed. In the former case it will be of the order of 0.03 per cent
of iron per ton of ingots, and in the latter as much as 0.35 per cent.

There is always some free metallic iron in run-off slags and frequently in the final slags. Not only does the amount of this free
iron vary but, of course, the slag volumes also vary considerably.
An average figure seems to be about 0.2 per cent of iron per ton
of metallic charge.

It is also obvious that the erosion of some parts of the furnace structure, particularly the side walls and roof, will result in a further loss of iron. Measurements of wall and roof erosion are very difficult to obtain accurately, and in various tests conducted show a range of 0.06 to 0.1 per cent of iron per ton of metallic charge.

339. Estimate of Open-Hearth Yields. An estimate of an open-hearth yield is shown in Table 59, from which it will be seen that there is a wide variation possible because of the different scrap produced as well as the magnitude of the miscellaneous losses. To ascertain these, it is necessary to conduct carefully controlled heat tests. In connection with the magnitude of this yield it does not necessarily follow that the best yield will give the lowest cost ingots. This will depend entirely on the relative prices of materials making up the gross metallic charge for equal scrap recovery as well as the character of the open-hearth cycle. There must also be considered the difference in cost in converting any type of metallic charge to ingots. In addition, where plants are physically handicapped in charging large amounts of scrap, thus slowing up production and adding in obvious ways to the cost of conversion, it may be found desirable to forego the use of the cheaper metallic mixture. The lower yield with higher ore and pig charge does not, therefore, necessarily mean higher ingot cost in actual practice. The inexpensive iron in the ore may give a lower cost for the mixture, thereby offsetting the disadvantages of lower yields; therefore, it is apparent that the open-hearth yield does not necessarily determine the charge to be used, but blast-furnace, open-hearth, Bessemer, and metal-market conditions will also be factors in making a choice.

SPECIAL PROCESSES

340. General. Ever since the Martin brothers developed the present open-hearth process, metallurgists have experimented with modifications of it in an effort to reduce the time required and to improve yields. Having in mind the very rapid oxidation in the Bessemer converter, as well as the violent oxidation brought about when raw ore is added to an open-hearth bath, they have conducted extensive experiments aimed at this goal. Of these methods, space permits only a discussion of the duplex and triplex processes and brief mention of the Talbot, Campbell, Bertrand-Thiel, and Monel processes.

341. The Duplex Process. Although the term duplex process may be applied to any combination of two processes for the manufacture of steel, actually it has been restricted to a combination of the acid

Bessemer and the basic open-hearth process in which the latter plays only the part of a finishing process in completing the elimination of carbon and phosphorus.

In the conventional pig-and-scrap process a charge of approximately 50 per cent pig iron and 50 per cent scrap is generally used. Practically all the scrap is of basic open-hearth grade with a phosphorus content of approximately 0.015 per cent, with the result that in a 200,000-pound charge there is about 240 pounds of phosphorus to be removed. In the duplex process the charge may consist of duplex metal blown entirely from basic pig iron. The phosphorus content of such a 200,000-pound charge is over 450 pounds; consequently, the slag for the duplex process must be capable of oxidizing and removing twice as much phosphorus as that of the regular basic process. The iron oxide content is thus of necessity comparatively high, and for that reason sulfur elimination is retarded except when unusually large amounts of limestone are added. Duplex metal is charged into the open-hearth furnace from ladles of approximately 25 tons capacity, this weight corresponding to that of the Bessemer blow. Owing to the extreme rapidity of the latter process, it is difficult to stop the blow at a predetermined carbon content, and it is the usual practice to blow full, which means that the resulting product contains about 0.05 per cent carbon as a maximum, 0.10 per cent manganese as a maximum, and a phosphorus and sulfur content about 10 per cent higher than that of the initial pig iron (this increase is due to the oxidation loss in the Bessemer converter). When the metal is transferred, in tilting the converter at the end of the blow, a considerable amount of slag is of necessity run into the ladle with the metal, and various amounts of this objectionable material are then charged into the open-hearth furnace.

As soon as this charging is complete, approximately 10 to 20 per cent of its weight of pig iron is added, which causes a violent reaction through the oxidation of carbon by the iron oxide. The violence of this boil is determined by the degree of oxidation of the duplex metal, its temperature, and the temperature of the pig iron. As a result of this vigorous reaction, the metal and slag are intimately mixed and the high concentration of ferrous oxide, together with low silica, insures a rapid oxidation and removal of the phosphorus.

At this point an interesting comparison with a regular basic open-hearth process is possible. In the regular process iron oxide in the form of iron ore is used to oxidize an excess of carbon, whereas in the duplex process an excess of carbon in the molten pig iron is used to reduce the iron oxide which saturates the duplex metal. At present it is not practicable to determine the degree of oxidation of the duplex metal; consequently, the amount of pig iron necessary to effect complete deoxidation and to provide for a slight excess of carbon is more or less a matter for intelligent guessing. So far as the oxidation of carbon is concerned the ideal procedure would be to determine the extent of oxidation and then calculate the amount of carbon or pig iron necessary. This is not practicable at present, and the best procedure is to add an amount of pig iron which is greatly in excess. On the whole the proper slag for the shaping-up period is much more difficult to attain than in the standard open-hearth process; exact conditions of slag viscosity and temperature from heat to heat are difficult to duplicate and maintain because of the variability of the duplex metal.

The chief advantage of the duplex process lies in the fact that when there is a pressing demand for steel, tonnage can be increased very quickly and cheaply, shortening the time of the open-hearth operation by about one-half. For example, one conventional open-hearth furnace will turn out an average of about fifteen heats in a week of straight running by the ordinary method, but the same furnace operated as a duplexing unit will produce about forty heats in the same period. This shortening of the time of heat saves fuel, and, of course, the elimination of silicon in the converter tends to prolong the life of the furnace by reducing the erosion of the bottom and banks. Another advantage is that it does not require the use of scrap, which is a considerable one when scrap is scarce and high in price. Offsetting these advantages, however, are the double conversion costs and the decrease in yield because of the increased oxidation, both of which factors are important in the economics of the process. Furthermore, in dull times especially, the extra cost of maintaining two separate units may more than counterbalance the gain from increased output. Still a third disadvantage lies in the general suspicion which has been directed toward duplex steel. There is a thought in the mind of the consumer that duplex steel, having been in contact with a Bessemer converter, is little better than Bessemer steel, with the result that a great many specifications, industrial as well as governmental, prohibit the use of this type of steel. The amount of duplex steel has ranged from 2.2 per cent of the total tonnage produced in 1932 to 5.4 per cent in 1929 (in 1940 it was 3.3 per cent).

342. The Duplex Process in the Southern District. The ore in the Birmingham district contains about 0.35 per cent phosphorus, with the result that no pig iron is available that is suitable for the Bessemer process, whereas in the northern part of the United States there are limited tonnages of Bessemer ore. Second, there is no low phosphorus iron or spiegel commercially available for recarburizing in the southern district as there is in the north, and this lack of a recarburizer makes it necessary to catch the carbon on the way down in the manufacture of high-carbon steels in the south. Third, pig iron made from the Birmingham ores averages about 0.80 per cent phosphorus, which is very high compared with the phosphorus content of the Lake pig irons, the average of which is about 0.25 per cent. Consequently, in the manufacture of high carbon steels from high-phosphorus pig iron, the duplex process offers exceptional advantages for catching the carbon high, thus reducing to a minimum the amount of coal or coke dust required and also avoiding rephosphorization from the high-phosphorus slag. Still another advantage of the process is the production of a slag which contains a high enough percentage of phosphoric acid to make it suitable in the manufacture of fertilizer. As a matter of fact, the southern furnaces are manipulated in order to obtain a slag most suitable for use as a soil conditioner.

343. Triplex Process. When operating with pig irons containing more than 0.8 per cent phosphorus, it is found difficult to prevent the reduction of some of the phosphoric oxide after recarburizing because of the high content of this constituent in the slag. Such reduction occurs chiefly in the steel ladle, especially where the metal is in direct contact with the mass of floating slag and reducing agents present in the steel or added in the form of recarburizers. This condition can be overcome only by finishing the steel under a new slag that is low in phosphorus. Although this might be done in the same open-hearth furnace in which the steel was originally purified, it is frequently much more convenient to employ a "triplex" process in which the purified molten metal is transferred from the Bessemer to the first open hearth and then to a second, where a new slag is made up and the metal finished under a slag low in phosphorus. Triplexing processes, although tried in this country and used for a time, are now seldom employed, as the rehandling of the molten metal leads to high heat and material losses and does not make for efficient operation of the furnaces without much special equipment.

344. Other Processes. In the course of time, since its original development by the Martin brothers, the original pig-and-scrap process has undergone various modifications, chief among which are the Talbot, the Campbell, the Bertrand-Thiel, and the Monel processes. All of these use a large basic-lined tilting furnace in which a large bath of purified metal is always retained. Talbot speeded up the oxidation of silicon, manganese, phosphorus, and carbon by pouring molten pig iron into this bath so that the operation is made nearly continuous and the time between tappings greatly reduced. Campbell's tilting furnace could be tilted forward so that the frothing of the bath brought about by the violent reactions of oxidation could not throw the slag through the doors as it would in the case of a stationary furnace. The Bertrand-Thiel process is a two-stage one, in the first of which the furnace is tapped in order to separate the metal from the slag, which contains such a high percentage of phosphoric acid that it is marketable as a fertilizer or soil conditioner. The metal is then either poured back into the same furnace, or better, into another basic furnace, for final purification. The Monel process resembles the Talbot except that the Monel employs a stationary furnace charged with limestone and ore. These are heated until the bath becomes pasty, when molten pig iron is added. Rapid oxidation occurs; the slag foams up and runs from the furnace through slag notches provided for this purpose.

A modification of the Monel process is sometimes used in the United States with pig irons containing a fairly high percentage of phosphorus or in mills that produce considerable high-phosphorus scrap. Limestone is first charged on the bottom of the basic open-hearth furnace, then ore and scrap on top of the ore. The charge is heated and molten pig iron added to make the total pig about 50 per cent of the charge. A lively reaction results in which almost all the silicon, manganese, phosphorus, and a part of the carbon are oxidized. About 80 per cent of this slag is drawn off at the end of about three hours and finally, with ore additions, the carbon is worked out of the bath until, if the heat is to be caught on the way down, it has been reduced to the proper level for tapping.

345. Tilting Furnaces. The greater use of molten metal in American steel plants as well as the more common use of such modifications as the Talbot, Monel, and triplex processes have resulted in the development of a tilting-type furnace. Such a furnace is rectangular in shape and has about the same proportions as an ordinary basic open-hearth furnace but a much greater depth in order to furnish a reservoir to hold a considerable amount of molten metal. Furthermore, the structural work must be much stronger to resist the twisting stresses and vibrations brought about when the heavy furnace is tilting. Only that section of the furnace comprising the hearth, side walls, and roof tilts. The ports and flues are stationary, and together with the checker work are of much the same construction as that employed in stationary furnaces. These furnaces are supported on trunnions and rollers so formed that the center of rotation of the furnace coincides with the center line of the ports. With this arrangement the operator is able to maintain heat on the furnace while it is being tilted, if such proves to be necessary. The clearance between the movable and stationary parts of the furnace is kept very small by means of water-cooled metal joints to facilitate the heating of the furnace even during the tapping of the heat.

Such furnaces, although much more expensive in initial cost than the stationary type, have some very definite advantages:

1. It is much easier to handle molten metal in them than in the conventional open-hearth. It is somewhat difficult to pour a 25-ton ladle of molten steel through a runner into the vertical door of a stationary furnace. The tilting type can be elevated so that the door, making less inclination to the horizontal, is much easier of access.

2. The operator is able to remove a raw or unsatisfactory slag much more easily than in the stationary type of furnace. In the stationary type enough charge must be added to elevate the slag level for such withdrawal, but in the tilting type the furnace itself can be canted until the slag runs out through the slag notch.

3. As in the conventional open hearth, the slag tap hole is often at the slag line so that in tapping a charge of metal all that is necessary is to plug this tapping hole temporarily with a piece of wet sacking, depress that side of the furnace; and, as the slag rises along the sloping back wall, this sacking prevents the egress of the slag until the metal has reached this point to burn the sacking away. Obviously, this does away with heats that are slow to tap because of the small tap hole or low metal temperature or heats that are hard to open because of tap-hole difficulties. Furthermore, it permits tapping on much closer temperature limits. Where a close tapping temperature is necessary, a slow tap will often cause a skull in the bottom of the ladle and produce bad pouring conditions for a large part of the heat.

4. Since slag and metal are under the control of the operator, tilting furnaces do away with soft heats (ones melting low in carbon), high heats (high in silicon), and raw heats (high in carbon). The size of heat charged into a stationary furnace is normally governed by the size of the ladle into which it will be tapped. It often happens that additions of pig iron must be made for melting or finishing of the heat. Often for fear that the heat will exceed the capacity of the ladle, this iron is not added and the furnace

is driven at a higher temperature, with the danger of overoxidizing the metal. If too much iron is added, the excess must be run out into the pit. With the tilting type, the furnace may be returned to an upright position when the ladle is full, and any steel remaining is retained for the following heat.

5. There is less danger of breakouts of slag in the front and ends because, when violent boils do occur, the furnace can be depressed and the doors elevated above the slag level.

6. On the whole there is much less bottom trouble, and, when this trouble does occur, repairs are much more easily made. This loss of time through bad bottoms and banks is especially bad in the manufacture of low-carbon steel. Often hours are spent in washing a bottom free of accumulated lime and steel left from previous heats.

INDUCED DRAFT FURNACES

346. General. Reference has already been made to the improvements and refinements in open-hearth operation in connection with the control of temperature, maintenance of the checker work, insulation of the furnaces, better refractories, etc. Another type of open-hearth furnace development having to do with the control of another important furnace condition—the atmosphere prevailing on the hearth —made its appearance about fifteen years ago—the Isley furnace. The old type of open-hearth furnace was dependent for combustion control upon the draft of a 150-foot stack and a rather complicated valve system which possessed the following inherent shortcomings:

1. The necessarily high temperature at which the gases must be delivered to the stack in order to make it operative.

2. The great temperature difference incidental to the reversal of flue gas and air, and consequently the large variation in preheated air and fuel delivered to the furnace during the cycle.

3. The leakages and resistances created by the reversing apparatus and the complicated flues.

4. The inadequate range of control afforded by the natural draft system especially under adverse atmospheric conditions (there must always be a negative pressure on the hearth for the stack to be operative).

347. The Isley Furnace. The inventor of this system of furnace control had in mind the following novel features:

1. To create positive furnace draft as and when wanted.
2. To furnish air for combustion as and when wanted.
3. To make the heat-generative function of the furnace system a maximum.
4. To simplify the construction and lessen the maintenance of the plant.

Such a furnace, shown in Figure 80, has the general shape and

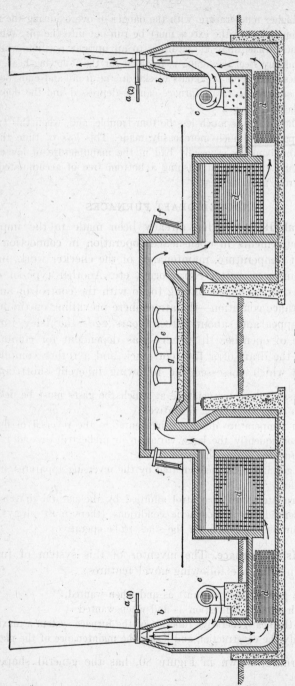

FIG. 80. Isley Furnace.

a. Stack valve—(1) closed—(2) open
b. Air injector

c. Air blower
d. Regenerative checkerwork

e. Hearth
f. Oil burner

g. Hearth

dimensions of the conventional open-hearth furnace, and the arrangement of the ports and checker work are much the same. The novel feature of this furnace consists of two separate Venturi-type ejector tubes connected with the flues from the two ends of the furnace and its intervening checker chambers, one tube for each end. For the sake of simplicity we shall consider furnaces operated with liquid fuel, that is, with fuels which are not customarily sent through a separate set of checkers. Each Venturi tube contains a blast pipe of the proper shape and size and is served by a low-pressure fan which is directly connected to an electric motor. The throat of the tube, which is lined with brick and insulated up to the throat, contains a butterfly damper. No valves, dampers, or abrupt changes of direction disturb the streamlined flow from, and to, the ejector tubes. When the furnace is in operation both fans are running, the one connected with the temporarily out-going side delivering air at a rate sufficient to lift the flue gas out of the furnace and into the atmosphere through the open throat of the tube; the fan which is connected with the then in-going side is adjusted to deliver just enough air for combustion (the damper in the throat of this tube being closed). When the temperature exchange in the regenerative chambers has passed its most economical point, as indicated by a recording pyrometer, the ejector-tube condition is reversed by a simple remote-control switching arrangement. The basic law involved is the one determined experimentally and mathematically by Zeuner which states that for every pound of propelling air sent through the Venturi throat, a certain corresponding weight of flue gas is discharged, regardless of temperature or density of the latter.

In addition to the feature of atmospheric control, a further interesting and important improvement is the extension of the regenerative work done. Since the point of entry of the air for combustion into the system is almost the very same point at which the waste gas is being released to the atmosphere, not only the checkers in the regenerator chambers but also the flues from them to the tubes and even the tubes themselves with their brick lining become regenerative, with the result that the average, final waste-gas temperature may be as low as 200°C. In order to achieve these economies in the conventional type of open-hearth furnace, it would be necessary to utilize waste-heat boilers with their grave shortcomings, which are:

1. Their very high cost of construction and maintenance.
2. The complexity of the apparatus connected with them.

3. The lack of synchronism between steam requirements and open-hearth operation.

Incidentally, it may be pointed out that the open-hearth steel furnace is only one of many kinds of furnaces which lend themselves to this type of furnace control, notably, soaking pit, reheating, and forging furnaces. Whenever high temperature and accurate furnace atmosphere are desirable, it is necessary that combustion be controlled by the delivery of a definite quantity of the hottest air obtainable; and, if this process is to be speeded up without loss of control and flexibility, it must be served by a positively adjustable draft that is independent of the furnace temperature and conditions of the atmosphere.

RIMMED STEEL

348. General. Rimmed steel is a product of the basic open-hearth and acid Bessemer processes in this country, although some rimmed steel may be made by the acid open-hearth process. In contrast to killed steel, this grade is partially deoxidized either in the furnace or in the ladle and is poured in this condition. In view of the fact that the steel is only partially deoxidized, chemical actions are bound to continue in the metal, after pouring. The predominate reaction is between dissolved ferrous oxide and carbon as follows:

$$FeO(c) + C(c) \rightarrow Fe(c) + CO(g); \quad \Delta H = +37,600 \text{ cal.} \quad (77)$$

The quality of the steel and the speed and completeness of this reaction are directly related, as will be shown later.

Killed steel covers a wide variety with carbon contents throughout the range of the steel portion of the iron-carbon diagram. On the contrary, the compositional range of rimmed steel is limited because of the effect that certain elements have on the amount of dissolved ferrous oxide in the metal. The range of analyses varies somewhat with local practice, but for the purposes of this discussion the following range may be assumed:

Elements	Per Cent
Carbon	0.02 –0.20
Manganese	0.15 –0.50
Sulfur	0.025–0.050
Phosphorus	Any desired
Silicon	Trace

The above limits may be exceeded in carbon, manganese, or sulfur, but to do so a departure from ordinary practice must be made. Phosphorus up to 0.08 per cent, such as is necessary in sheet bar heats, does not show any marked effect on any of the qualities of the steel.

349. Structure of Rimmed Steel Ingots. The fundamental differences in the structure of killed and rimmed steel are shown in Figure 81. In the rimmed ingot there are two lines of blowholes approximately parallel to the sides and coming together at the top and at the bottom of the ingot. These blowholes are not present in killed ingots. Furthermore, the rimmed ingot has no well-defined pipe as compared to the deep pipe on the killed ingot (see Figs. 93 and 94), and there are numerous primary blowholes in the lower portion of the rimmed ingot perpendicular to the surface and close to it. In contrast, the killed ingot has no blowholes of this type, only very small ones close to the surface on the lower part of the ingot. A certain amount of pipe may also occur in rimmed ingots, although it is normally porous and not as well defined or as deep as in the killed variety. The lines of blowholes parallel to the surfaces, or the secondary blowholes, are a definite characteristic of rimmed ingots and result from the difference in the furnace and pouring practice of this type of steel as compared to that for killed steels.

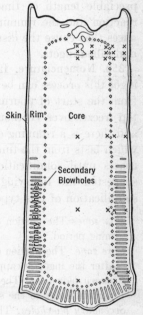

FIG. 81. Structure of a Rimmed Ingot. (*Courtesy of American Institute of Metallurgical Engineers.*)

In the processing of killed steels various deoxidizers are added to the furnace, ladle, or mold, and this deoxidation results in the reduction of most of the iron and manganese oxides with the formation of more stable ones which may be partly eliminated from the steel during the processing. The deoxidizing additions may also tend to increase the solubility of the gases in the steel. Consequently, when this type of steel is poured into the mold, very little gas is formed either from reactions or from gases coming out of solution. The top of the ingot freezes over almost immediately after it is poured, and the ingot solidifies without any reactions that affect the composition of the ingot as a whole.

In the processing of rimmed steel the steel is usually more highly oxidized in the furnace than for the production of killed steel, and only enough deoxidizers are used to maintain the iron and manganese oxide contents within certain limits. When this type of steel is poured into the mold, the reaction takes place between the carbon and iron and manganese oxides with the formation of carbon monoxide gas. The evolution of this gas, together with other gases such as hydrogen and nitrogen which may come out of solution, results in the "rimming" or boiling action of the steel in the mold during, and for an appreciable length of time after, pouring the ingot. It is this carbon reaction and the rimming action resulting from the evolution of the gases that cause the distinctive differences in the structure of rimmed and killed ingots.

350. Nomenclature. In order to discuss the freezing of a rimmed ingot this process can be divided into two periods: the first, which lasts from the start of pouring until the cap is placed on the ingot or the top freezes over (without artificial cooling, gases evolve continuously and there is a rimming or boiling action in the steel); and the second, which lasts from the time the top freezes over and the rimming action ceases until solidification is complete. Washburn and Nead[35] have suggested the following nomenclature to be used in discussing the solidification of this type of ingot:

Rim zone: The portion of the ingot that solidifies during the first or rimming period.

Core zone: The portion of the ingot that solidifies during the second period after the ingot is capped.*

Primary blowholes: The blowholes in the rim-zone running approximately perpendicular to the surface of the ingot.

Secondary blowholes: The blowholes between the rim and core zone which form a line approximately parallel to the surface of the ingot.

Skin: The portion of the rim zone between the surface of the ingot and the point where the primary blowholes begin to form.

351. Mechanism of Solidification. It is difficult to explain all the phenomena associated with the solidification of the rimmed steel ingot and the formation of the blowholes referred to above. According to Washburn and Nead,[35] the first metal to solidify when the liquid steel comes in contact with the mold wall forms equiaxed crystals as a result of the rapid solidification. As this solidification continues, the crystallization changes to a dendritic type which persists during the

---

* This cap differs from the cap on a mechanically capped ingot in that it is not firmly held in place. Usually consists of a light plate laid across the mouth of the ingot mold.

rimming period and the formation of the rim zone. Selective crystallization occurs in both kinds of crystals, but to a greater degree in the columnar dendritic type. This results in the solid phase being lower in carbon, phosphorus, sulfur, and oxides than the original melt, with the rejection of these components to the adjacent liquid phase.

Carbon monoxide is formed at the boundary of the solid phase as a result of reaction 77. It is also probable that hydrogen is evolved at this point as a result of the lower solubility of this gas in the solid phase. These gases form at the boundary of the solidification zone between the branches of the dendrites. The escape of the evolved gas from between the branches sweeps away the impure liquid adjacent to the solidifying metal. The rising of this gas along the solid-liquid interface and its escape at the top of the ingot cause the rolling action of the liquid metal at the surface which is so characteristic of this type of steel, and from which it gets its name, "rimming" steel. This rolling action of the liquid metal at the top keeps the metal from freezing over.

Some of the gas is entrapped, permanently or temporarily, between the branches of the dendrite, displacing the liquid. A rim-zone structure in which the gas has remained and formed primary blowholes consists of a solid phase with less carbon, manganese, and phosphorus than the remainder of the ingot, since the liquid between the dendrite branches is displaced by the gas. The portion of the rim zone that is free from primary blowholes is also low in the elements mentioned above, however, which would indicate that gas had formed between the dendrite branches during the solidification and had either escaped or was reabsorbed, probably the former. In either case the void would be filled with metal from the liquid phase in the body of the ingot which would be less impure than the impure metal it replaced. The type of solidification forming the rim zone ceases when the rimming action stops. This may be accomplished artificially by placing a cap on the top of the ingot or adding aluminum to the liquid phase. It will also occur naturally, however, if the ingot is allowed to rim, for, when the temperature is low enough, the gas evolution decreases until the top freezes over.

The secondary blowhole zone occurs at the boundary of the rim zone at the point where the rimming action stops; presumably it is formed from the gas along the face of the solidifying metal that it trapped when the ingot was capped. There is also a higher concentration of carbon, phosphorus, sulfur, and oxides at the solid-liquid interface which will tend to persist in the secondary blowhole zone.

After the ingot is capped, the core zone solidifies with the formation of equiaxed rather than dendritic crystals. During the solidification of this zone, the temperature is close to the freezing point, and crystallization probably occurs to a certain extent throughout the liquid. The usual type of segregation, however, is found in this zone, and the concentration of carbon, phosphorus, and sulfur increases toward the middle and top of the core zone. When the solidification is completed, the top of the core zone is porous and does not resemble the type of pipe found in killed steel. Probably this can be attributed to the fact that gas evolved during the solidification of the core zone collects in the mushy metal under the cap and prevents the formation of a true contraction pipe. Rimmed steel does not have the true pipe characteristics of killed steel because the volumetric shrinkage resulting from falling temperature in the liquid state and phase change contraction is largely offset by the space occupied by the entrapped gas or blowholes.

352. Segregation. This is the principal evil in rimmed steels. Killed steel segregates according to the laws of freezing, and, steel not being homogeneous, the constituents in it that have the lowest melting point will freeze last. Segregation in rimmed steel, in addition to being subject to this condition, is further complicated by the fact that chemical action accompanies freezing, and some elements are actually eliminated from the steel because of the action of the dissolved ferrous oxide.

Figures 82 to 84 show the distribution of carbon, manganese, and sulfur in a normal rimmed ingot. The curves represent the change in composition from the bottom to the top and from the edge to the center of the ingot. As the distribution is the same on both sides of the center, the curves show the analysis at any point in the ingot. The curves were obtained by averaging the analyses of ingots from three different heats, the average ladle analysis being: carbon, 0.09 per cent; manganese, 0.40; phosphorus, 0.009; and sulfur, 0.025. The ingots were poured from a height of 67 inches into 24 x 43 inch molds. Near the top of the ingot, as indicated in Figure 82, the carbon decreases uniformly from the surface to the secondary blowholes. At the secondary blowholes, which divide the rim and core zone, there is a sharp increase amounting to 0.04 per cent carbon. From the secondary blowhole zone to the center of the ingot, the carbon increases comparatively rapidly. At the center of the ingot, and 85 per cent above the bottom of the ingot, the carbon reaches a maximum of 0.19 per cent.

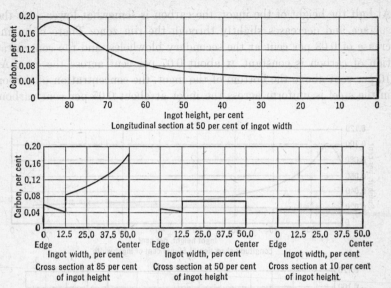

Fig. 82. Carbon Distribution Curve. (*Courtesy American Institute of Metallurgical Engineers.*)

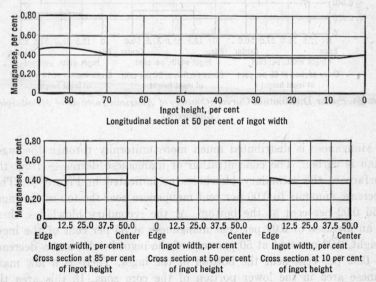

Fig. 83. Manganese Distribution Curve. (*Courtesy American Institute of Metallurgical Engineers.*)

At half the height of the ingot, the carbon is somewhat lower near the surface and decreases slightly through the rim zone. There is an increase of 0.03 per cent at the secondary blowholes, and the concentration of carbon is constant at about 0.07 per cent across the core. At 10 per cent above the bottom of the ingot, the concentration of carbon in the steel is uniform across the ingot at about 0.05 per cent carbon.

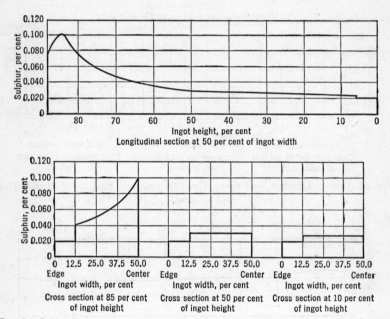

FIG. 84. Sulfur Distribution Curve. (*Courtesy of American Institute of Metallurgical Engineers.*)

Manganese is distributed much more uniformly through the ingot than is carbon. The concentration of manganese decreases from the surface to the secondary blowholes as indicated in Figure 83. This decrease amounts to 0.06 per cent manganese near the top of the ingot and 0.02 per cent at the bottom. At the secondary blowholes, there is an increase of 0.09 per cent manganese at 85 per cent of the ingot height, 0.03 per cent at 50 per cent of the ingot height, and a decrease of 0.02 per cent near the bottom of the ingot. There is a low manganese area in the lower portion of the core zone. In this area the manganese concentration is lower than in the adjacent rim zone.

Figure 84 shows corresponding variations for sulfur. The sulfur is approximately uniform in the rim zone at 0.02 per cent. There is a sharp increase from the secondary blowholes amounting to 0.02 per cent sulfur at the top of the ingot and 0.008 per cent at the bottom. The sulfur reaches a peak at the center of the ingot and at 85 per cent of the ingot height. At this point the steel contains 0.100 per cent sulfur. At 50 per cent of the ingot height the concentration of sulfur is uniform across the core zone, and near the bottom of the ingot the sulfur decreases slightly in the core between the secondary blowholes and the center.

Because of the small amount of phosphorus commonly present in rimmed steel ingots, it is rather difficult to follow the distribution of this element, but it is believed that it is similar to that of sulfur except that there is less difference between the rim and core and between the top and bottom of the ingot.

353. Factors Governing Distribution. The reaction of carbon with ferrous oxide is the most important reaction that occurs during rimming, and probably controls the distribution of carbon in the rim zone. The decrease in carbon across the rim, near the top of the ingot, indicates that the concentration of ferrous oxide in the liquid steel at the solid-liquid interface increases as rimming proceeds, probably because, near the bottom of the ingot, the pressure exerted by the liquid steel is high enough nearly to suppress the reaction between carbon and ferrous oxide. The presence of the primary blowholes indicates that some gas is evolved, but the uniform carbon content across the bottom shows that little carbon is removed. It is probable that the gas evolution is so slow that the bubbles are entrapped between the growing dendrites.

Although variations in the concentration of manganese will result from changes in concentration of ferrous oxide during rimming, the product of the reaction between manganese and ferrous oxide is a solid rather than a gas; consequently, the reaction is affected little by pressure, and the distribution in the rim zone changes little between the top and bottom of the ingot. The manganese oxide formed is carried to the top of the ingot by the rising stream of molten steel and gas, during the rimming, and combines with ferrous oxide to form the slag found on the top of the ingot. Manganese is also removed with sulfur as manganese sulfide. When the ingot is capped, the distribution of manganese is determined by the factors that control distribution in killed steel and by the action of the remaining manganese oxides.

On the other hand, the distribution of sulfur is not affected by the ferrous oxide content of the molten metal; therefore, there is virtually no change in the concentration of sulfur across the rim zone. The elimination of sulfur from this zone is probably largely mechanical, the immiscible manganese sulfide being swept away by the rising stream of gas and molten steel.

There are some other operational factors that affect markedly the character of rimming steel. For example, pouring the ingots from a greater height raises the point of maximum analysis higher in the ingot, and in the taller ingots the peak will be sharper and give higher extreme concentrations than in shorter ingots. Low-pouring temperatures give peaks of higher concentration in the distribution curves than high-pouring temperatures. With high-pouring temperatures there is a sharp drop in carbon and manganese through the rim from the edge of the ingot to the secondary blowholes. With low-pouring temperatures there is little or no drop in analysis across the rims. Furthermore, capping the ingot early reduces the width of the rim zone but does not alter the distribution within the rim and core zones. Late capping increases the width of the rim zone and raises the analysis throughout the core zone, but has little effect on the relative distribution within the core zone. Ingots that rim-in flat, or rise slightly during rimming, have peaks of higher concentration than ingots that drop slightly during rimming. Heats that are underoxidized in the furnace have very sharp peaks of high concentration, and the area of uniform analysis in the core extends higher in the ingot.

354. Advantages of Rimmed Ingots. A large and increasing tonnage of steel is cast in the form of rimmed ingots because of the following advantages:

1. The ingots may be made at a lower cost.
2. Fewer deoxidizers and addition agents are used.
3. There will be a minimum of non-metallic inclusions.
4. There will be a greater ingot yield.
5. A better surface can be obtained on the finished product more easily and cheaply.

The chief disadvantage accruing to this type of steel is the low compositional range in which it may successfully be made.

355. Mechanically Capped Ingots. Another method of ingot making commonly used today consists in casting the steel in specially shaped ingots, shown in Figure 85, provided with tightly fitting caps which can be firmly held in place during the solidification of the ingot by means of the lugs on the top of the ingot mold.

Such ingots can be cast with much higher yields than with conventional practice, are more nearly free from pipe, are sounder, can be cast over a wider chemical composition than rimming steels, exhibit less segregation, and are more uniform.

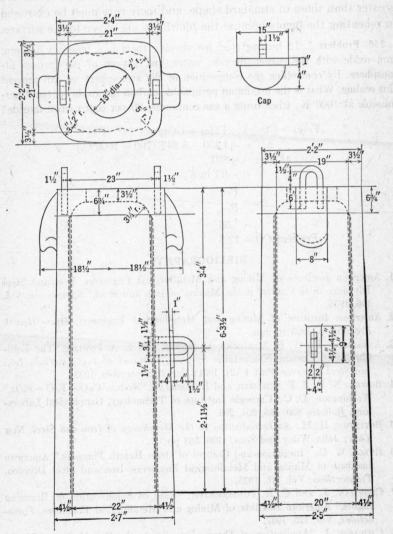

FIG. 85. Mechanically Capped Ingot Mold.

There is, however, a definite hazard in their use for sufficient gas may be evolved to exert considerable pressure on the cap; as a matter of fact it is not uncommon to have this pressure raise the ingot mold off the stool. They cannot be cast over a weight range because the ingot mold must be completely filled with metal at each cast; standard molds can be poured short. The cost and upkeep of these molds are greater than those of standard shape, and more care must be exercised in reheating the ingots because the blowholes are closer to the surface.

356. Problem 7. In heating steel for shaping there is a tendency to form iron oxide with the carbon dioxide, water, and oxygen of the furnace atmosphere. By controlling the composition of the atmosphere we can prevent this scaling. What is the maximum permissible carbon monoxide content* permissible at 1000°K., when using a gas containing 20 per cent carbon dioxide?

$$\mathrm{Fe}(c) + \mathrm{CO_2}(g) \rightarrow \mathrm{Fe}(c) + \mathrm{CO}(g)$$
$$\Delta F^\circ = +4,350 - 5.24T \ (700 - 1000°C.)$$
$$\Delta F_{1000°K} = -890$$
$$= -RT \ln K_p$$
$$K_p = \frac{P_{CO}}{P_{CO_2}}$$
$$= 1.56$$

Per cent CO = 12.8

BIBLIOGRAPHY

1. American Institute of Mining and Metallurgical Engineers, Iron and Steel Division, "Slag Control in the Making of Iron and Steel," *Symposium*, Vol. 116, 1935.

2. American Institute of Mining and Metallurgical Engineers, *Open Hearth Proceeding*, 1925 to date.

3. ANDREW, J. H., W. R. MADDOCKS, D. HOWAT, and E. A. FOWLER, "The Equilibrium of Certain Nonmetallic Systems," *Journal of the American Iron and Steel Institute*, Part 1 (2), 1931; Part 3, September, 1932.

4. BOWEN, N. C., J. F. SCHAIRER, and E. POSNJAK, "System CaO − FeO − SiO2," Washington, D. C.: Carnegie Institute of Technology, Geophysical Laboratory. *Bulletin* 830, 195, 204, 205.

5. BOYLSTON, H. M., *An Introduction to the Metallurgy of Iron and Steel*. New York: John Wiley and Sons, 1936. 563 pp.

6. BUELL, W. C., "Insulation and Control of Open Hearth Furnaces," American Institute of Mining and Metallurgical Engineers, Iron and Steel Division, *Transactions*, Vol. 116, 1935.

7. CHIPMAN, J., and C. R. FONDERSMITH, "Rate of Solidification of Rimming Ingots," American Institute of Mining and Metallurgical Engineers, *Transactions*, Vol. 125, 1937.

8. CHIPMAN, J., "Application of Thermodynamics to the Deoxidation of Liquid Steel," American Society for Metals, *Transactions*, Vol. 22, 1934.

* Note that equilibrium for CO2 + C = 2CO would not be reached because of the rapid passage of the gas and the low velocity of the reaction at this low temperature.

9. Cook, E., "Open-Hearth Temperature Control," American Society for Metals, *Transactions,* Vol. 24 (3), September, 1936.

10. Cook, E., "Basic Open-Hearth Slag Control," American Society for Metals, *Transactions,* Vol. 25 (2), June, 1937.

11. Diehl, A. N., "Action of Sulfur in Basic Open-Hearth Steel Practice," American Iron and Steel Institute, *Yearbook,* 1926.

12. Entwisle, E. F., "Insulation of Open-Hearth Furnaces," American Iron and Steel Institute, *Transactions,* 1933.

13. Fitterer, G. R., "A New Thermocouple for the Determination of Temperatures up to at least 1800°C.," American Institute of Mining and Metallurgical Engineers, *Transactions,* Vol. 105, 1933.

14. Foote, P. D., C. O. Fairchild, and T. R. Harrison, "Pyrometric Practice," Bureau of Standards, *Technical Paper* 170. 1921.

15. Francis, C. B., *The Making, Shaping, and Treating of Steel.* Pittsburgh: Carnegie-Illinois Steel Corporation, 1940. 1440 pp.

16. Geiger, H. I., "The Basic Open Hearth Process," *Steel,* March, 1937.

17. Hand, H. J., "Utility of Statistical Methods in Steel Plants," American Institute of Mining and Metallurgical Engineers, *Transactions,* Vol. 131, 1938.

18. Hayward, C. R., *An Outline of Metallurgical Practice.* New York: D. Van Nostrand Company, 1940. 612 pp.

19. Henry, W. H., and T. J. McLoughlin, "A Thermal Study of an Open Hearth Furnace," American Iron and Steel Institute, *Transactions,* 1931.

20. Herty, C. H., "The Deoxidation of Steel," Carnegie Institute of Technology, *Cooperative Bulletin* 69, 1934.

21. Herty, C. H., C. F. Christopher, and H. Freeman, "The Physical Chemistry of Steel Making," Carnegie Institute of Technology, *Cooperative Bulletin* 68, 1934.

22. Hultigen, A., and G. Phragnien, "Solidification of Rimming Steel Ingots," American Institute of Mining and Metallurgical Engineers, *Transactions,* Vol. 135, 1939.

23. Joseph, T. L., "Oxides in Basic Pig-Iron and in Basic Open Hearth Steel," American Institute of Mining and Metallurgical Engineers, *Technical Paper* 804, 1937.

24. Keats, J. L., and C. H. Herty, "Elimination of Metalloids in the Basic Open Hearth Process," American Institute of Mining and Metallurgical Engineers, *Transactions,* Vol. 73, 1926.

25. King, C. D., "Basic Open Hearth Yields," American Institute of Mining and Metallurgical Engineers, *Technical Paper* 186, 1929.

26. King, F. A., "The Economic Size of the Open Hearth," American Institute of Mining and Metallurgical Engineers, *Mining and Metallurgy,* December, 1928.

27. Maurer, E., and W. Bischof, "The Distribution of Phosphorus between Metal and Slag in the Basic and Acid Processes of Steel Manufacture," Iron and Steel Institute, *Journal,* May, 1936.

28. Maurer, E., and W. Bischof, "The Distribution of Phosphorus between Metal and Slag in the Basic Process of Steel Manufacture," Iron and Steel Institute, *Journal,* September, 1935.

29. Reinartz, L. F., "Recent Developments in Open Hearth Design and Operation, American Iron and Steel Institute, *Transactions,* May, 1936.

30. Smith, C., "Some Problems of Steel Melting," American Institute of Mining and Metallurgical Engineers, Iron and Steel Division, *Transactions,* Vol. 116, 1935.

31. Stoughton, B., *Metallurgy of Iron and Steel.* New York: McGraw-Hill Book Company, 1934. 519 pp.

32. Stoughton, B., and A. Butts, *Engineering Metallurgy.* New York: McGraw-Hill Book Company, 1930. 441 pp.

33. Tranter, G. D., "Ladle and Teeming Practice in the Open Hearth Department," American Institute of Mining and Metallurgical Engineers, Iron and Steel Division, *Transactions,* Vol. 116, 1935.

34. Washburn, F. M., and W. O. Philbrook, "Basic Open Hearth Slag Control," *Iron Age,* February 22, 1940.

35. Washburn, T. S., and J. H. Nead, "Structure of Rimmed-Steel Ingots," American Institute of Mining and Metallurgical Engineers, *Technical Paper* 779, 1937.

36. Zapffe, C. A., and C. E. Sims, "Silicon Monoxide," *Iron Age,* January 22, 1942.

CHAPTER IX

THE ACID OPEN-HEARTH PROCESS

357. General. So far as general features are concerned, such as the shape of the hearth, disposition of the ports, checker work, valves, etc., the acid open-hearth furnace is much the same as the basic. The fundamental difference lies in the character of the hearth, which is acid. Furthermore, for the reason the acid open-hearth steel is commonly considered superior to basic open-hearth, and being more expensive is confined to forgings and castings, the furnaces are on the whole smaller than those employed in the basic open-hearth process.

358. The Hearth. After the tapping hole has been made ready—this is similar in size and shape to the one employed in the basic open-hearth except that it is lined with siliceous material—a layer of sandstone or granite chippings is scattered over the bottom and banks to cover the prepared surface. The furnace is then brought to heat until these chippings begin to fuse. This must be done slowly in order to permit the bricks in the banks and bottom to absorb more heat than would be the case if the final sand were spread directly upon them, and, furthermore, the partly fused chippings form a better bond between the silica brick and this sand. When this operation has been

TABLE 60

ANALYSES OF ACID OPEN-HEARTH SANDS AND SLAGS

Per Cent

Material	SiO$_2$	FeO	Al$_2$O$_3$	CaO	MgO	MnO	Ignition Loss	P$_2$O$_5$
Sand (good)	95.83	0.40	2.76	tr	0.13		0.88	
" (bad)	88.46	0.96	8.27	tr	0.23		2.08	
Slag A	54.25	25.87	3.28	5.37	0.12	11.27		0.045
B	52.06	20.38	3.07	4.35	tr	20.52		0.035
C	55.60	28.90	4.16	0.70	0.12	10.23		0.022

completed, silica sand is spread evenly over the surface of the bottom and the banks to a depth of about one-quarter of an inch, and the heating continued until this sand layer begins to fuse, forming a glaze over the entire surface. Another layer of sand is then spread on, sintered into place, and these operations repeated until the bottom and banks have been built up to a thickness of 12 to 20 inches.

The quality of sand used is a vital factor in the stability of the bottom. It has been found that, if the sand is too pure, considerable difficulty is experienced in sintering in the bottom; and, if it contains too great a percentage of impurities, it will be rapidly worn away by the slag, after the furnace is in operation. The sand, as indicated in Table 60, usually contains 94 to 97 per cent silica.

359. Slags. The slags (shown in Table 60) employed in the acid open-hearth process are of necessity very acid, with the result that only a trace of the phosphorus and none of the sulfur are eliminated in the process. As a matter of fact, the finished steel may contain a slightly higher percentage of these elements than was present in the original charge, because the weight of sulfur and phosphorus remains practically constant but the weight of the metal decreases through losses by oxidation of iron, silicon, and manganese. Great care must, therefore, be exercised in selecting the scrap and fuel so that the phosphorus and sulfur content of the charge may be somewhat below that required in the finished steel. The specifications for acid open-hearth pig iron usually call for silicon under 2 per cent, manganese 1 to 2, and phosphorus and sulfur both under 0.03. Scrap for the process must be carefully selected by source, rather than by analysis, because it is very difficult to get a representative sample of such a conglomerate mixture as a charging box full of scrap. Consequently, such materials as tubes, pipes, sheets, Bessemer rails, and castings should be avoided, and more attention must be paid to the character of this scrap than in the basic process for the reason that light scrap is oxidized by the furnace atmosphere, and the ferrous oxide thus formed tends to combine with the siliceous lining and rapidly erode the bottoms and banks. In some furnaces, making the very highest grade of acid open-hearth steel, Swedish sponge iron and charcoal pig iron have been used.

A new bottom must be carefully prepared for the first metallic charge. This is done by covering the hearth with acid open-hearth slag, broken red brick, or any easily fused siliceous material, together with some light scrap consisting of turnings, stampings, light sheet scrap or small gates, runners, and risers. When this mixture is melted it is vigorously rabbled so that the molten slag may be splashed over the banks. The furnace is drained, leaving a smooth, well-consolidated, and properly shaped bottom.

360. Charge. The initial metallic* charge normally consists of cold pig iron or cold pig iron and scrap. No ore can be added with the charge as in the basic process, for the reason that iron oxide would combine with the siliceous lining and rapidly destroy it. For the same reason the melting of scrap alone would be bad practice, but the proportion of scrap to pig iron may vary over wide limits.

The manner (some small furnaces are still charged by hand) and order of charging differ from plant to plant and, apart from protecting the hearth and promoting heat transfer, this order is immaterial. If the scrap is heavy or makes up less than half the total charge, it is charged after the pig iron; but, if the scrap is light, many prefer to charge it ahead of the pig iron, which, being spread out on top of the charge, tends to protect the scrap from excessive oxidation. Other plants make a practice of charging part of the pig iron on the bottom and part on top of the scrap. The pig iron on top melts first, trickling down over the scrap beneath, the silicon and carbon which it contains reacting with the oxides of iron and manganese in the rust and scale and thus preventing these from eroding the banks or bottom; that on the bottom serves to protect it from damage during the charging of the furnace. This part of the process, which normally requires 2 to 4 hours in large furnaces, is much the same as in the basic open-hearth. If the charge contains a large proportion of pig iron, and especially if the iron carries high silicon and low manganese, the slags formed will be thick and viscous; consequently, in order to hasten the process and increase the yield, it is necessary to add a little ore or lime. Great care must be exercised in adding either of these reagents, else the banks will be badly eroded. On the other hand, if the charge was composed chiefly of scrap or pig containing a low percentage of silicon, it may be advisable to add some sand or other siliceous material in order to save the banks and bottom from such damage.

361. Adjustments of the Slag. After the charge is completely melted, it usually contains 0.3 to 0.6 per cent carbon more than that required in the finished steel. Unless the charge contains a large amount of silicon, or the heat was not given proper attention at the end of the melting period, practically all the silicon and manganese will have been oxidized, forming the initial slag. At this point the slag is black

* The first two or three charges will be small, usually about two-thirds of the capacity of the furnace (usually of cold pig iron), to test out the bottom.

in color and will normally contain about 50 per cent silica. As a matter of fact, the slag is almost self-adjusting. If the acids are increased, the slag will tend to retard the elimination of silicon and carbon from the metal; or, if the bases are increased, it will hurry the elimination of these elements; but, if they are increased too much, the slag will absorb silica from the banks. As the temperature rises during this period, the carbon in the bath reduces the amount of iron oxide in the slag, causing the latter to grow lighter in color. Also, as the slag gains more manganese, the color changes to brown and finally to yellow. The conditioning of the slag may be hastened somewhat by adding a little coal or lime, if the temperature is high enough.

362. Shaping the Heat. Now that the silicon and manganese have been eliminated to the desired extent, the melter seeks to reduce the carbon content as rapidly as possible and at the same time attain the temperature desired for tapping and teeming. The adjustments are not complicated by the necessity of eliminating phosphorus as they were in the basic process. Fracture tests are used to guide the melter in the earlier part of the heat; they are used along with chemical determinations to finish it. If the carbon is still relatively high and the metal quiet and hot enough, a few lumps of ore are added to start a boil. On the other hand, if the metal appears cold (before any ore is added), attempts will be made to raise its temperature by more frequent reversals or additional fuel. If the carbon is still too high, more ore is added, or, if it is decreased too much, it may be necessary to add some pig iron to hold the carbon ("block" it) until the temperature desired for tapping can be reached. Thus, by frequently sampling the metal and treating it as required, the carbon and temperature should, in the course of the next three or four hours, reach the desired point. Low-carbon heats (under 0.3 per cent carbon) will be worked down to a carbon content of about 0.1 per cent, then tapped, and the carbon brought back to meet specifications through the addition of recarburizers. This point is selected because it is much easier to read the fractures and also because the carbon is eliminated very slowly under 0.1 per cent; consequently, the composition of the steel is not likely to change very much in getting the heat out of the furnace.

With higher carbon contents it is customary to reduce a little of the silica in the slag to give 0.07 to 0.10 per cent silicon in the metal either by changing the fuel ratio, by adding a little coal, or by raising the temperature as high as possible. Ferrosilicon may be added to block the heat. No phosphorus is eliminated in the process; consequently the addition of large amounts of pig iron or spiegel for recarburizing is not wise unless the phosphorus content of the steel can be increased beyond the usual limits. As a result, medium- and high-carbon heats are usually caught on the way down.

363. Finishing. The last hour or so of the heat is occupied in shaping up the steel so that it will be in the proper condition for tapping and teeming. Little ore, or, better, none at all, is added; otherwise the steel will dissolve ferrous oxide and be "wild." Since the amounts of phosphorus and sulfur are extremely important in this type of steel, a sample is usually sent to the laboratory for preliminary analysis, which requires about 20 minutes. Allowance is made for this time in the heat by holding up the carbon with pig iron, or allowing the charge to boil down to the point desired for tapping. If the result of this analysis is satisfactory, the heat is tapped at once; but, if unsatisfactory, it constitutes an "off" heat, for there is no way of removing this phosphorus or sulfur. Most of the additions of recarburizers and deoxidizers will be made in the ladle and will consist of anthracite coal, coke dust, ferromanganese, and ferrosilicon. These ferroalloys should be carefully sized and, in small furnaces, added red hot or even in the molten condition to prevent chilling of the bath. All ladle additions should be made early, before much of the slag has flowed from the furnace. The losses will be about the same as in the basic process. On the whole, teeming is much the same as in the other process, although because of the higher price of most of the steels made, and more stringent specifications, more care is taken in this step.

364. Chemistry of the Acid Open-Hearth Process. The reactions involved in this process are given below:

$$CO_2(g) + Fe(c) \rightarrow FeO(c) + CO(g); \quad \Delta H = +3920 \text{ cal.} \tag{78}$$
$$H_2O(g) + Fe(c) \rightarrow FeO(c) + H_2(g); \quad \Delta H = -6210 \tag{79}$$
$$2Fe(c) + O_2(g) \rightarrow 2FeO(c); \quad \Delta H = -128,000 \tag{80}$$
$$Si(c) + 2FeO(c) \rightarrow SiO_2(c) + 2Fe(c); \quad \Delta H = -70,200 \tag{81}$$
$$Mn(c) + FeO(c) \rightarrow MnO(c) + Fe(c); \quad \Delta H = -26,800 \tag{82}$$
$$C(c) + FeO(c) \rightarrow CO(g) + Fe(c); \quad \Delta H = +37,600 \tag{83}$$
$$SiO_2(c) + FeO \rightarrow FeO \cdot SiO_2(c); \quad \Delta H = -6,600 \tag{84}$$
$$SiO_2(c) + MnO(c) \rightarrow MnO \cdot SiO_2(c); \quad \Delta H = -2,200 \tag{85}$$
$$6Fe_2O_3(c) \rightarrow 4Fe_3O_4(c) + O_2(g); \quad \Delta H = +123,400 \tag{86}$$
$$Fe_3O_4(c) + Fe(c) \rightarrow 4FeO; \quad \Delta H = +9800 \tag{87}$$

The oxidation of the charge by furnace gases and the elimination of silicon, manganese, and carbon are effected much the same as in the basic process. Only traces of sulfur and phosphorus can be eliminated because the slag is so acid that any phosphate present will be broken up by silica and reduced by silicon, manganese, or carbon.

365. Acid versus Basic Open-Hearth Steel. There has been a great deal of controversy concerning the quality and cleanliness of acid and basic open-hearth steel. It is significant that the consumers at least regard the acid open-hearth steel as the better one. One explanation lies in the fact that if the temperature of the steel, under an acid slag, is raised to a critical point approaching 3000°F., silicon can be reduced from slag to metal. It has been argued that more complete deoxidation is thus possible and that fewer oxidation products from alloy additions are formed in the bath. However, it seems to the author that the reduction of silicon to the metal under equilibrium conditions does not necessarily imply a corresponding diminution of the iron oxide in solution (similar migrations of phosphorus and manganese between steel and basic slags are without measurable effect upon the bath oxidation). Whether a lesser proportion of the iron oxide in an acid slag is available for solution in the metal, according to the distribution law, remains for future investigators to determine.

This last statement brings up another possible explanation having to do with the diffusion of ferrous oxide from slag to metal. The average acid open-hearth slag contains about 25 per cent ferrous oxide and 54 per cent silica, as contrasted to 14 per cent ferrous plus ferric oxide and 16 per cent silica in the basic open-hearth slag. Two forces are at work at the slag-metal interface. One of these is diffusion, tending to cause ferrous oxide to migrate from the slag to the metal. Another force is the chemical one of synthesis; that is, the formation in the slag of a definite chemical compound between ferrous oxide and silica. Certainly, the ferrous silicates are very stable compounds, and it may be that the high percentage of silica in the acid open-hearth bath stabilizes and fixes a higher proportion of the ferrous oxide and thus prevents it from diffusing over into the metal bath.

BIBLIOGRAPHY

1. BOYLSTON, H. M., *An Introduction to the Metallurgy of Iron and Steel.* New York: John Wiley and Sons, 1936. 563 pp.
2. COOK, E., *Open Hearth Steel Making.* American Society for Metals, 1937.
3. FRANCIS, C. B., *The Making, Shaping, and Treating of Steel.* Carnegie Illinois Steel Corporation, 1940. 1440 pp.
4. STOUGHTON, B., *Metallurgy of Iron and Steel.* New York: McGraw-Hill Book Company, 1934. 519 pp.

CHAPTER X

THE ELECTRIC FURNACE

HISTORY

366. General. The electric furnace has gained for itself a secure place in industry for the manufacture of quality steels. These furnaces are also widely used in foundries for melting cast irons as well as non-ferrous alloys. In connection with the higher-priced steels it can be said that the electric furnace has practically replaced the crucible process (only 1024 tons of steel were produced by the latter process in 1940). In 1910 there were in operation in the United States ten electric furnaces, which produced 52,141 gross tons. By 1929, there were approximately 650 in operation, with an output of 1,065,603 tons, which production was in the ratio of one-third ingots and two-thirds steel and iron castings. In 1941, it is estimated that there were 1010 arc furnaces alone in operation and nearly 4 million tons of steel were produced, with large expansions planned for 1942. In part this remarkable increase has been due to improvements in electric-furnace construction and operation, but another contributing factor has been the tremendous expansion in alloy steels, many of which cannot be made in the conventional open-hearth process.

Although the principle of heating by electricity was discovered early in the nineteenth century, it was not until 1879 that Franz Siemen was able to melt iron with the electric arc. His equipment was nothing more than a small crucible containing a charge, into which he introduced two carbon electrodes. In the following years the steel industry refused to take the electric furnace seriously, first because the basic open-hearth process had been developed, with all its apparent advantages and virtues, and second because at that time the cost of power was prohibitive.

From 1888 to 1894, P. L. V. Heroult successfully employed the electric current in the manufacture of aluminum, calcium carbide, and some ferroalloys, and in 1898 Stassano took out a patent for "melting and refining a liquid alloy of iron and of iron and carbon by the electric current." In 1900, Kjellin invented his first induction furnace and in the same year Heroult modified his furnace for the melting and refining of steel. This modification was introduced in this country soon after, when the United States Steel Corporation secured the American rights. The years 1900 to 1912 were very fruitful ones in experimenting with this new method of producing steel. Many investigators, among them Girod, Rodenhauser, and Renefelt, modified and improved these furnaces; some used the indirect arc, some the direct arc with a non-conducting hearth, some the direct arc with a conducting hearth, and some the induction principle.

In 1916, Dr. Edwin F. Northrup invented the coreless induction furnace, the principle being that of an air transformer whose primary is the furnace coil and whose secondary is the melt or the conducting crucible containing the melt. If a high-frequency current is applied to the terminal of this coil, induced currents of sufficient magnitude are generated in the metal to cause rapid and efficient heating. As far as the steel industry is concerned, the outstanding arc furnace at the present time is the Heroult and the outstanding induction furnace the Ajax-Northrup.

367. Advantages of the Electric Process. The advantages of the electric furnace for the manufacture of steel, about in the order of their importance, are:

1. A much higher temperature can be attained than in a combustion-type furnace. In the latter, although a theoretical temperature of 4200°C. is possible, the maximum attainable, with conventional regeneration, is about 1800°C. The temperature of the electric arc is probably in the neighborhood of 4000°C., and consequently the attainment of 2000°C. in the arc furnace is relatively easy.

2. It is much more flexible than the open-hearth, for it can be operated equally well with cold charges or with hot metal.

3. It produces steel of a much higher quality than any other process except the crucible.* Compared with steel made by the open-hearth or Bessemer process, electric steel has greater density, can be made more nearly free from blowholes and slag, occluded or absorbed gases, and is stronger, tougher, and more ductile. Alloy additions are made directly to the bath, a smaller percentage of them is lost, and this bath addition results in a steel which is freer from segregation because all furnace additions have sufficient time for thorough mixing and melting and the melt is hotter and less viscous.

4. The efficiency of the electric furnace, 74 to 77 per cent, is much higher than any other iron and steel furnace. Blast furnaces may have an overall efficiency as high as 65 per cent, but the basic open-hearth is not much more than 10 and the puddling furnace about 5 per cent efficient.

* Very little steel is melted in crucibles today.

5. Regulation of the heat is easily carried out by varying the electrode spacing or voltage.

6. The temperature can be kept more nearly constant.

7. The heat is localized and produced where and when desired.

8. There are no products of combustion to take care of; these products reduce considerably the efficiency of all other steel-making furnaces.

9. Any atmosphere can be produced and maintained at will.

10. It is possible to produce "interchangeable steels." If a bar or carload of a certain type of steel is purchased today in the open-hearth grade, another order may or may not possess the same properties—a higher hardening temperature, a different grain size. Electric steels can be made to much closer tolerances. An electric furnace can duplicate Bessemer, open-hearth, or crucible steel, but the reverse statement does not hold true.

11. Any alloy steels can be made in the electric furnace; open-hearth furnaces are seldom used to make steels with a higher alloy content than 5 per cent.

12. An important advantage is the fact that notably higher recoveries of alloying agents such as vanadium, tungsten, and chromium can be effected, thus serving to reduce the cost differential which exists between the electric and open-hearth processes.

368. Disadvantages of the Electric Process. These are not numerous, but one of them, the cost of power, has held back the development of the electric furnace until comparatively recent times. The outstanding ones are:

1. The cost of operation is much higher than for the open-hearth type of furnace. Power consumption ordinarily is 400 to 600 kilowatt-hours per ton of output, and graphite electrode consumption 4 to 9 pounds.* It is evident then that heat applied in the form of electric current, even with the very cheap current now available from hydroelectric developments, costs six to ten times as much as heat applied through the combustion of carbon.

2. Until comparatively recently electric furnaces have had a capacity of 5 to 25 tons per heat, but this difficulty is now being overcome with the erection of a number of furnaces with a capacity of over 75 tons.† These large furnaces introduce serious problems in design. First, higher voltages must be used to conduct the heavy currents economically, and these result in longer arcs which transmit less heat to the bath and more to the wall and roof.‡ Second, the metal directly under the electrode is superheated, resulting in a more active, "sloppy" bath. Third, with the heat thus concentrated in small areas

---

* Carbon electrode consumption ranges from 8 to 15 pounds per ton of output.

† One large furnace has six electrodes, a total transformer capacity of 20,000 kilowatts, and has been charged with as much as 135 tons.

‡ Although the life of an arc furnace lining may be much shorter than that of an open-hearth furnace, the cost per ton of output compares very favorably.

under the electrodes, a point is soon reached where heat cannot be absorbed by the bath and conducted to other parts rapidly enough. A limit commonly recognized is 4000 kilowatts per electrode.

3. A minor disadvantage lies in its effect on the power system. Unless unusual precautions are taken, the power factor will be reduced below 0.70 to 0.90, required by central stations. As a matter of fact, companies usually are obliged to install their own generating equipment because 25-cycle current is much better than 60-cycle, permitting greater power input and a better power factor. Although this low-frequency current is not entirely suitable for other uses when the furnace is not in operation, many operators use the low-frequency for the entire plant.

ARC FURNACES IN GENERAL

369. General. The action of the arc in heating may be outlined briefly as follows: In passing from one electrode to another, the current jumps the small air gap and forms an arc between the slag and the electrode. Most of the heat is formed above the slag by these arcs, and furthermore the slag serves to protect the metal from the carbon vapors and excessive temperatures prevailing at the electrode tip. The heat thus imparted to the slag bath is distributed to the metal by conduction and convection,* as well as radiation from the roof.

There are four possibilities of arc heating, as indicated in Figures 86a-d. In Figure 86a the arc is formed between two or three carbon electrodes placed above the bath, which principle is employed in the Stassano furnace; in Figure 86b the arc from two horizontal electrodes is directed down upon the charge by a third vertical one, which method is used in the Renerfelt furnace; in Figure 86c is the familiar Heroult furnace employing a direct arc with a non-conducting hearth; and in Figure 86d the direct arc with a conducting hearth as used in the Girod furnace.

The indirect-arc furnace is not commonly used in the iron and steel industry because it has some very serious disadvantages. The arc is very hot and the atmosphere of the furnace is a relatively poor conductor of heat; consequently, the metal and slag directly below the arc are greatly overheated while that near the banks and bottom may be relatively cold. In addition, in order to supply sufficient heat to obtain the desired temperature, the refractory lining and roof become overheated, with corresponding decrease in life. Heating by radiation is not conducive to rapid heat transfer or rapid refining. Another important operating difficulty has to do with the breakage of the elec-

---

* Aided, probably, by a slight motor effect produced in the iron bath by the electric current.

trodes, which is particularly bad wherever one or more of these electrodes is horizontal.

There are two types of direct-arc furnaces, one with a non-conducting hearth and the other with a conducting one. In turn the conducting-hearth furnaces may be of two kinds. In the one the hearth is of regular construction and becomes conducting at a high temperature; in the other a carbon block is set into the refractory bottom. Of these

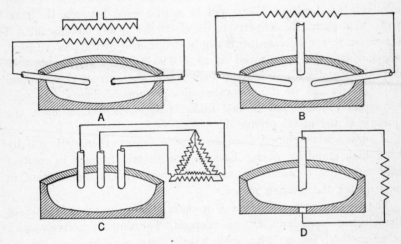

FIG. 86. Types of Arc Furnaces.

the direct-arc furnaces with a non-conducting hearth, the Heroult type, is the most popular at the present time. The conducting-hearth class, having a bottom electrode, has not been very successful because trouble is almost universally experienced with this bottom while the furnace is in operation.

In addition to the general advantages of arc heating discussed in Article 367, the direct-arc furnace has its own and peculiar ones:

1. The direct arc permits any slag conditions to be maintained, and both oxidizing and deoxidizing slags may follow each other in the same heat. In addition slag reactions take place very rapidly.
2. The efficiency is higher than the indirect type because most of the heat is generated within the bath and available immediately for melting or refining.
3. The heat is not localized, being even all over the bath.
4. Automatic electrode controls have made this type of furnace much easier to control.

370. Power Supply for Arc Furnaces. For ease of transformation from one voltage to another and to prevent any electrolytic effects, alternating current is almost universally used in arc furnaces. The current is commonly brought in at potentials of 16,000 or more volts and transformed to a current of low voltage and high amperage, the voltage range being 90 to 300 volts and the current up to 10,000 amperes per phase. It should be noted in connection with the use of alternating current that all the current from the transformer is not available for heating. There will be a difference between the total power that should be delivered to the electrodes at any one instant and the actual power delivered; this will be determined by the power factor, which should be maintained as near 0.90 as possible. Under such conditions and with cold scrap being used, the current consumption is ordinarily 525 to 750 kilowatt-hours per ton of ingots, and with hot-metal practice 100 to 300 kilowatt-hours, depending upon the quality of the metal produced.

If power is purchased from an outside source, there will usually be a high stand-by charge because the electric furnace in melting cold scrap has considerable, sometimes very violent, fluctuations in load during the melting period.

The cost of power is the factor upon which the whole future of the electric steel industry will depend. To compete actively with other methods of melting, even taking into consideration the inherent advantages of the electric process, the power cost should be less than 1 cent per kilowatt-hour. It is encouraging to note that the power available in some of the large hydroelectric projects financed by our government in recent years falls well below this figure, and consequently a large increase in the use of electric furnaces should be expected in the next few years. Power companies will frequently offer very attractive power rates for off-peak periods. For example, a number of electric furnaces have been installed in recent years in industrial centers operating on local scrap. The rapidity of melting, as well as the flexibility of the electric furnace, permits these operators to melt several heats of steel between 10 P.M. and 6 A.M., when these low rates are available.

THE HEROULT FURNACE

371. General. The Heroult is easily the most popular of the electric steel-making furnaces in use today; more than half of the larger sized furnaces, 6 tons and upward, are of this type. In point of tonnage it is safe to say that at least 65, perhaps 75, per cent of electric steel ingots are produced in furnaces of this type.

It is interesting to note that when Paul Heroult took out his patent on this furnace in 1900, the specifications clearly stated that, to avoid carbon absorption by the molten bath, the slag used to refine the metal should be inserted between the metal bath and the electrodes; and Heroult in his first efforts used a bottom electrode. Because this arrangement was never successful, he finally turned to the one used today—electrodes in series and a non-conducting hearth. These furnaces are built in a wide range of capacities from as small as 1 ton to as large as 100, but the most popular and efficient are those with capacities ranging from 40 to 70 tons.

372. Furnace Shell. This shell, about 16 feet in diameter,* is constructed of 1-inch steel plates as shown in Figures 87 and 88. On top of the shell is the roof ring molding, fastened to the shell by adjustable bolts and containing the slightly arched roof set flush with the top of the shell. This shell is pierced by a tapping door and by one or more working doors. These doors, lined with silica brick, fit tightly to the side of the furnace and are usually mechanically operated, especially in the larger units. The door jambs, electrode holders, transformers, electrode economizers, and roof coolers are cooled by circulating water.

373. The Lining. Almost all electric furnaces are basic lined with magnesite brick. Practically the only exception to this general rule are small acid furnaces used in steel foundries for producing special castings or forgings. In general the lining consists of one course of silica brick or fire brick laid next to the shell and, on top of that, one of magnesite brick. The bottom, which may be 13 to 18 inches thick, is made up by tamping and burning in a saucer-shaped hearth made of dead-burned grain magnesite.† This material, mixed with a little ground basic slag and sufficient tar or molasses to make it plastic, is shoveled into the furnace and leveled off into a layer about 2 inches thick. Pieces of scrap electrodes are then placed on the hearth, the electrodes lowered, and the power turned on. About 18 hours are required to sinter this first 6 or 8 inches of magnesite to the main bottom. The electrode scrap is then raked out and more of the magnesite-tar mixture spread out in another layer about 3 inches thick

---

* A furnace of 40 tons capacity is about 20 feet in diameter.

† A popular refractory is Ramix which is mixed with water, rammed into a properly shaped bottom and then burned in.

over the bottom; and this, in turn, is fritted into place, this time for a longer period, say 20 or 30 hours. Altogether 48 to 72 hours of burning is required to sinter the bottom into place permanently.

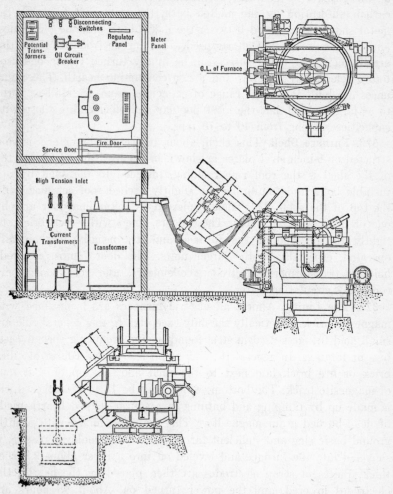

FIG. 87. Heroult Furnace. (*Courtesy of Carnegie-Illinois Steel Corp.*)

Magnesite bricks are used up to and a little above the slag line. Above the slag line silica brick extends up to the roof. It is common practice to use one or more courses of chrome brick to separate the basic from the acid material. Many plants use metal-cased magnesite brick extending up to the roof with a layer of neutral material between it and the silica roof. As a rule no mortar is used, with either magnesite or silica brick, expansion being sufficient to close up the cavities; and, after the sintering period, all these bricks are firmly fused together. The roofs of the larger furnaces are usually made of 12-inch brick that will last twenty to two hundred heats, depending upon whether the acid or basic process is used, the kind of steel being made, and other plant conditions. In the roof three openings are provided for the insertion of the electrodes which are located at

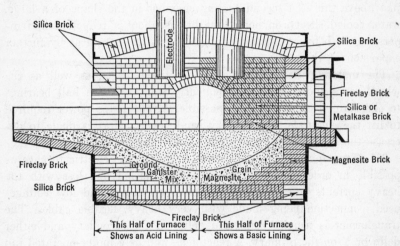

Fig. 88. Lining of Arc Furnaces. (*Courtesy of Harbison-Walker Refractories Co.*)

points corresponding to the vertices of an equilateral triangle, its center coincident with the center of the furnace.

374. Electrodes. The electrodes are held in heavy bronze clamps, supported on the end of arms, which in turn move up and down on an electrode mast fastened to the side of the furnace. Since the electrodes burn off at the hot ends and since the depth of metal, or the height of the charge, varies considerably during the heat, provision must be made for moving the electrodes vertically and almost constantly in order to preserve the proper length of arc.* All these motions may be controlled automatically by means of voltage regulators controlling three motors, which in turn operate winches and pinion gears actuating the electrode arms; but the initial adjustments with

* This consumption will vary from 8 to 15 pounds per ton of steel refined with amorphous carbon electrodes to 4 to 9 pounds with graphite electrodes. This consumption will be greatest with a basic bath, least with an acid one.

a cold charge are so sudden and variable that means for manual adjustment must be provided.

Considerable quantities of gas are given off during the heat; this rushes out past the electrode, and unless precautions are taken, will cause oxidation or "necking" of the electrode at the roof level. In order to prevent this, an electrode economizer surrounds the electrode where it enters the roof. Just above the roof, and surrounding the electrode, is the first cooling chamber around which water circulates; just above this is a second cooling chamber in the shape of a large, water-cooled sheet-iron hood that brings about a reduction in temperature both by conduction through the water as well as by further expansion of the gases.

The motors used to operate the electrode masts, as well as the winch gears and drums, are frequently equipped with ball bearings to eliminate friction as far as possible. Although the power required to lift the electrode arms is very small, every effort is made to decrease the lag so as to provide close and easy control.

375. Transformer. This is placed as close to the electric furnace as possible in order to avoid an excessive transmission loss with the heavy currents (up to 18,000 amperes per phase) and low voltages used, connection being made with very heavy, flexible cables. The transformer is usually connected delta on the secondary and either delta or Y on the primary. A reactor as well as a motor-operated tap changer is provided to afford multiple voltage control.* Current may be any frequency; but 3-phase, 25- to 60-cycle current at 2200 to 26,400 volts is commonly employed.

ELECTRODES FOR ELECTRIC FURNACES

376. General. Electrodes for the direct-arc type of furnace can be made of either graphite or amorphous carbon; except in small furnaces carrying on special heats, the electrodes are usually made of the latter material. In a general way an ideal electrode should:

1. Not contaminate the furnace charge by reason of contained impurities.
2. Not cause undue waste of energy.
3. Have a high electrical conductivity.
4. Have a low thermal conductivity.
5. Withstand severe handling† and sudden temperature changes.

* Eight to twelve operating voltages ranging from 90 to 290 volts.
† A 6-foot length of 12-inch graphite electrode weighs nearly 450 pounds.

377. Amorphous Carbon Electrodes. These are made of various proportions of calcined anthracite coal, petroleum coke, and a binder of pitch or tar. These materials are thoroughly mixed, the binder added, molded, pressed, and then baked at a temperature of about 1100°C. for a period of 12 to 20 days. Both heating and cooling must be carried on very carefully to avoid setting up any thermal stresses. On being removed from the furnace the electrodes are cleaned, machined, and threaded, the large ones being drilled and tapped at both ends in order that a small nipple may be screwed in for the attachment of the next electrode length, which method serves to economize in the electrodes because there is no scrap formed. Commonly, they are made in 5-foot lengths with diameters varying from 8 to 10 inches in the 1-ton furnace up to as much as 20 inches in the 75-ton size. In screwing carbon electrodes together a graphite paste is used in the nipple joints,* but even with these precautions there is a voltage drop in this joint, accounting for a loss of 3 to 4 per cent of the total energy put into the furnace.

The chief advantages of the amorphous carbon electrodes are their smaller cost per pound and their greater strength; but tending to offset these to some extent are the disadvantages of lower electrical conductivity, more rapid oxidation, higher transportation costs, and the necessity of greater care being exercised in making up the joints.

378. Graphite Electrodes. The graphite electrodes are made of practically the same raw materials as the amorphous carbon electrodes, but in addition they must be put through a graphitization process whereby all the carbon is changed to graphite. This procedure consists of heating the carbon electrodes in an electrical resistance furnace up to 2000°C. and holding them at this temperature for 4 to 6 days. This treatment represents quite an additional cost, for it requires 3 to 5 kilowatt-hours per pound of graphitized electrodes. The chief advantages of graphite electrodes are:

1. Their much higher electrical conductivity, about four times that of amorphous carbon.
2. Less heat and current losses at the joints.
3. Much smaller electrodes can be used, which is especially advantageous in furnaces where large holes might seriously weaken the roof.
4. There is less oxidation loss, about one-half that of amorphous carbon. Graphite begins to oxidize at 665 to 690°C. as against 375 to 450°C. for amorphous carbon.

* No paste is used with graphite electrodes.

5. Graphite permits the use of much lighter control mechanism.
6. There is less transportation loss and cost.

Operating against these advantages are some very serious disadvantages that normally outweigh the former. These are:

1. Graphite electrodes are more costly, although in some instances the cost per ton of steel produced may be less.
2. They are more fragile.
3. They have a high heat conductivity, and consequently each electrode acts as an opening in the roof through which considerable quantities of heat may be transmitted to the atmosphere.

379. The Soderberg Electrode. It is obvious that the preparation of either amorphous carbon or graphite electrodes entails a considerable expenditure of time and money. With the object of overcoming this objection, the Soderberg electrode was developed in 1920. It consists of a metallic sheet cylinder, provided with interior extensions or ribs, into which the green electrode paste is poured. The ribs provide a good electrical and mechanical connection between the outer sheet and the electrode proper. The electrode is baked by heat from the furnace itself, as the electrode is allowed to slip through the holder to compensate for electrode consumption. When a section has been consumed to a point where the upper end is approaching the holder, a new section of shell is welded to the old and tamped full of the electrode mixture. On the whole this electrode is not commonly used in steel-making furnaces because of the difficulties and dangers encountered in making replacements when working from a platform on top of the furnace, but it is frequently used with aluminum and carbide furnaces.

OPERATION OF THE BASIC ELECTRIC PROCESS

380. General. Consideration will be given only to the basic electric process because it involves a more nearly complete refining of the metal, and it is the process generally used in the production of high-quality tool and alloy steel. In this connection it is timely to point out that, because of the features outlined in Article 367, this type of electric furnace is especially adapted to the production of fine steels containing expensive elements which might be oxidized and lost in the ordinary basic open-hearth process. At the present time the following steels are almost exclusively made in electric furnaces:

1. High-speed tool steels.

2. Manganese steels containing 12 to 14 per cent manganese.
3. Practically all stainless steels, particularly those containing very small amounts of carbon.
4. Corrosion- and heat-resisting steels.
5. Carbon and highly alloyed tool steels.
6. Magnet steels.
7. Special alloy steels for instruments, machines, and scientific apparatus.

381. Charging. More often than not the furnace is charged with cold metal. One reason for this practice is the desire to start with as high-grade material as possible; and a second is to utilize home scrap, large quantities of which are available around the steel plants in the shape of scrap ends of ingots, billets, bars, and trimmings from heavy plate, etc. If the charging is done by hand or chute, the material can be placed on the hearth through the door, but in many modern furnaces the whole roof is removable so that the furnace can be charged from a bucket. Charging cars, similar to those used on open-hearth furnaces, are used on the larger furnaces.

In general much more attention is given to the matter of purity of the charge than in the conventional basic open-hearth process. In selecting the scrap, precautions have been taken to keep phosphorus and sulfur at a minimum, and in general to have present only the elements desired in the finished steel so as to permit full control of final adjustments in compositions. Today there is a tendency to use the electric furnace more like an open hearth and charge it with scrap of any reasonable composition. As tonnages increase in the future it will be necessary to do this. The physical condition of the charge will affect its thermal and electrical conductivity; consequently, great care is taken to select light and heavy scrap in proper proportions and to mix these materials on the hearth so that they may be properly distributed in the furnace, particularly when iron ore, limestone, or ferroalloys are charged along with the metal. Too much heavy scrap decreases the life of the lining because the intense heat of the arc is reflected to the lining, playing havoc with it. To overcome this, light scrap is used for the upper part of the charge, permitting the electrodes to cut their way down through this light material and form protective walls, smothering the arc, and preventing damage to the refractories. The fluxing materials also must be of high purity and are confined largely to lime,* roll scale,

* Lime is more favorably regarded than limestone, for the latter appears to bring hydrogen along into the bath.

fluorspar, and silica sand. If any deoxidizing or reducing agents are used, they are usually ferrosilicon and petroleum coke.

382. Melting. When charging is completed, and the doors closed, the transformer taps are set at some intermediate voltage and the current turned on the secondary system. With manual control the electrodes are lowered until the current starts to flow through the furnace, as indicated by lights on the control board. If the scrap has been properly selected and distributed, the motor control can shortly be thrown in, after which it will maintain a constant current, depending upon the setting of the control mechanism. For the next 10 to 20 minutes the arc melts a hole, down through the scrap, forming a small metal pool on the bottom of the furnace, after which the electrodes start to rise as additional molten metal joins this pool to raise its general level. At some plants the operators will push unmelted scrap about the edges of the furnace toward the pool at the center; but on the whole this is discouraged because air entering through the open door not only consumes the electrodes but also combines with some of the metal, thus increasing the volume of slag, as well as wasting iron.

383. Refining. This part of the process constitutes the great value and flexibility of the electric furnace. The bath is not exposed to an oxidizing atmosphere as in the combustion type of furnace. Furthermore, the metal itself may be exposed to the slag, as a vehicle, to oxidizing or reducing conditions, or to both successively, at the will of the operator and for indefinite periods. Elements not oxidizable may be added to the charge or, rarely, to the melt; and those which may be oxidized can be added under the reducing slag. Some elements like sulfur, not ordinarily affected in the basic open-hearth process, can be eliminated in the electric process. One disadvantage is that it is difficult to hold carbon under 0.04 per cent when a reducing slag is used, owing to carbon diffusing over from the electrode and the slag; but this so-called pick-up becomes a problem only when the carbon in the steel must be kept very low. For the ordinary grades, containing more than 0.1 per cent carbon, this difficulty can be readily overcome or provided for.

384. Use of an Oxidizing Slag. This part of the electric process does not differ materially from the conventional basic open-hearth. Lime, roll scale, silica, and fluorspar will be charged in the right proportions to yield a slag comparable with the one used in the latter process. The little silicon there is in the charge, therefore, will be largely eliminated during melting; but, if some remains, this is soon oxidized and slagged. Phosphorus will also be oxidized and fixed by the lime of the slag. Ordinarily, the charge is calculated so that it will have about the right carbon content at meltdown, but, if it is desired to eliminate some of the carbon, iron oxide in the form of roll scale or iron ore is added. Incidentally, if it is necessary to remove phosphorus, this is removed before the carbon, and the relatively high-phosphorus slag is raked out of the furnace. Oxides of chromium, vanadium, tungsten, or molybdenum may be added to the slag during this period for the purpose of reducing them so that they will be assimilated by the metallic bath, when the white slag is used. This direct method of reduction from the crude oxides avoids the use of the more expensive ferroalloys—an additional attractive feature of the electric process.

385. The Reducing Slags. Depending upon the condition of the black (oxidizing) slag, the character of the steel being made, as well as its specifications, this black slag may be removed from the furnace entirely and replaced by a new (reducing) slag, made up from calcined limestone, sand, fluorspar, and coke dust. If the black slag is not removed, the initial reduction may be effected by the addition of low-ash anthracite coal, petroleum coke, or high-grade metallurgical coke and perhaps a little ferrosilicon. As the iron oxide in the black slag is reduced, more lime and carbon are added and the temperature raised considerably to form calcium carbide, whose presence can be tested for by dropping the slag into water. There should be enough calcium carbide present to give a noticeable odor of acetylene. Such a reducing slag is white, flakes in the air, and is capable of reducing oxides of iron, silicon, and manganese incorporated in the slag itself. It will not, however, in any reasonable length of time, remove the dissolved ferrous oxide in the metal, for the reaction will take place only at the metal slag interface, and for deoxidation to be complete the ferrous oxide must diffuse through the bath—a slow process. Consequently, to hasten this removal some deoxidizer, such as an aluminum-silicon alloy, may be used, the products of which form fusible compounds which coalesce and rise out of the metal to join the main body of the slag.

Another attractive feature of the electric process is the ability of the reducing slag to remove the sulfur almost completely, as indicated in the reaction below. As a matter of fact, by the use of a double slag, phosphorus and sulfur can be reduced to a point lower than that of the famous Swedish irons. Ordinary control will lower both these elements to 0.03 per cent, and it is possible to reduce them to 0.01 per cent.

$$3FeS(c) + 2CaO(c) + CaC_2(c) \rightarrow 3Fe(c) + 3CaS(c) +$$
$$2CO(g); \quad \Delta H = -6160 \tag{88}$$
$$FeS(c) + CaO(c) + C(c) \rightarrow Fe(c) + CaS(c) + CO(g);$$
$$\Delta H = +34,800 \tag{89}$$

These reactions, as well as those of deoxidation, are somewhat slow because they occur only at the slag-metal interface; consequently, the time necessary to hold the metal under the white slag will vary considerably. For the highest quality steel about two hours appears to be sufficient. Incidentally, the removal of sulfur may be speeded up by having manganese present in the bath, because the manganese sulfide formed is less soluble in the metal than iron sulfide and rises to the surface faster.

386. Finishing. The objects sought in this period are much the same as in the conventional open-hearth process; that is, final adjustments in the composition and temperature of the steel. Rough chemical analyses, checking the observations of the furnace operators, are carried out in order that the calculations for the necessary additions may be made in a minimum of time and with the maximum certainty of meeting specifications. These additions will consist of carbon for the medium and high plain carbon steels and of ferroalloys for alloy steels. Ordinarily, the problem is to keep the carbon as low as possible; but, if it is necessary to increase moderately the amount of this element, low-phosphorus, low-sulfur pig iron or carbon briquettes may be added. When a greater increase is found necessary, carbon in some pure form, such as petroleum coke or a broken electrode, may be added.

Finally, temperature adjustment is made so that the heat will be at the proper tapping temperature. No completely satisfactory pyrometric method having been developed (see Article 296) the operator is dependent largely upon personal observation, such as holding the metal in a spoon and observing the formation of a film on the surface, or pouring the metal from a spoon under standard conditions and observing the amount of skull remaining in it.

387. Pouring. With the heat in proper condition, tapping is accomplished by tilting the furnace to deliver the metal through the spout into a clean, dry ladle. Efforts are made to hold the slag back by providing the spout with a brick skimmer or filling the tap hole with wet sacking which does not burn out until the metal itself has risen to the tap hole level. Every effort is made to get a swirling motion in the ladle in order to obtain maximum mixing and, as a result, homogeneous steel. During the pouring, the temperature of the metal will be obtained by means of an optical pyrometer; and, after the heat is allowed to stand for the proper length of time to rid the metal of rising inclusions, the metal is teemed into some form of ingot mold designed to keep piping and segregation to a minimum.

388. Chemistry. The reactions involved when basic, oxidizing slags are used are practically the same as those indicated in Article 300 for the basic open-hearth process. Reactions involved when a reducing slag is used are given in Article 385.

THE HIGH-FREQUENCY ELECTRIC FURNACE

389. History. The development of the high-frequency electric furnace, sometimes known as the coreless induction furnace, is a noteworthy example of modern research. In 1916, Dr. Edwin F. Northrup of Princeton University was retained by a group of industrialists to analyze the electric furnace, as revealed by literature and patent office records, to ascertain if any basic principle for developing heat by electrical energy had been overlooked and, if so, whether such basic principle had any promise of commercial application. After months of patient study, Dr. Northrup suggested the use of induced currents of high frequency for such heating. The wireless method of communication was being developed, and all efforts were directed toward obtaining high voltage and high frequencies to minimize heating effects. No one had so far deliberately stepped down the voltage of a high-frequency current for the express purpose of using it for heating purposes. As a result of this research, Dr. Northrup was able to obtain a broad coverage, as evidenced by the following typical claim from his original patent: "The method of applying energy by electromagnetic induction to be converted into heat within a resistor mass which consists in passing high frequency current through a conducting coil surrounding the resistor to be heated." As frequently happens in connection with such pioneering inventions, no practical power equipment at the time was available on the market for successfully practicing the invention, and no suitable condensers were available for correcting the power factor.

390. Electrical Equipment. A simplified wiring diagram of a converter and furnace is shown in Figure 89 and a simple sketch of a small furnace in Figure 90. The equipment consists essentially of a high-reactance transformer, a spark gap, and a bank of condensers. These in conjunction with the furnace coil set up an oscillatory circuit, the frequency of the oscillation being a function of the capacity and inductance of the oscillatory circuit, and in practice this frequency ranges from about 20,000 to 60,000 cycles per second.

At first an open rotary spark gap was used to produce the required high-frequency oscillatory current, but the noise created was terrific and the efficiency low. The present discharge gap, shown in Figure 89, consists essentially of a double-walled container, holding a bath of mercury and having space above the pool to afford room for the electrodes. The purpose of the double walls is to provide space for

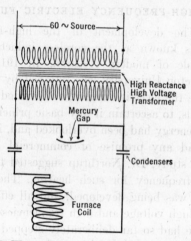

FIG. 89. Wiring Diagram of High-Frequency Furnace.

circulating water for cooling purposes, and the electrodes also are water-cooled down to the arcing points. The arc operates in a sealed chamber between a tungsten-tipped copper electrode and the mercury bath in an atmosphere of pure hydrogen. Means are provided for adjusting the level of the mercury whereby, by varying the distance between the electrodes and the mercury pool, the power may be controlled. Such a discharge gap is not only quiet but is also highly efficient and effective.

Condensers are, of course, required in the oscillatory circuit and are also required in the larger commercial units to correct the power factor of the system. These were at first constructed of alternate plates of proper quality glass and very thin brass sheets immersed in water-free oil. Such construction was heavy, costly, and decidedly inconvenient, and with the development of the radio industry the design has been changed to impregnated paper, aluminum foil, and water cooling.

Unfortunately, the use of such a method of generating oscillatory currents is restricted to an output of approximately 35 kilovolt-

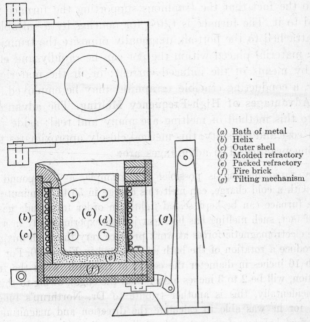

(a) Bath of metal
(b) Helix
(c) Outer shell
(d) Molded refractory
(e) Packed refractory
(f) Fire brick
(g) Tilting mechanism

Fig. 90. High-Frequency Furnace. (*Courtesy of Carnegie-Illinois Steel Corp.*)

amperes per phase because satisfactory vacuum power tubes of much larger capacity are not yet available. In view of the fact that the high-frequency Alexanderson type alternators are prohibitively costly, the machines now used consist of a 3-phase motor and a single-phase generator developing current at 900 volts and about 2000 cycles.

391. Furnace. The sketch shown in Figure 90 serves only to illustrate the chief features of the construction and operation of such a furnace, and specifically applies to the smaller-sized units; in the larger ones some of these details are modified. The essential parts of the furnace are a crucible or pot and a water-cooled coil of copper tubing serving as a conductor for the primary high-frequency current, the metal in the pot forming the conductor for the heavy, secondary current. Within the helix thus formed is the thin layer of special refractory, the space between it and the pot being filled with some suitable, granular refractory. The outer shell of the furnace is usually made of asbestos, plastic, brick, or some strong non-magnetic material because, if a magnetic material, like steel or iron, were used, it too would absorb energy and become hot. This is one of the minor difficulties in design, because strength in this material is important owing to the fact that the trunnions supporting the furnace must be attached to it. The furnace is tilted for pouring by a suitable lifting device attached to the bottom, diagonally opposite the trunnion. Any metallic material placed within the pot can be rapidly and efficiently melted by means of the induced current; or, if the material is not metallic, a conducting crucible (graphite) may be employed.

392. Advantages of High-Frequency Melting. The advantages accruing to this method of melting are many and real; aside from the items of cost and capacity, this method closely approximates the ideal of melting practice. The advantages are:

1. Very rapid melting is possible. For example, a 1000-pound furnace, starting with a cold charge, can melt this charge in 55 to 80 minutes.

2. The furnace can be kept sealed tightly in order to exclude gases. As a matter of fact, such melting has been carried on experimentally in a vacuum.

3. The electromagnetic forces at work produce very thorough mixing. These forces produce a rotation of the bath as indicated in Figure 90. For example, in a bath 16 inches in diameter the center of the bath, when the furnace is in operation, will be 2 to 3 inches higher than the edges, owing to this stirring effect. Incidentally, this is another tribute to Dr. Northrup's fundamental research, for he was able to calculate the direction and magnitude of this stirring effect before a furnace was actually constructed.

4. As a corollary to item 2, controlled atmosphere melting can be carried out.

5. The furnace is remarkably quiet.

6. Working conditions are better than in open-hearth practice.

7. Electrical equipment has been developed so that the furnace can be easily and effectively controlled.

8. Not only steel but also every known metal, limited only by the properties of the refractory container, may be melted.

9. The state of aggregation of the charge is not important.

10. The furnace has a very high efficiency—84 to 89 per cent, with a consumption of 550 to 1000 kilowatt-hours per ton of steel.

11. The induction furnace permits melting without carbon pick-ups; in the arc furnace it is difficult to hold the carbon under 0.04 per cent.

12. It is sometimes more rapid, making three to six heats while an arc furnace is making one, but the tonnages produced are less.*

Operating against these advantages are two very serious disadvantages, namely, the small capacity and the high cost of operation. The induction furnace at the present time appears to be limited, in holding capacity, to about 5 tons, and electrical engineers believe that this capacity will probably never exceed 15 tons. It is, therefore, difficult for a small high-frequency furnace to compete with arc furnaces melting as much as 75 tons per heat. Mechanical and electrical difficulties stand in the way of the design and manufacture of generating units much larger than those required for a 5-ton furnace. Preliminary analysis of metal which are necessary results in some delay in the heat, but with the uncertainty of scrap this is unavoidable. Finally, it should be noted that refining with slag is very difficult in the coreless furnace as contrasted to the arc furnace which is well adapted to either single- or double-slag treatments.

393. Lining. In small units a crucible may be inserted within the helix, but in the larger units another difficulty encountered is the substitution of some lining for this container. As indicated in the sketch, Figure 90, the bottom is strengthened by fire-clay brick, and the top may also be built up of molded refractory to form the tapered top and pouring spout of the crucible. For acid linings a dry mixture of ganister with a suitable flux is first put in to form the bottom, then a form made of asbestos or steel is inserted, leaving an annular space between it and the coil lining, which space is then filled with ganister mixture, in granular form. With the first heat the steel form melts away and the asbestos form slags off, leaving a lining composed wholly of ganister, the average life of which will be about 75 heats.

On the whole, at least in this country, basic linings are preferred, and grain magnesite† is substituted for the ganister, the inner form being made usually with Portland cement and asbestos fiber. These linings will last 100 to 500 heats, depending upon the type of steel made.

394. Charging. In a sense this method of making steel resembles the crucible process in that practically no refining is carried out. One reason for this lies in the fact that a slag cannot be used and the second in the cost of the process. Since the latter is high, the

---

* A 40-ton heat may be refined in an arc furnace in 6 hours; a 4-ton induction furnace requires about 3 hours for a heat.

† Such materials as Normagal and Lavgal (mixtures of electrically fused magnesia-alumina cement and silica) have given excellent results.

operator might just as well start with some very high-grade material; consequently, the charge may consist of anything that will enter the crucible, except that, in melting, a moderate amount of fairly large pieces should be added to provide initial conditions favorable to the generation of heat. The charge is collected in pans, much the same as in the crucible process, and dropped into the furnace through the top opening. If the charge contains pieces of varying size, the larger ones are charged first and the smaller ones packed about these as closely as possible. Even with the closest packing the furnace may not contain all the charge at once and some must be left to be added later on as melting progresses.

395. Melting. As soon as charging is completed, the current is turned on and the rapidly changing magnetic flux density generates heavy secondary currents in the charge which are converted into heat by the ohmic resistance of the charge itself. This heat is developed mainly in the outer rim of metal but is quickly carried by conduction to the center of the charge. As the molten metal forms in the furnace the charge sinks into the pool and melting is further accelerated by the motor effect upon this liquid metal, which movement of the metal promotes melting and also efficient stirring.

396. Future. Modern steel making requires a melting tool which will give easily the highest temperatures needed for practical metallurgy and which will provide good control over the chemical composition of the alloy. It is demanded further that all the mass heated shall be heated uniformly, and that at no point of it shall the highest temperature attained exceed that to which the whole mass will finally be brought. A need is strongly felt for a melting furnace that can recover scrap without changing in the least its composition. For all the requirements stated above, and probably many more, no method of melting seems more sound and basic in principle and more effective in application than this one of melting by high-frequency, coreless induction. Unquestionably, furnaces which employ this principle will change in design, improve in construction, and increase in size. They must all, however, be limited by the fundamental principle that in high-frequency induction the power absorbed by the melt is substantially proportional to the frequency used and to the square of the ampere-turns of the inductor coils. The method and apparatus now used for supplying high-frequency power to such a furnace will undoubtedly change in character, probably become cheaper, and be supplied in larger units.

BIBLIOGRAPHY

1. ARNOLD, S., III, "The 3-Phase Electric Arc Furnace," American Electrical Engineers, *Electrical Engineering,* December, 1933.
2. BOYLSTON, H. M., *An Introduction to the Metallurgy of Iron and Steel.* New York: John Wiley and Sons, 1936. 563 pp.
3. CAMPBELL, D. F., "A High Frequency Induction Furnace," Transactions of the Iron and Steel Institute, *Journal,* Vol. CXII (11), September, 1925.
4. CAMPBELL, D. F., "High Frequency Steel Furnaces," Transactions of the Iron and Steel Institute, *Journal,* September, 1930.
5. CLAMER, G. H., "The Development of the Coreless Induction Furnace," *Metals and Alloys,* May, 1935.
6. FRANCIS, C. B., *The Making, Shaping, and Treating of Steel.* Pittsburgh: Carnegie-Illinois Steel Corporation, 1940. 1440 pp.
7. GILL, J. P., "The Melting of Tool and Other High Grade Steels in the Basic Electric Furnace," *American Society for Metals Handbook,* 1936.
8. GRAY, A., *Principles and Practice of Electrical Engineering.* Revised by G. A. Wallace; fourth edition. New York: McGraw-Hill Book Company, 1933. 538 pp.
9. HAYWARD, C. R., *An Outline of Metallurgical Practice.* New York: D. Van Nostrand Company, 1940. 612 pp.
10. KOEHLER, W. B., *Applications.* Volume 2 of Creighton and Koehler's *Electrochemistry.* New York: John Wiley and Sons, 1935.
11. LYON, D. A., and R. W. KEENEY, "Electric Furnaces for Making Steel," Bureau of Mines, *Bulletin* 67, 1913.
12. MOORE, W. E., "Twenty Year Advance in Electric Arc Furnaces," *Transactions of the Electrochemical Society,* 1931.
13. NORTHRUP, E. F., "Tonnage Melting by Coreless Induction," *The Iron Age,* January 15, 22, and 29, 1931.
14. PALMER, F. R., "Electric Furnaces and Their Part in Metallurgical Progress," American Iron and Steel Institute, *Transactions,* 1936.
15. ROHN, W., "Influence of Gases on Metals and Influence of Melting in Vacuo," American Institute of Mining and Metallurgical Engineers, *Transactions,* Vol. 99, 1932.
16. SISCO, F. T., *The Manufacture of Electric Steel.* New York: McGraw-Hill Book Company, 1924. 304 pp.
17. SPRAGUE, E. C., "The Graphitizing Furnace," *Electrochemical Society Transactions,* Vol. LXX, October, 1936.
18. STANSFIELD, ALFRED, *The Electric Furnace; Its Construction, Operation, and Uses.* New York: McGraw-Hill Book Company, 1914. 415 pp.
19. STOUGHTON, B., *Metallurgy of Iron and Steel.* New York: McGraw-Hill Book Company, 1934. 519 pp.
20. STOUGHTON, B., and A. BUTTS, *Engineering Metallurgy.* New York: McGraw-Hill Book Company, 130. 441 pp.
21. WILCOX, C., and G. V. LUERSSEN, "Steel Melting in the Coreless Induction Furnace," *American Society for Metals Handbook,* 1936.
22. WILLCOX, D., "Accomplishments of the High Frequency Induction Furnace," *Industrial and Engineering Chemistry,* News Edition, December 10, 1928.

CHAPTER XI

SCRAP

GENERAL ASPECTS

397. General. Underlying the entire iron and steel industry is that indispensable trinity—iron ore, coal, and scrap. Of these, scrap is the most spectacular, yet it is an industrial paradox. It is not a product in itself but a toll taken by obsolescence or the by-product of metal-working processes. It may be defined as any alloy of iron that is the waste or by-product of processes for manufacturing or fabricating such alloys or that has been discarded on account of failure, obsolescence, or for any other reason. It includes almost every category from automobiles to hairpins; ships that have outlived their usefulness; automobiles that have been sent to the scrap pile; rails that have been removed from abandoned branch lines; superannuated locomotives and freight cars; trimmings and stampings from the manufacture of sheet-metal articles; shavings or small particles of iron and steel from machining operations; farm implements that have become obsolescent or covered with rust in the corner of the farmyard; in short, anything made from iron and steel, regardless of size and condition, from tin cans up to battleships.*

There is hardly a phase of our modern civilized life into which scrap iron and steel does not enter. In transportation by airplane, railroad, and steamship; in the channels of communication by telephone, radio, and telegraph; in the transmission of power and electricity; in the gossamer network of cables that suspends the bridges of our large cities; in the refinements of urban life with its sky-scrapers and highways; in the vast domain of agriculture; and in the

* In 1939 the relative tonnages were estimated as:

	Tons	Per Cent of Total
Home scrap	17,519,550	55.5
From railroads	2,357,264	7.5
From automobiles	2,675,000	8.5
From public utilities	300,000	1.0
From ship breakers	75,000	0.2
Country scrap	8,626,396	27.3
	31,553,210	

TABLE 61

STATISTICS OF THE SCRAP INDUSTRY[2]

(In Gross Tons)

Year	Domestic Consumption of Scrap	Exports	Imports	Steel Ingot Production	Ratio Consumption Steel Ingot Production
1910	13,100,000	25,825	72,764	26,094,919	0.503
1918	25,400,000	2,160	63,730	44,462,432	0.572
1921	12,400,000	37,592	41,469	19,783,797	0.628
1929	37,600,000	557,044	90,479	56,433,473	0.667
1932	10,000,000	227,522	9,775	13,681,162	0.732
1934	18,800,000	1,835,170	44,421	26,055,289	0.722
1937	38,006,272	4,092,590	81,640	50,568,701	0.764
1938	21,000,000	3,003,523	24,451	28,349,991	0.742
1940	41,687,000	2,793,718	....	66,982,686	0.633
....	....	....	....	....	....

thousands of uses of steel in the offices, households, and factories of the nation—in all these scrap is basic; from scrap they all arise and to scrap they must return in the course of time. Statistics of this important industry are given in Table 61.

398. Character of Scrap. Scrap may be broadly classified into "home" and "country" scrap. Home scrap is produced in the process of steel making in all the various steps, from the blast furnace to the rolling mill. When molten steel is cast from an open-hearth furnace or Bessemer converter into an ingot mold, 15 to 30 per cent of the ingot must be cropped off, and this—the highest grade of scrap—is charged again into a furnace. Home scrap is made in the various manufacturing processes where steel sheets, plates, rails, etc., must be trimmed to shape. Especially in the rolling of the high-grade products such as a "full-finished" sheet or rail particular care must be taken to eliminate the inferior portions. So exacting are the specifications and standards of steel consumers that the yield of finished steel is rarely more than 70 to 75 per cent of the weight of the original ingot. All classes of foundries also generate home scrap in the form of sprues, risers, spillage, etc. This scrap never leaves the premises of the mill or foundry and accounts for practically one-half the total that is consumed.

The country scrap that accounts for about 20 per cent of the total volume of the industry normally filters into the yards in the small cities from every nook and corner of the country. After small yard dealers have accumulated several carloads, they sell to brokers or to large yard operators having mill orders, and these in' turn ship directly to the consumer. The base of this scrap pyramid is the army of small peddlers, collectors, and dealers who, in order to eke out a living, must also handle other waste materials such as rubber, rags, paper, and non-ferrous metals. It includes the peddler's mixed wagon-load of old pipe, kitchen stoves, farm implements, and other cast-off iron and steel as well as the residue from the auto-wrecking yard that is to be found in the outskirts of every small community.

399. Use of Scrap. A small proportion (perhaps 3 per cent) of scrap can be used in its original form. For example, the clippings and trimmings from some forming operation may themselves be stamped down into washers and similar smaller articles. Railroad rails, no longer serviceable or too light in section, may be heated, slit into three parts, and rerolled into reinforcing for concrete structures, fence posts, and small bars. Over 95 per cent of all scrap iron and steel is charged back into some iron or steel furnace, such as the open-hearth, the blast furnace, the gray iron cupola, the malleable iron furnace, or the electric furnace to be transformed into some new form of iron or steel. In 1939 open-hearth steel furnaces accounted for 70 per cent of all the scrap consumed in this country, gray iron cupolas 17, blast furnaces 6, electric furnaces 4, malleable iron furnaces 2. Almost 90 per cent of all the steel that is produced in the United States is produced by the open-hearth process, and as previously mentioned scrap usually makes up about half the charge. As a matter of fact there are a number of steel-producing companies in this country operating entirely on scrap as raw material.

PREPARATION OF SCRAP

400. General. To the general public an old crankshaft or connecting rod from a junked automobile is much the same as a lot of old wood screws or washers. To the sellers and consumers there are for good reasons many distinct varieties.[1] Actually, there are seventy-five separate classifications, based upon analysis, size, and ease of handling. Consequently, the preparation of scrap is a very technical operation. This preparation has for its main objective the separation of scrap into a group based on analysis and one based on size. With a trend toward lighter and more highly alloyed steels, the responsibility of the scrap dealer in segregating alloys becomes much more pronounced because a few tenths of one per cent of manganese, copper, tin, lead, or zinc may ruin a heat of steel. In a modern automobile there are now more than 125 different kinds of steel; and, whereas the scrap-yard worker soon learns to distinguish cast-iron from rolled-steel products, only by laboratory analysis can one classify many of these alloys.

The size of scrap is equally important and is usually dictated by the processes used for handling it. For example, to fit into the charging boxes of an open-hearth furnace, No. 1 Heavy Melting steel must be not over 18 inches in width nor more than 5 feet in length, but at the same time it must be ¼ inch or over in thickness for economical melting. To illustrate this point a full description of a few of the more important classes of scrap are given in the pages that follow immediately.

SCRAP FOR USE IN THE BLAST FURNACE

401. Cast-Iron Borings. Clean cast-iron borings free from badly corroded material, lumps, scale, other metals, dirt, or foreign material of any kind.

402. Mill Scale. Iron oxide produced in rolling-mill practice, from drop-forge hammers or from a busheling mill squeezer. It should contain not less than 65 per cent metallic iron and must be reasonably free from dirt, grease, and other foreign material. Scale from alloy steel may be excluded from these specifications by mutual agreement between buyer and seller.

SCRAP FOR USE IN THE BASIC OPEN-HEARTH FURNACE

403. No. 1 Heavy Melting Steel Scrap. Steel scrap ¼ inch and over in thickness, not over 18 inches in width, and not over 5 feet long. Individual pieces must be cut into such shape that they will be free from attachments and will lie flat in a charging box. Cut boiler plate must be practically clean and free from stay bolts, not over 3 feet long, and must lie reasonably flat in charging box. Smaller dimensions of plate scrap may be required upon mutual agreement between buyer and seller. No piece to weigh less than 5 pounds.

No. 1 Heavy Melting may include structural shapes, angle bars and plates, steel castings, heavy chain, carbon tool steel, heavy forgings, forge butts, and similar heavy material.

This grade may also include new mashed pipe ends, original diameter 4 inches and over, thoroughly flattened; sheet bars; billets; blooms;

rail ends; railroad steel; and wrought scrap, such as angles, splices, couplers, knuckles, short rails, drawbars, cut cast-steel bolsters, coil and leaf springs (all coil springs to be ⅜ inch or larger in diameter).

No needle or skeleton plate scrap, agricultural shapes, annealing pots, boiler tubes, grate bars, cast iron, malleable iron, or curly or unwieldy pieces will be accepted.

Must be free from dirt, excessive rust or scale, or foreign material of any kind. Alloy-steel scrap may be excluded from these specifications by mutual agreement between buyer and seller.

404. No. 1 Busheling. Clean iron and soft-steel pipes and flues, tanks, cut hoops, and bands No. 12 gage and heavier, steel-plate punchings and clippings, soft-steel and iron forgings, and flashings; no dimension over 8 inches. To be free from burnt material, hard steel, cast, malleable, and galvanized or metal-coated stock of any kind.

405. No. 1 Machine-Shop Turnings. New, clean steel or wrought-iron turnings, free from lumps, badly tangled or matted material, cast-iron borings, other metals, excessive oil, dirt, or foreign material of any kind. Badly rusted or corroded stock will not be accepted.

406. Loose Sheet Clippings. New, black steel sheet clippings, shearings, and stampings, 3/16 inch and lighter, free from excessive rust, paint, or protective coating of any kind, to be not over 18 inches wide or long, or if edge trimmings or shearings to be not over 12 inches by 5 feet long. No detinned scrap, electrical sheets, or material over 0.50 per cent silicon will be accepted. Further limitation of silicon content may be made by mutual agreement between buyer and seller.

407. No. 1 Cast-Iron Scrap. To contain all kinds of machinery and similar cast-iron scrap, nothing under 10 pounds or over 500 pounds in weight nor over 48 inches long or 18 inches wide. To contain no brake shoes, cast-iron soil or water pipe, stove scrap, or burnt iron of any description, and to be free from steel parts.

SCRAP FOR USE IN ACID OPEN-HEARTH FURNACE

408. Billet and Bar Crops. Billet, bloom, axle, heavy forge, or bar crops not over 0.04 per cent phosphorus or sulfur, not over 0.50 per cent silicon, free from alloys. Not less than 2 inches square or 2 inches in diameter, not over 18 inches wide, and sheared to lengths not over 36 inches. No piece to weigh less than 10 pounds nor more than 500 pounds. Must be new material and free from excessive rust. Longer lengths may be allowed by mutual agreement between buyer and seller.

409. Structural and Miscellaneous Scrap. Bar ends, forging crops, structural crops, and plate shearings smaller and lighter than grade A and B, not over 0.50 per cent silicon, 0.04 per cent phosphorus, and 0.05 per cent sulfur, free from alloys. Not less than ¼ inch thick, not over 18 inches wide or 36 inches long. To be fully described at time of sale and purchase. Must be clean and free from excessive rust. Longer lengths may be allowed by mutual agreement between buyer and seller.

410. Car Wheels. Solid cast steel, forged, pressed, or rolled-steel car and locomotive wheels, not over 36 inches in diameter. (Specify kind when offered for sale.)

SCRAP FOR USE IN ELECTRIC FURNACE

411. Punchings and Clippings. Open-hearth steel punchings and clippings, ¼ inch and heavier, 4 inches and under in length. Not over 0.04 per cent in phosphorus or sulfur and suitable for shovel charging. Must be clean and free from galvanized or coated stock, dirt, and excessive rust or corrosion.

412. Guaranteed Axle Turnings. Heavy steel or iron axle or forge turnings, guaranteed not over 0.04 per cent in phosphorus or sulfur. To contain no foreign material and must be clean and free from excessive rust and corrosion. To weigh not less than 75 pounds per cubic foot.

413. Guaranteed Heavy Scrap. Open-hearth steel plates, structural shapes, crop ends, shearings, broken steel tires, knuckles, tool steel, and spring steel. To be not less than ¼ inch thick, other dimensions subject to agreement. Not over 0.04 per cent in phosphorus or sulfur, clean, free from excessive rust and corrosion, and containing no foreign material.

414. Miscellaneous. Compressed sheet scrap must have a density of not less than 75 pounds per cubic foot. Steel rails for the remelting must be cut to 3-foot lengths. Railroad car and locomotive couplings must be stripped clean of all attachments. Steel coated with lead, zinc, tin, or other materials is properly segregated and used sparingly in the steel furnace. Ordinarily, the reclamation of tin cans from city dumps is uneconomical for the reason that the cost of collection exceeds the ultimate scrap value; but there are a few plants at which the tin, the really valuable part, is removed from the scrap, and the resulting detinned scrap is baled and remelted.

TABLE 62

Ratio of Ore to Iron and Steel

Year	Pig Iron Other than Basic and Bessemer	Steel Ingots and Castings	Total Iron and Steel	Total Ore Consumed	Total Lake Ore Consumed	Ratio Total Ore to Total Iron and Steel	Ratio Lake Ore to Total Iron and Steel
1918	7,383,504	44,462,432	51,845,936	71,983,356	62,520,682	1.39	1.21
1921	3,339,840	19,783,797	23,123,637	29,629,738	25,832,215	1.28	1.12
1929	7,825,089	56,433,473	64,258,562	73,058,586	63,662,346	1.14	0.99
1932	8,549,649	13,680,517	22,230,166	12,787,915	10,284,000	0.58	0.47
1940	12,083,932	66,982,686	79,066,618	79,672,248	62,426,314	1.01	0.79

ECONOMIC ASPECTS

415. The Conservation of Our Iron Resources. No factor concerning the American steel industry is so often "viewed with alarm" as the country's dwindling reserves of iron ore. Iron ore is an essential ingredient in the food on which the giant Steel lives and labors. As its supply of food cannot presumably last forever, the question naturally arises—how long will it hold out, how long will it be before the giant must depend for subsistence on food supply from foreign countries? The encouraging fact is that this giant needs a little less of this food every year because, as shown in Table 62, the ratio of ore to iron and steel has been decreasing ever since the early years of the present century. Over the past ten years there has been an average annual decline of 40 pounds of ore consumed in making a ton of iron and steel. Discounting the present unusual conditions, we may hope that the time will come when only one ton of iron ore will be consumed for each ton of iron and steel manufactured. What this means in tonnage can be illustrated by taking the period from 1920 to 1929. If the ratio had remained the same in 1929 as it was in 1920, the consumption of Lake ore would have amounted to over 73 million tons instead of approximately 64 million actually consumed. In this instance there was a saving of about 8 million tons of ore, worth about $35,000,000 at Lower Lake ports, directly attributable to the increased use of scrap. Incidentally, as the amount of iron in the Lake ore decreases, a correspondingly larger tonnage will be required.

We should show some concern over the fact that in the past decade a very large tonnage of scrap has been exported from this country. To replace this scrap by virgin pig iron involves the consumption of 25 million tons of raw materials. It is particularly distressing, at this time of national peril, to recall that during the past 5 years over 8 million* tons went to Japan and is, presumably, now being manufactured into munitions for the present conflict. It is not too much to say that the United States is literally digging itself into its natural environment on a scale which has no precedent in history and is leading the world in the speed with which it is exploiting and exhausting its natural resources. Coal reserves of all kinds, high and low grade, favorably and unfavorably located, will last for 1000, perhaps 4000, years. Iron ore, including the lower grades, will last for hundreds of years, but the known reserves of high-grade Mesabi ores, now supplying about one-half of our requirements, will last for only

* In 1938, the record year, 2,026,859 gross tons were exported to Japan.

about 40 years; and for the rest of the Lake Superior region, supplying about 30 per cent of our requirements, the estimate is less than 20 years.

416. Price. Scrap, unlike most raw materials used in the steel industry, is never deliberately produced as such and hence has no raw material cost. It may be said to have no intrinsic value. Its price is determined more than anything else by the relationship between scrap and the material which it displaces—pig iron—and scrap rarely exceeds the price of pig because consumers purchase more of the latter when scrap rises in price. Under these conditions the dealer in scrap reverses the normal practice; that is, he works backward from his selling price, which is the level consumers will pay under the prevailing market conditions. As a result this relationship only determines the general price level for scrap. Perhaps more accurately it determines the price for the best grade of scrap, which is No. 1 Heavy Melting steel. All other grades of scrap will be priced accordingly, depending mostly on their desirability as open-hearth charge and secondarily on the market conditions. For example, at this writing No. 1 Heavy Melting steel is selling in Chicago at $18.75 per ton, No. 2 Heavy Melting at $17.75, No. 1 Busheling at $18.25, Cast-Iron Borings at $14.50, and Mixed Borings and Turnings at $14.00. At the same time, No. 2 Foundry Pig iron is selling in Chicago at $24.00 per ton and Basic Pig iron at $23.50.

417. Exports of Scrap. There has been a steady increase in the amount of scrap iron and steel exported to Europe, the Far East, and South America ever since the turn of the century. As long ago as 1900, 25,000 tons of scrap were exported; by 1929, this had reached half a million and a peak was reached in 1937, when over 4 million tons were exported. The chief reason is that foreign purchasers of American scrap find it less costly to tap the vast American reservoir of metals than to build their own facilities for producing theirs from ore. In recent years the principal buyers of American scrap, in order of the tonnage involved, were Japan, Italy, the United Kingdom, Germany, the Netherlands, Poland, and Canada. Over the past decade Japan has been the leading customer.

418. Scrap as a Source of Steel. The fact that steel produced from scrap, or its somewhat cruder synonym "junk," was inferior to that made from primary or virgin pig iron has largely disappeared, owing in the main to the tremendous strides made by the scrap industry in properly preparing, classifying, and sorting the scrap, as well as to the great advances made by metallurgists in the technique of reshaping, remelting, and refining it. Even so, "the memory lingers on" in industry, and a good salesman may still convince a gullible customer that steel made from scrap is inferior to that produced from pig iron. As a matter of fact, a bill was recently introduced in California* prohibiting the use of scrap iron, or any material derived from it, in the construction or repair of any public buildings, bridges, or other structures. It is to be regretted that such a misconception regarding quality still persists, because it can be categorically stated that under comparable conditions steel of just as high quality can be made from scrap as from virgin pig iron.

BIBLIOGRAPHY

1. Department of Commerce, *Classification of Iron and Steel Scrap,* 1940.
2. Institute of Scrap Iron and Steel, *Yearbooks,* 1939 to date.
3. Institute of Scrap Iron and Steel, *Story of Scrap,* 1939.
4. Institute of Scrap Iron and Steel, *Conservers of National Wealth,* 1930.
5. WILLIAS, C. E., "The New Technical and Economic Importance of Iron and Steel Scrap," American Iron and Steel Institute, *Transactions,* 1936.

* One was introduced in another state, years ago, to legalize the value of π at an even 3.0.

CHAPTER XII

INGOTS AND INGOT MOLDS

GENERAL ASPECTS

419. General. A point has now been reached in the lengthy process of the conversion of iron ore into a usable form where the refining operation has been completed and we have, on the hearth of an open-hearth furnace, in a Bessemer converter or in an electric furnace a molten bath of steel. Using the methods and tools placed at his disposal by modern science, the melter can usually produce a bath of steel conforming very closely to the specifications set down by the consumer and in proper condition for teeming or casting. This large body of molten metal must now be cast, in a convenient shape for rolling, into what are known as "ingots." This is accomplished by pouring the metal, while it is still molten, into metallic molds of the desired dimensions, which are then allowed to solidify in part, or in whole, before the mold is removed. It is unfortunate that this process must be carried on in contact with the atmosphere. In the preceding chapters much stress has been laid on the role of ferrous oxide in the refining of steel and the bad effects it may have on the properties of the alloy if allowed to remain in the metal. Precautions must therefore be exercised in this process of casting not to reintroduce ferrous oxide, in too great amounts, into the solidifying metal.

Furthermore, the matter of uniform temperature is of great importance. Before the rolling or shaping operation begins, the ingot must have been allowed to solidify throughout and the whole body to reach a uniform temperature. Naturally, these conditions are not fulfilled because, in cooling, the outside of the ingot is the first to solidify and the interior is the last to drop to any given temperature. As a matter of fact, the molds are frequently stripped from many ingots, in an effort to decrease costs of heating and rolling, while the central portion is still in the liquid state. This was taken advantage of by early steel workers by stripping the ingots as soon as possible and placing them in a tightly covered hole or pit in the ground, where the heat from the interior of the ingot was slowly diffused to the outside by conduction, sufficing not only to heat up the cold or exterior part of the ingot but also to supply heat to this pit. This process was called "soaking," hence the name "soaking pit." This feature is mentioned only in passing in order to complete the picture; a consideration of the reheating of these ingots for rolling and shaping will be left to other books. This one will close with the production of the solid ingot.

420. Ingot Molds. Primarily, the function of an ingot mold is to provide a receptacle for the molten steel which shall, after freezing, be in a form suitable for subsequent working. A further function of the mold is to abstract heat from the molten steel and to dissipate it by radiation, or other means, from its outer surface. The mold abstracts heat from the steel by two, not entirely independent, methods. The first is a chilling action due to the mold's being at a much lower temperature than the steel which has been poured into it and at the same time acting as a receptacle into which the heat flows from the steel. The second, which becomes more vital as the cooling proceeds, is the outward passage of heat, by conduction, through the walls of the mold, with subsequent radiation from its outer surfaces.

Although the above are essential functions of an ingot mold, it has become, necessarily, more and more the practice to design the mold so that it may fulfill the further function of producing sound ingots free from cavities, surface defects, and with the harmful influence of segregation phenomena reduced to a minimum. The form of the ingot mold should also be such that the amount of steel to be discarded from the ingot in the subsequent forming operations shall be as small as possible.

Any factor which influences the functions of the mold as outlined in the above discussion is of importance in determining its weight, dimension, and contour. Such factors are numerous and are not confined to the properties of the mold itself, but they are also inherent in the steel inside the mold. Unfortunately, economic factors also enter into the picture so that it may be advisable in many cases to sacrifice the advantages of using a mold of a certain shape in order to simplify and considerably reduce the cost of the subsequent working of the steel ingots. Furthermore, the relative importance of many of these factors is not very definite, with the result that it is often extremely difficult to decide, a priori, which of two ingot molds is the better for a particular purpose. It is possible only to enumerate the various factors which operate and the direction in which they act and then perhaps, from a consideration of all of these, arrive at the proper conclusions. In the design of the shape of the mold, however, the following important points certainly stand out:

1. Freedom from shrinkage cavity (pipe).
2. Suitability for, and ease of, further working.
3. The elimination of stresses set up on cooling.
4. The elimination of planes of weakness.
5. The shape or contour of the ingot.

All these important factors are discussed in more detail in the pages that follow.

421. Mold Material. Since the early days of modern steel production, the intermediate phase of ingot making has received comparatively less attention than any other stage in the whole process. Altogether too little progress has been made in the field of ingots and ingot molds regardless of the general tendency towards metallurgical and economical improvements in other departments of the modern steel plant. Perhaps the most conclusive proof for this statement may be found in the large deviations which prevail in the chemical com-

TABLE 63

CONDITION AND LIFE OF INGOT MOLDS[7]

Grade of Steel Teemed	Per Cent						Life of Mold in Heats	Country
	Total C	Si	Mn	S	P	Cr		
Basic open hearth	3.84	1.63	1.20	0.038	0.216		137	U. S. A.
"		1.34	0.96	0.046	0.117		119	"
"	3.24	1.96	1.43	0.030	0.098	0.15	181	"
"	3.30	1.89	0.85	0.063			140	Germany
Acid open hearth		1.77	0.91				98	Sweden
Acid Bessemer	3.60	1.57	1.03	0.05	0.112		92	U. S. A.
"	3.37	1.69	0.96	0.078	0.172		123	England
Basic Bessemer	3.78	1.90	1.10	0.040	0.166		177	Czechoslovakia
"	4.11	1.03	0.93				151	Belgium
Electric		1.53	1.22	0.054	0.180		129	U. S. A.
"	4.29	1.31	1.06	0.044	0.156		158	Austria
"	0.38	0.32	0.73	0.041	0.029		226	U. S. A.
"	0.43	0.27	0.88	0.021	0.032		246	"

position of that part which is so important in the production of sound ingots at favorable costs—the ingot molds. A glance at Table 63 shows conclusively the variety of alloys used in some of the world's leading steel-producing countries. Practically all ingot molds of today are produced from one of the following metals:

1. Gray iron.
   a. Direct blast-furnace metal.
   b. Mixer metal.
   c. Ordinary cupola iron.
   d. Ordinary air-furnace iron.
   e. Alloyed gray iron.
2. Cast steel.
   a. Acid or basic open-hearth steel.
   b. Acid or basic Bessemer steel.

Because of their origin, all the above-mentioned metals necessarily contain one or more kinds of carbon in addition to silicon, manganese, phosphorus, and sulfur. Occasionally mold metal may contain, by accident or design, copper, nickel, chromium, titanium, aluminum, and other more or less rare constituents.

Molds almost always fail through cracking, checking, pitting, or deterioration of the inside surface. That the composition of the metal of the mold does have a very direct influence on its performance is demonstrated by a research project which has been in progress for a number of years at Purdue University. This research has to do with the life of brake shoes employed on railroad trains. In the past it has been an accepted fact that these wear away rapidly, and the chief factor heretofore considered has been cost. This investigation brought out the fact that the composition of a metal has a very direct effect on its cracking, checking, and pitting and, of course, on its hardness, with the result that this research has developed a new metal composition which, although a bit more expensive per unit of weight than that heretofore employed, is actually much cheaper when the life of the shoe, and its effect on the car wheel, is taken into consideration. The same set of conditions unquestionably prevails in the selection of metal for an ingot mold.

The present tendency of modern foundry practice to produce iron of better resistance to deterioration, with a most desirable small size of graphite flakes, is governed theoretically by the relationship between the ultimate carbon and silicon analyses. John Hruska,[7] on the basis of a large number of experiments, has worked out a very interesting correlation showing that the most durable molds are made of metal whose carbon-silicon ratio falls close to the line A-B in Figure

91. The chemical specifications for the most efficient mold metal should be determined in accordance with this expressed relationship, but with due consideration of the mass effect upon the exact location of line *A-B* in the diagram. Molds made of cast steel of basic open-hearth quality apparently show the longest life at carbon concentrations ranging from 0.32 to 0.40 per cent.

From a similar study it appears that the manganese does affect mold life so greatly as to warrant a term, "critical manganese content," at approximately 1.95 per cent manganese. At this concentration the molds frequently gave a serviceability exceeding 180 heats, pro-

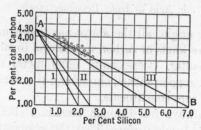

FIG. 91. Ingot Mold Compositions. (*Courtesy of The Iron Age.*)

viding the design of the mold was correct and the metal represented good cupola iron of rather fine grain.

Apparently the influence of sulfur upon the durability of ingot molds has been completely misinterpreted. Most authorities have been guided entirely by speculative theories and have advocated low percentages of sulfur in order to prevent what they term "undue diffusion of sulfur into the solidifying ingot." It appears certain now that sulfur, instead of being rejected from the mold wall into the ingot, is being assimilated by the interior layers of the mold wall, presumably in the gaseous form, thus affecting favorably the ingot surface. The continuous assimilation of sulfur, however, increases the red shortness of the ferrous matrix of the mold interior until a point is reached at which the "fire cracking" or "crow footing" of the surface extends beyond operable limits; therefore a longer life may be obtained with a low initial sulfur content, thus retarding the saturation of the mold metal by a sulfurous constituent.

Up to about 0.15 per cent phosphorus the influence of this element is practically negligible, and it appears that phosphorus changes very slightly during the life of the mold. When changing concentration does occur, it is always a positive one; that is, a little of this element is diffused from the ingot into the surface of the mold. However, this difference was never above 8 per cent of the original amount present in the mold.

The addition of nickel is uncommon. Although it is true that the effect of nickel in gray iron results in a strengthening of the ferrous matrix and a dissociation of the carbides, the economical results of such additions, with nickel at 35 cents per pound, are quite another matter. Those obtained with chromium, on the other hand, have been very satisfactory. Most of the commercial sizes of modern ingot molds represent castings with rather heavy sections, and these heavy walls account for the practical impossibility of producing uniform grain structure with a favorable size of graphite flakes. The slow cooling rates of such sections are accompanied by a dissociation of the carbides of iron into graphitic iron and ferrite at temperatures exceeding about 600°C. Owing to the fact that this temperature is frequently reached, the graphitic flakes are of larger size, the combined carbon low, the fracture coarse, resulting in poor properties for the ingot mold.

CLASSES OF STEEL

422. General. The author has delayed the consideration of the different classes of steel to this part of the book because the production of good steel is just as much a matter of casting and ingot manipulation as it is open-hearth, Bessemer, or electric-furnace practice. The melter may produce, in the open-hearth furnace, a heat of steel which might be expected to result in a superior ingot and yet, in the relatively short space of time represented by teeming, be converted into an off-heat.* All steel, however it may be produced today, can be divided into three general classes: (1) fully deoxidized, (2) semideoxidized, and (3) open, effervescent, or rimming steel.

423. Fully Deoxidized Steel. This name has been selected because, when produced under the proper conditions, the steel is practically free from oxides and gases. The melter accomplishes this through the use of proper slags in the furnace and suitable deoxidizing agents in both the furnace and the ladle so that the evolution of gases during the solidification of the ingot in the mold is almost entirely prevented, with the result that the solidification of the ingot is accomplished without any blowhole formation and the only physically defective portion of the ingot is that part represented by the pipe or shrinkage cavity. It is commonly recognized that fully deoxidized or killed steel is the only class from which reliably sound products can be obtained.

---

* One not conforming to specifications.

The other two classes of steel are admittedly compromises and are represented by large tonnages only because, under certain conditions, it becomes more economical to produce steel in this way.

The usual method for finishing fully deoxidized steel in the basic open-hearth furnace is to charge sufficient ferrosilicon to reduce most of the ferrous oxide 20 to 30 minutes before the heat is to be tapped, and the silica resulting from this reaction then fluxes more ferrous oxide from the bath. Manganese is sometimes added to effect complete deoxidation of the bath, but it does not combine as readily with oxygen as does silicon, nor does it have as much effect on the removal of iron oxide by fluxing. On the other hand, there must be a residual manganese content of at least 0.35 per cent; otherwise the ferrosilicon cannot function effectively. Reference to the order of oxidizing agents (see Article 332) shows that aluminum is the most powerful deoxidizing agent known; and, although it does have some fluxing value, its relative high cost, low specific gravity, and the difficulty it has in functioning with the bath at the slag-bath line limit its use to that of a correctant after the major part of the deoxidizing and refining has been carried out in the furnace with less expensive and more easily handled elements. The more common practice is to add a few ounces of aluminum in each ingot mold to finish the deoxidizing. In a basic open-hearth heat of killed steel aluminum should not, under any conditions, be added to the furnace. If it is added to the ladle, it should be done when the ladle is approximately one-third to two-thirds filled.

424. Semi-deoxidized Steel. This, as the name implies, refers to steel that is only partially deoxidized or degasified by furnace treatment. The common practice is to bring the bath of molten metal down to 0.10 to 0.15 per cent carbon and then recarburize, either in the bath or in the ladle, to the analysis required. Sometimes semideoxidized steel lies relatively quiet in the mold without much evolution of gas, but it usually requires the addition of aluminum or some other strong degasifier to prevent the steel from boiling or rising in the mold. As a result, blowholes are formed in the body of the ingot, particularly in the upper, outer portion, and the shrinkage cavity, although relatively smaller in volume than with fully deoxidized steel, is rather deep. The greater, or more extensive the formation of blowholes, the smaller the volume of the pipe because these blowholes tend to compensate for the shrinkage of the metal as it cools. Secondary axial pipe or cleavage planes of porosity frequently extend throughout the greater part of the vertical lengths of the ingot. Ingots of this description are frequently removed from their molds and placed in the soaking pit while the central portion of the ingot is still in a liquid condition; some metallurgists believe that such stripping before complete solidification prevents the formation of an extensive pipe and improves the quality of the bloom. The truth of the matter probably is that it simply serves to hide the evidence of the pipe and, to some degree, of the blowholes and, of course, lessens the reheating cost which may be the real reason for carrying out this practice. Actually, the remedy is worse than the disease, for, once rolled, no subsequent treatment of any kind can compensate for the damage done.

425. Rimmed Steels. The terms "rimmed," "open," and "effervescent" are applied to low-carbon steels manufactured by the basic open-hearth and Bessemer processes to which little deoxidation, with the exception of manganese, is applied either in the furnace, the ladle, or the mold. The last two terms were prompted by the fact that, after the steel is in the mold, the evolution of gas proceeds for a considerable length of time and in appearance is quite unlike that of the killed or deoxidized steels which lie dead and flat in the mold. In the early days of steel manufacture the principal product of the basic open-hearth process was low-carbon steel.

Before ferrosilicon and aluminum were available, steel was deoxidized by ferromanganese alone, which deoxidation, within the ordinary ranges of 0.30 to 0.80 per cent, is far from complete. In order to hold the steel in the mold, it was necessary to cover the top of it with a heavy cast-iron cap or cover and hold this in place by means of a steel bar placed across the cap and fitting tightly into two lugs, one on each side. When the ingot had solidified sufficiently, the cap was removed. The violent evolution of gas during solidification caused irregular freezing on the mold walls, which resulted in large slivers in the blooms and billets, and blowholes near the surface resulted in small slivers, seams, and laps when the ingot was heated in the soaking pit and rolled in the blooming mill. Rimmed steel was the result of attempts to improve the quality of this type of steel by controlling the evolution of gas and directing its escape in an orderly manner through the top of the ingot. This necessitated doing away with the cap and pouring the ingot short because the steel rose a few inches in the mold before solidifying. The improvement was slow and the action of the steel in the molds could never be predicted with certainty; even today it is often a question whether or not a heat will rim properly. A more detailed discussion of this type of steel is found in Article 348.

INGOT DEFECTS

426. General. The very nature of the solidification of the steel in an ingot mold prevents the formation of a perfect ingot; by this is meant one free from all cavities, blowholes, or openings, and composed of material that is entirely homogeneous and of the proper composition. Unfortunately, the physical and chemical forces at work during this solidification operate against attaining this goal. As soon as the molten steel is poured into the cold mold, the metal next to the surface of the mold and the stool is chilled, and solidifies on these surfaces to form what is known as the skin of the ingot. As more and more heat is absorbed by the mold and stool, a relatively rapid process as contrasted to subsequent radiation from the outer surfaces of these parts, this skin increases in thickness, but at a rapidly decreasing rate. Finally, the temperature of the mold approaches close to that of the ingot, after which the rate of heat transfer decreases.

In addition, in certain types of molds an insulating air gap soon forms between the ingot and the mold because, at this stage in ingot formation, the ingot contracts and the mold expands. Finally, cooling takes place by dissipation of the heat through this skin along lines perpendicular to the surface of the solidified shell, by conduction through this shell, which is gradually growing in thickness and progressing toward the center until all the metal is in a solid state. The rate at which this solidification will go on is dependent upon the temperature at which the metal was teemed, the thickness of the mold wall, and the design of the mold.

On the whole this rate of solidification, measured in inches, will vary roughly as the square root of the time in minutes. An ingot 18 x 20 inches in cross section will be solid throughout, when poured at ordinary teeming temperatures, within 65 to 80 minutes after it has been poured. As a result of these physical phenomena, ingots as produced by modern methods are bound to develop certain natural defects, notably, piping, segregation, blowholes, ingotism, inclusions, checks, scabs, and butt cracks.

427. Pipe. Certainly the most noticeable of the above defects, very likely the one most difficult to overcome because of the nature of the process of solidification of the ingot, is the formation of a pipe or contraction cavity. Molten metal occupies more space than an equal weight of solid metal, and the contraction taking place on the cooling of molten steel amounts to about 2 per cent of the lineal dimensions of the ingot. Manifestly if the process of cooling did not oppose this contraction (by friction of the ingot wall and lack of freedom to conform to new conditions), no cavity would form, and a perfect ingot would result. In ingots of fully deoxidized steel much of this difference in volume is represented by the pipe, but in semi-killed and rimming steels the pipe is much smaller because the difference in volume is to some extent made up, or neutralized, by the blowholes formed during the solidification process (see Article 348).

Furthermore, a thin skin forms very quickly after the molten metal is poured into the ingot mold, and this skin is soon made rigid by the progressive solidification of the metal. This skin as it cools, of course, occupies less space, and the contraction causes the remaining liquid in the center to sink in the cavity which, in turn, grows progressively larger as solidification progresses. Furthermore, after the solidification of the metal is complete, further contraction on cooling sets up stresses which tend to open this pipe still farther towards the bottom because the exterior, being colder, is stronger and capable of stretching or tearing the hot, plastic interior. Being exposed to the atmosphere, the surface of this pipe becomes more or less oxidized and will not weld in the subsequent rolling or forming operations. The upper end of the ingot, therefore, must be removed if a satisfactory rolled section is to be produced; and this cropping, as it is termed, will result in a further loss of steel, of the order of 12 to as much as 30 per cent of the total weight of the ingot.

Many methods have been suggested and used for overcoming this serious defect in ingot making. One method involved the application of pressure to the walls of the ingot during solidification and the insertion along the center axis of a bar of steel having the same composition as that of the ingot, shortly after the steel had been poured. This method has failed because the fusing point of steel is raised by pressure; this pressure must be applied to all surfaces and involves the use of a great deal of cumbersome machinery if it is to be powerful enough to be effective. Other schemes involve the use of physical force that will feed molten metal to the central portion of the ingot as it solidifies. The centrifugal method has been fairly successful in casting small billets, but it has not met with acceptance in the larger sections. Of them all, the most successful employed to date has to do with the big-end-up, hot-top mold (see Article 433).

428. Segregation. This is another defect in ingots which is not likely to be entirely overcome because steel is a very complex mixture of various compounds and elements. When the steel is in a molten condition, these constituents are held in solution; but, when the ingot

TABLE 64

PROPORTIONATE SEGREGATION OF ELEMENTS

	Average Per Cent	Lowest Per Cent	Highest Per Cent	Highest Divided by Lowest	Percentage Difference from Average		
					Negative	Positive	Total
Carbon	0.30	0.27	0.43	1.59	10	33	43
Manganese	0.55	0.53	0.58	1.09	4	5	9
Silicon	0.17	0.16	0.20	1.25	6	18	24
Phosphorus	0.031	0.026	0.058	2.23	16	87	103
Sulfur	0.019	0.017	0.037	2.18	10	95	105
Nickel	2.07	2.03	2.09	1.03	2	1	3
Chromium	0.40	0.39	0.43	1.10	3	7	10
Molybdenum	0.25	0.23	0.27	1.17	8	8	16

starts to freeze, the compounds and elements referred to, having different melting points, progressively crystallize from the solidifying mass following the laws of selective freezing. It is easy to see how the process of solidification would result in an isolation of certain components because those substances having the highest melting point would be, of course, the first to freeze. This selection would have the effect of concentrating the solution of substances having a lower freezing point in the remaining liquid, which process would continue until the remaining liquid is made up only of that substance that has the lowest freezing point. Eventually this will freeze, forming in the ingot (usually at the bottom of the pipe) a solid mass that is very different in composition from the metal that crystallized out in the first stages of solidification. This latter metal is also different from that originally present in the ladle. The extent and character of this segregation are shown in Figure 92 and the proportionate segregation of elements in Table 64.

Two phenomena are at work to offset, to some extent, this segregation. One is the trapping of small amounts of liquid between the crystals as they freeze, and the second is a diffusion and redistribution of these zones of different composition during the heating and rolling process. Segregation is one of the reasons that specifications usually call for a given range of composition; for example, for SAE 1035 steel, carbon should range from 0.30 to 0.40 per cent, manganese from 0.60

to 0.90. It is obvious that, when such an ingot is rolled out into a bar, the portion of the bar coming from the bottom of the ingot would have a very different composition from the portion coming from the center of the top of the ingot.

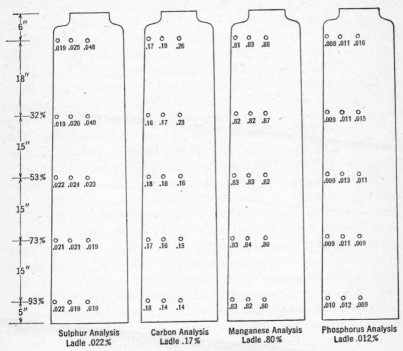

Fig. 92. Segregation in a Mechanically Capped Ingot.

429. Blowholes. In Chapter VIII, devoted to the basic open-hearth process, the presence, in molten steel, of considerable volumes of gases such as oxygen, hydrogen, and nitrogen has been referred to. Oxygen probably combines almost completely with iron to form ferrous oxide; but in the case of the other gases no such stable compound is formed, and the gases are largely thrown out of solution when solidification of the metal occurs. Unfortunately, this liberation of gas does not take place until the instant of solidification, and, although the steel is in a plastic condition at this high temperature, it still has great enough resistance to deformation to prevent the complete escape of these gases; consequently, they collect in the form of bubbles or small cavities in the metal, known as "blowholes." These vary in size from those just visible under a microscope to pockets the size of one's thumb. The smallest ones usually occur just beneath the skin of the ingot, where the rapidly cooling metal has given tiny bubbles of evolved gases time neither to escape nor to coalesce in the form of larger bubbles. Unable to escape upward on account of the viscous character of the solidifying metal, these gases form long, tubelike cavities at right angles to the skin, or wall, of the ingot and toward the center. Fortunately, in the rolling of the steel most of these blowholes are closed up and welded together because the gas is usually carbon monoxide, hydrogen, or nitrogen, producing a clean unoxidized surface on these walls. On the other hand, if oxygen from the air or from the ingot enters these cavities, the walls will be oxidized, will not weld together in the forming process, and will produce serious defects in the finished section. Cavities near the center of the ingot, known as deep-seated blowholes, are less liable to oxidation, and are considered the least harmful. The least difficulty with blowholes is encountered in completely deoxidized or killed steels, and the greatest difficulty in semi-deoxidized and rimming steels. On the whole, the blowholes can be almost eliminated in thoroughly deoxidized steel and their presence turned to good advantage in rimming steels.

430. Crystallization. Liquid steel, as it is tapped from the open-hearth furnace, is just as much a solution as an aqueous one and, in freezing, obeys the same laws of crystallization. The size of the crystals will depend upon the composition of the steel, the rate of cooling, the temperature at casting, and the size and shape of the ingot and ingot mold. In general the slower the cooling rate, the larger the crystals will be; and, if they are large, the force of cohesion between the crystals is decreased and they will offer less resistance to deformation than small ones. This condition, known as ingotism or crystallization, renders the ingot more liable to tearing in the shaping or working operations. A crystal aggregate formed by progressive solidification, having many branches in a treelike pattern, is called a "dendrite" or "pine tree" crystal and the structure a dendritic or columnar one. It gives rise to cleavage planes or lines of weakness and may be the source of cracks, particularly butt cracks, during the rolling process.

431. Inclusions. Ordinary steel always contains four elements besides iron, and frequently seven or eight. It is clear, then, that in the solidification process a large number of compounds may form. Some of these, like the silicates and oxides formed in the process of deoxidation, may be harmful to the steel; others, like manganese sulfide, may be very useful or wholly beneficial when properly controlled. On the whole, large inclusions are generally harmful and can be avoided in a properly finished bath. Most of the particles, whether they are caused by dirt in the ladle or mold, or are the result of the slag-forming reactions referred to, will rise to the top of the metal in the ladle during the chilling or liquating period. Some particles may be so small that they cannot rise through the liquid metal in this time, and these are carried over into the metal in the ingot mold where they have still less opportunity to rise because the chilling of the steel by the mold is rapid and they will be entrapped in the viscous metal. When they are present in large quantities and likely to detract from the valuable properties of the steel, the steel is said to be "dirty."

432. Checks and Scabs. At best the surface of the interior of an ingot mold is rough and becomes increasingly so during the life of the ingot, owing to checking and cracking of the surface through the sudden application of heat. This condition is intensified in the stripping operation because liquid metal penetrates into these cracks and holes, and, since considerable force must be used in stripping the ingot mold from the ingot, this force will be enough to disrupt further the metal of the ingot mold. Furthermore, the resistance offered to the natural contraction of the steel in solidifying by reason of these cracks and holes in the ingot mold may result in transverse cracks in the skin of the ingot. Cracks may also be caused by molten metal splashing on the mold wall in pouring, particularly if the ingot is poured from an excessive height; and this splashed metal after solidifying becomes loosened as the liquid steel rises and bends over to be immersed in the solidifying ingot. If these splashes only stick to the ingot wall and do not bend over, they become oxidized and form "scabs" on the outside of the ingot after it is stripped. In any case they will form serious surface defects in plates, and seams and slivers in other rolled products. While the condition can be partially avoided by cutting down the pouring height, by multiple pouring from a basket, or entirely eliminated by bottom casting of the ingot, these methods of casting large heats into small ingots have many obvious disadvantages.

Mold washes are frequently employed to overcome these defects. Various mixtures, such as slurries of clay, slaked lime, tar, and powdered metals, are used to coat the interior surfaces of the mold and cut down the likelihood of these splashes adhering to the ingot mold. They are used fairly commonly in the cheaper grades of steel, but in the production of high-quality ones their use is to be avoided. Such refractory materials as clay and lime are very likely to contaminate the steel and increase the number of inclusions whereas carbonaceous washes, such as tar, recarburize the skin of the ingot, thus increasing its tendency to crack in subsequent forming operations. Some of the other washes are likely to evolve volatile matter that will disturb the normal conditions essential to the formation of a satisfactory solid skin on the ingot. On the whole, careful control of teeming or pouring, with good nozzles and stoppers, is a much surer way to reduce or eliminate scabs and cracks caused by splashes.

THE BIG-END-UP (GATHMANN TYPE) MOLD

433. Solidification of Steel. Mr. Emil Gathmann[4, 5] and his associates of Baltimore, Maryland, have done a tremendous amount of fruitful experimental work, since 1906, aimed at the production of steel ingots of uniform high quality.[4, 5] Early in this investigation it became evident that more nearly sound ingots could be obtained by the use of what was termed "inverted" molds rather than the standard or big-end-down mold that had been in general use in casting all grades of steel. Through the use of materials of low melting point that crystallize, contract, and segregate during their transition from the liquid to the solid state, such as paraffin and stearin, Mr. Gathmann was able to watch the process of solidification of these materials and make interesting and profitable comparisons with the probable mechanism of freezing or solidification of steel. He designed and constructed model molds having one major wall of glass and the remaining ones of aluminum. One of these was of the big-end-up type and the other the big-end-down. In these molds the glass wall tends to conserve the heat of the molten bath, solidification occurring primarily from contact with the metallic ones. This gives a view of solidification equivalent to watching the central, vertical section of an ingot and allows a study, not only of the influence of mold design on the structure of an ingot, but also the effect of temperatures and rates of teeming on the amount of shrinkage and the segregation in the solidified ingot.

The sequence shown in Figure 93 shows the stages of solidification in both types of ingot molds. In the case of the big-end-up type, note that the solidified ingot is piped and highly segregated for approximately 20 per cent of its volume, although in producing steel ingots this figure might be cut to about 10 per cent of the ingot volume if a shrink-head casing of proper volume were used. In the case of the big-end-down design the solidified ingot contains actual porosity and excessive segregation in at least 75 per cent of its volume, leaving a maximum of 25 per cent of material that is substantially sound. In steel ingots the primary pipe usually extends just about half way through the ingot body, but, because of variables in casting tempera-

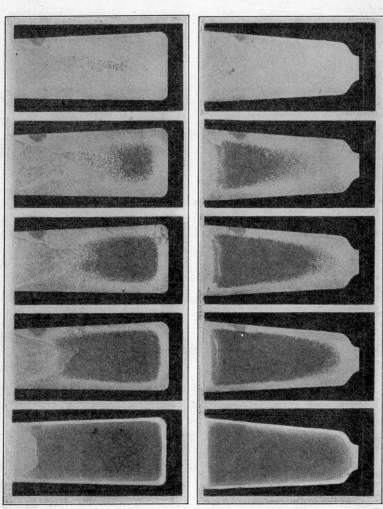

FIG. 93. Solidification of Standard vs. Gathmann Ingot. Standard Mold Above; Gathmann Mold Below. (*Courtesy of Gathmann Engineering Co.*)

tures, mold temperatures, and other factors, there is no assurance that even that part of the ingot will be entirely free from pipe.

On the basis of these experiments a diagrammatic sketch can be constructed as shown in Figure 94, in which the curves or contour lines for both the big-end-up and the big-end-down ingot molds show the crystallization of successive ingot skin thicknesses, the progress of solidification, and the extent of the shrinkage cavities formed in

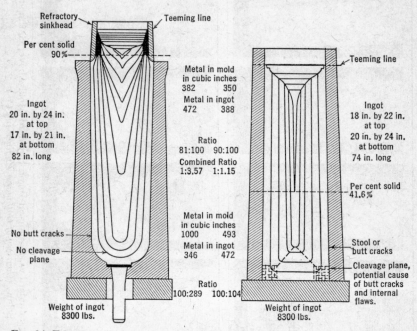

FIG. 94. Freezing of a Standard vs. Gathmann Ingot. (*Courtesy of Gathmann Engineering Co.*)

both types of ingot molds. The lines were obtained from visual inspection of the above wax ingots, supplemented by dumping a series of steel ingots out of the molds at various stages of solidification and splitting them for inspection.

Besides utilizing the big-end-up principle, this type of ingot mold has two other distinctive features. First, it will be noted that very heavy walls of variable cross section are employed which favor the important factor of rate of solidification. The greater heat absorptive value of the heavy compared with the light mold wall shortens the time of solidification. This not only results in the formation of a greater number of independent nuclei from which solidification may proceed but also permits the ingot to solidify from the bottom up and tends to offset any tendency to entrap molten metal within the solidifying ingot. A second feature provides a necked-in chamber, closed by a refractory bottom plug, which may be of either the one- or two-plug closure type as shown in Figure 95. The upper or refractory part of the mold closure is adapted to receive the impact of the molten metal without cutting or scouring of the mold wall, and, as this plug is seated in the recess, lateral movement is prevented, thus obviating the danger of its floating up into the molten metal. The bottom or metallic plug is adapted to act as an ingot lifter or stripper should an ingot bind to the mold wall. An ingot produced in a mold of this design is readily rolled into blooms or billets without "fish-tailing," and requires a minimum bottom discard that is frequently less than 2 per cent of the ingot weight.

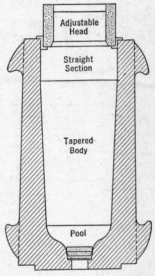

FIG. 95. Gathmann Mold. (*Courtesy of Gathmann Engineering Co.*)

434. Segregation. Analyses show that the initially formed chilled crystals comprising the skin of an ingot are practically the same as the molten material. Segregation begins almost immediately, however, and persists at an increasing rate toward the central longitudinal axis of the ingot, being most pronounced in the molten metal that solidifies last. This accounts for the fact that the shrink head or crop portion of the big-end-up ingot is the most highly segregated part of the ingot, whereas, in the big-end-down type, the greatest segregation is in the lower half of the ingot. Figure 96 shows the distribution of carbon in both types of ingots. These were cast adjacent to one another from the same heat of steel, the molten metal having been deoxidized in both the furnace and in the ladle with silicoaluminum. It will be observed that the carbon range in the body of the big-end-down ingot is between 0.67 and 0.80 per cent, a variation of 13 points, but it has a range of only 0.68 to 0.74, a variation of only 6 points, in the body of the big-end-up ingot, below the shoulder or discard portion. Even in the big-end-up ingot, segregation cannot be entirely eliminated from any type of steel, but it may be materially reduced by increasing the rate of solidification of the metal and by keeping the molten mass in a state of substantial equilibrium during the period of solidification in the mold.

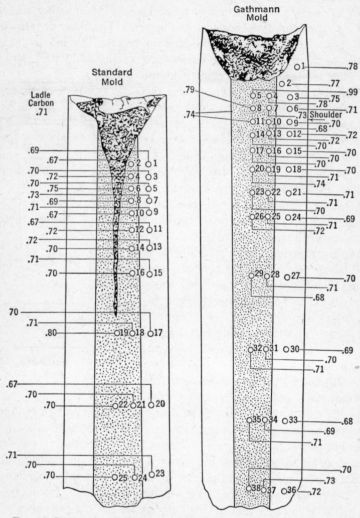

Fig. 96. Segregation of Carbon in a Gathmann vs. Conventional Mold.

The primary reason for employing a shrink-head casing is to increase the yield of sound steel by lessening the depth of the primary shrinkage cavity as well as lessening segregation. Shrink-head casings are efficient, however, only with molds of big-end-up design in which the solidification of the molten material is progressively upward from the bottom to the top of the mold and not interrupted by bridges which always form when the thermal action is greater at a lower portion of the ingot than it is higher up.

435. Mold Sizes. A proper determination of the size at which the ingots are to be cast is one of the first considerations, not only for convenience in operating the rolling mill but also because the tonnage and quality of products depends upon ingots' being of the proper size.

Advantages to be gained by the employment of large ingots lie in the fact that fewer ingots of a large size need be poured and handled. This results in greater production, lower costs, fewer movements, and less trouble in a general way in operation. Nevertheless, in every plant there is a limit to the ingot size to be used, beyond which it is not advantageous to go; it is desirable to maintain as few sizes as possible and thus limit the amount of equipment and the complication of handling both the equipment and the ingot.

Another factor to be taken into consideration in determining the size of the ingots is the grade of the steel. It is the general rule to cast high-carbon and high-metalloid steels in ingots of moderate size and of rectangular instead of square sections in an effort to hasten the solidification and arrest the segregation of carbon, phosphorus, and sulfur. The high-metalloid steels remain liquid at lower temperatures and therefore remain liquid longer than soft steels; and consequently the segregation has full opportunity to take place in large ingots, where, with a moderate-sized one of rectangular cross section, the cooling is hastened and the segregation not as pronounced. In this way a greater yield may be procured.

In the case of soft steels, the objection to a large ingot is not so pronounced because the steel is not liquid so long. Too large sizes tend very strongly to soft, mushy centers which in subsequent hot working often prove to be weak and show all the effects of a deep piping. This shows up particularly in pressed forgings of large pieces.

Large-sized ingots are more frequently observed to crack owing to the unequal cooling strains, and this results in rejection for surface flaws in the rolling mill. There is a variance of opinion on this point, but on the whole this general rule is accepted.

A very good general-purpose ingot is 22 x 24 inches, weighing around 4 tons; or even a 20 x 22-inch ingot may serve for most purposes. At the rail mill at Gary, Indiana, rails are rolled direct without reheating from 23¼- x 23¼-inch ingots. At the Jones and Laughlin

Steel Corporation plant, a 19- x 22-inch ingot is in use on all classes of products.

Insofar as height is concerned, it is obvious that relatively short ingots produce fewer scabs and seams by reason of less splashing during the teeming period, because the violence of this splash is determined by the square of the distance between the ladle nozzle and the bottom of the mold. Molds used in the production of high-quality steels are, therefore, almost invariably short, seldom over 36 or at most 48 inches long. Above this height the ingots will range from 48 inches to 72 inches for most tonnage blooming mill products, up to 16 feet or over for large forgings, armor plate, and pipe.

436. Ingot Yield. The croppage from the top of the ingot should always be a definite percentage of the ingot weight, about 10 or 11 usually being sufficient to clear the product of both pipe and excessive segregation. A crop of 1 to 2 per cent from the butt of the ingot is usually sufficient, even in producing large blooms and slabs, to square up the lower end of the bloom. With careful reheating scale loss need not exceed 2 per cent. This leaves 83 to 86 per cent of the ingot available for first-quality products, unless preventable mistakes have been made in finishing the heat, in teeming the ingot, in reheating them, or in reduction in the rolling mill or forge.

437. Essentials for Soundness. In order to produce the above satisfactory yield in ingots, certain factors are necessary to assure soundness. They are:

1. The molten metal must be thoroughly deoxidized before teeming so that no chemical reaction can take place in the mold during solidification; blowholes and gas pockets are prevented from forming; and segregation in the body of the ingot is kept at a minimum.

2. The chamber of the mold must be of big-end-up design and enough larger in top cross section than in bottom to assure the metal's solidifying progressively upward so that there will be neither loose texture nor actual shrinkage cavities in the body of the ingot.

3. A suitable shrink-head casing should be employed whose volume should be at least 10 per cent of the total ingot mass.

4. The ingot should be kept in a substantially vertical position until solidification is complete. It need not be kept in the mold for the entire solidification period, but it must be kept upright; otherwise the axial center of the product will be of a "cokey" or porous texture.

INGOT CONTOUR

438. General. Thus far, we have been concerned with internal defects in the ingot; notably, pipe, blowholes, and segregation. The condition of the surface of an ingot is just as important in steel as any other specification affecting appearance as well as serviceability.[5] It is of extreme importance in ingots intended for the production of rails, forgings, blooms, wire rod, sheet bar, strip steel, and similar products because it is a factor in determining strength during fabrication as well as in ultimate use. Unless surface defects are removed from the bloom or billet by chipping, which is always a very expensive and time-consuming operation, the actual strength of the finished product may be far below that expected. In addition to physical weakness, products having inherent surface defects are more subject to atmospheric oxidation which rapidly enlarges even minute initial defects. Automobile fenders offer a good example; tens of thousands of them must be repaired or replaced annually because of surface and subcutaneous defects inherent in the original ingot. Where reliability and strength are necessary to the safety of life, as in axles, gears, rails, structural shapes, and other products subject to severe stresses during use, the soundness of the surface is as vital to everyone concerned as that of the interior. In designing a mold contour which will insure good surface in the product, the following six factors must be kept in mind: .

1. Prevention of excessive splashing of the molten metal during the teeming period.

2. The ingot must be free to contract upon itself during solidification without any interference from the mold wall.

3. The prevention of the formation of cleavage planes and cracks in the skin or subskin of the ingot during solidification.

4. The corners and salients of the solidified ingot must be of such contour that they will not be decarburized to any harmful extent in the soaking pit.

5. These corners and salients must be also of such a contour that they will not become overheated when the ingots are reheated for rolling.

6. The shape of the ingot must be such that it can be reduced in rolling or forging without either overworking the corners or tearing the free sides during the initial passes.

439. Corrugated Ingot Contours. Molds having properly designed corrugated sides, such as those shown in Figure 97, do much to prevent surface defects and to improve generally the structure of the ingot. A corrugated cross section giving an ingot contour comprised largely of concave faces is able to withstand considerable bending without cracking, whereas large convex surfaces or extended planes may break on slight distortion. This greater flexibility of the skin of the corrugated ingots is perhaps their most important advantage because all steel

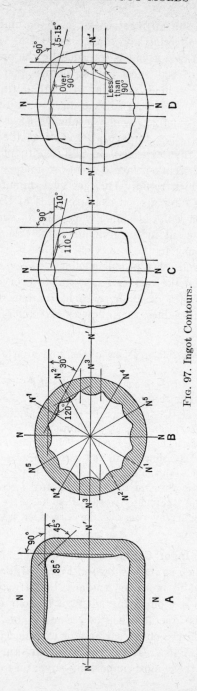

Fig. 97. Ingot Contours.

ingots are distorted during solidification in the mold and subsequently during reheating and reduction.

When the walls of a mold are suitably corrugated, as shown in Figure 98, and are sufficiently heat absorptive, the initial skin of the ingot, which forms practically immediately on teeming, is relatively thick at the center lines N-N (A) even though the mass of metal is greatest and the heat most intense in these areas. In plain-sided ingots

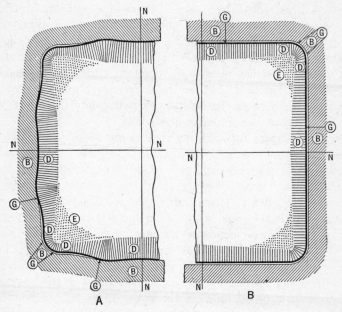

FIG. 98. Initial Crystallization and Air Gap.

the skin is thinnest at the lines N-N (B) and is more easily ruptured by the combined distortion and pressure of the molten metal during the period of solidification and later by the action of the rolls during the reduction of the ingot.

The surface of a corrugated ingot should consist, to as great a degree as practicable, of inwardly curved spaces struck on relatively long radii as compared to the chord of the arcs so as to prevent catches between the outwardly arched spaces of the corrugation. The outwardly arched spaces on the other hand should be as acute as is permissible for the size of the ingot being produced without running into the danger of burning the surface of these salients during reheating. Another primary advantage of the corrugated mold cross section is its advantageous effect upon the chilling and cooling of the ingot surface. It has been found that the convex mold wall portions, by extending inwardly into the mass of the ingot metal, serve to chill the metal quickly, resulting in improved crystalline structure and greater strength in the outer or chilled zone of the ingot. These convex portions of the ingot chamber should, therefore, constitute as large a part of the entire surface as practical without departing substantially from the smoothly corrugated contours. The concave portions of the mold should, as stated, be as small as possible without forming too acute salients in the ingot. In connection with the working of the ingot it is important to note that a steel ingot as it enters the rolls is merely a chilled casting having a relatively coarse crystalline structure. The first few passes are, therefore, critical to the condition of the finished product. The entire surface of the ingot should be worked and the size of the crystals reduced before there is any appreciable elongation of the ingot as a whole.

440. Ingot Taper. Taper in any type of ingot is objectionable from the point of view of rolling or forging, but, since a tapered contour is necessary for soundness and ease of stripping, the best that can be done is to decrease the taper as much as possible, consistent with progressive solidification from bottom to top. This decrease in taper is permissible if the mold walls are made relatively more heat absorptive at the lower section of the ingot than at its upper portion. A further decrease in taper is obtained by employing what is known as differential taper in the mold chamber. This method involves the use of the minimum taper necessary for soundness in the body of the ingot with little or no taper in the upper 15 to 20 per cent of the ingot adjacent to the sink-head* portion. This can be done because the shrink-head portion of the ingot will feed the body of the ingot for about 20 per cent of its volume without danger of bridging and the resultant secondary piping. For example, in a commonly used ingot mold the lower section is 23 by 23 inches, the upper 25 by 25 inches with a 2-inch taper in a 5-foot length, and the sides of the upper 12 inches of the ingot are substantially parallel.

441. Air Gap. The corrugated cross section is particularly efficacious in preventing breaks in the surface of the ingot, resulting in the so-called "run out." During the early stages of solidification the absorption of heat from the molten metal causes the mold chamber to contract in size owing to the inward expansion of the mold metal. This initial contraction of the chamber more than compensates for the

* The upper portion of the ingot which includes the pipe.

initial shrinkage of the ingot so that close contact of the mold with the ingot is maintained during this period. The longer the time the initial contact is maintained, the thicker the initial skin will be; and the thicker it is, the greater is its resistance to the ferrostatic pressure and heat of the molten metal. This is very important because, as soon as the mold walls have become heated through to the outside, the mold as a whole begins to expand and pulls away from the ingot, forming an air gap as shown in Figure 98. It is very essential that the ingot at this time have a sufficiently thick skin to withstand the interior pressure, or breaks in the skin will occur. Apart from the fact that big-end-up ingots have a relatively thick chilled skin, an important function of the corrugated mold chambers is to delay the formation of an air gap at the primary faces of the ingot so that the initial contact of the ingot in the mold will be maintained for a longer period of time and the desired thick chill crystallization be obtained.

442. Prevention of Teeming Splashes. The impact of the molten metal on the bottom of the mold during teeming causes splashings. It is frequently a serious cause of scabs and general surface troubles. The splashed metal is oxidized and solidifies almost instantly on contact with the walls of the mold. In order to avoid this splashing, the mold chamber should be necked in or materially reduced in cross section at the bottom so that a small pool of metal can be quickly formed in the mold chamber. Such a pool acts as cushion for the incoming stream of molten metal, and the body of the ingot can then be poured much more rapidly without harmful splashing.

SHRINK-HEAD CASINGS

443. General. The function of the shrink-head casings is to keep the upper part of the ingot in a molten condition so that it can supply hot metal during the solidification period, hence the term "hot top" generally used in practice. The progressive solidification of an ingot from the bottom to the top, in order to prevent secondary piping, is assured only when the chamber of the mold is of the big-end-up type and is properly proportioned. However, even when using such a mold, the extent of the primary shrinkage cavity will necessitate an excessive top crop unless a shrink-head casing is used. Not enough attention has been given to the proper design of shrink-head casings, because most of the ones in use today are inefficient thermally. The shrinkage of the molten metal from the liquid to the solid is only of the order of 3 to 5 per cent, and yet the volume of metal ordinarily required in the shrink-head casings is 10 to 20 per cent of the ingot. In an attempt to reduce the volume of the metal lost through top discard, heat-insulating material, such as infusorial earth,* straw, coke breeze, and various heat-producing compounds, is often thrown on top of the ingot immediately after teeming.

Shrink-head casings may be divided broadly into two types: one, known as the fixed casing, is placed on top of the ingot mold and allowed to remain in that position until the ingots are ready for stripping; the other type can be termed "adjustable floating" casings, which are fixed on the top of the mold with blocks until the ingot has been teemed. The blocks are then removed and the casing allowed to descend with the shrinking ingots. This adjustable floating type casing has several advantages over the fixed type. By adjusting the height of the blocks the casing can be suspended at any position required to produce an ingot of a given weight. This is a great advantage in plants producing special heats in which specific bloom and billet weights are required. Although this economy is considerable, the primary advantage of the floating type casing has to do with the physical condition of the ingot. In using the fixed type casing it is not at all unusual for molten metal to bind to the refractory material forming the inside of the shrink-head casing and "hang" the ingot, causing tears that are sometimes very deep, in the upper 20 per cent of the ingot body. This happens more often when heats are teemed on the hot side and the amount of contraction of the material during solidification is at a maximum. Another expedient to maintain the volume of the shrink-head casing at a minimum is to preheat the tops to 200 to 400°F. before they are placed on the mold, prior to teeming. As a matter of fact, in the production of the finest types of steel special furnaces are being used for preheating these casings to as much as 1000°F.

444. Stripping Big-End-Up Ingots. For many years this was a serious problem and stood in the way of a more extended use of this type of ingot mold because ingots that could not be started by the crane tongs caused all sorts of delays and were particularly troublesome. It was not unusual for an ingot to fin to such an extent that it could not be stripped from the mold without great difficulty. With the apparatus available today big-end-up ingots can be stripped just as readily as big-end-down and a great deal more economically because less handling of the molds is required.

There are two basic types of big-end-up strippers: one type exerts pressure against the bottom of the ingot while the mold is held against movement, the "pusher" type; the other, the "puller" type, holds the

* Tripolite, a fine-grained siliceous material resembling chalk in appearance.

mold against upward movement while the ingot is pulled out of the mold by multitooth tongs carried by an overhead crane which runs above the ingot car.

COPPER STOOLS*

445. General. Considerable experimental work[17] has been carried out in casting small ingots in copper molds on the assumption that the high thermal conductivity of copper would improve the ingot surface and effect the formation of a much finer grain structure. These tests confirm this as well as the assumption that the rapid cooling effect lasts only for a short period of time owing to the formation of an air gap between the ingot and the mold due to the contraction of the steel ingot. With these facts in mind, large-scale tests were then made on the use of stools, inserts, and mold plugs of copper.

Copper may be used as a stool material because of its ability to conduct heat from the molten steel very rapidly. On first thought one might not suppose that a material with a melting point so much below that of steel poured upon it would be suitable for this sort of service. The melting point of copper is about 850°F. below the pouring temperature of steel, but the thermal conductivity of copper is nine to ten times that of cast iron. This greater thermal conductivity offsets the low melting point through rapid heat conduction, in consequence of which the surface of a copper stool, in contact with liquid steel, is considerably cooler than the surface of a cast-iron one. To avoid overheating the surface of the stool, however, it is necessary to have a large volume of copper present, and for this reason the dimensions of the stool, particularly the thickness, become important. Ordinarily, a larger ratio of copper to steel is required than of iron to steel. It is more effective to get increased weight through increasing the thickness than the cross-sectional area which need not be much larger than the mold base. Experience indicates that the weight of the stool should be at least two-thirds that of the ingot cast if cutting and cracking of the stool are to be avoided.

A recent development, using a cast-iron frame in which cakes of copper are held vertically by a spring at one end, gives promise of increasing the life of the stools. These cakes are 10 to 15 inches long, depending upon the thickness of the stool desired, 4 inches thick, and of varying lengths, depending upon the width of the stool. Inserts made of copper have also been used with some success in cast-iron stools

* Stools are heavy plates mounted on trucks for supporting the ingot molds.

and in closed bottom molds. Copper has another advantage over iron in this application because its surface contour remains constant owing to the absence of much cutting action. The life of the copper insert is less than that of the stool made entirely of copper because of the smaller mass of copper. This is, however, compensated for by the resulting smaller amount of copper scrap.

It is obvious that copper stools can be returned to the refinery for credit when they are so badly checked or cracked as to be unfit for further use. On this basis copper stools should give six to eight times the life of iron stools, which means that on the average the copper stools should last at least 500 heats. Practically all the stools have lasted that long and many have reached 1500 heats. So far as it is possible to determine, the use of copper stools has not adversely affected the quality of the ingot, and plant tests show an increased life of molds of 30 to 100 per cent over the conventional type. This may be attributed to the more rapid extraction of heat from the steel by the copper stool. By reason of this the steel in the lower section of the mold cools more rapidly, freezes earlier, and thus establishes the gap between ingot and mold more quickly. Both these actions serve to hold down the inside surface temperature of the lower section of the mold. The greater clearance at the butt end of the ingot results in easier stripping, fewer "stickers," and hence less rough usage of the mold.

446. Centrifugal Castings. A number of machines have been developed to cast steel billets centrifugally. One of these consists of a cylindrical container revolving on small wheels mounted on roller bearings. Inside this cylindrical container are molds of cast iron, each about 6 feet long, 18 inches wide, and $\frac{1}{2}$ to 4 inches thick. At one end is a pouring head which receives metal from the ladle, and the whole contrivance is revolved at about 275 revolutions per minute. About 3 minutes are required for the machine to attain this speed, and it is found necessary to spin the mold for about 2 minutes after pouring has been completed. The bars formed are of uniform thickness from end to end except for a slight taper at the pouring end. The inner surface of the bar is curved slightly, but this curvature is removed in the first rolling pass. In a semi-commercial plant the total loss of metal, with the exception of trimming losses, did not exceed 3 per cent, as compared with losses of 25 per cent in normal casting. To the knowledge of the author, this method has not been extended to larger units; but it obviously possesses considerable merit.

BIBLIOGRAPHY

1. BOYLSTON, H. M., *An Introduction to the Metallurgy of Iron and Steel.* New York: John Wiley and Sons, 1936. 563 pp.
2. BREARLEY, A. W., and H. BREARLEY, *Ingots and Ingot Moulds.* New York: Longmans, Green and Company, 1925.
3. FRANCIS, C. B., *The Making, Shaping, and Treating of Steel.* Pittsburgh: Carnegie-Illinois Steel Corporation, 1940. 1440 pp.
4. GATHMANN, EMIL, *The Ingot Phase of Steel Production.* Baltimore and Caronsville, Maryland: Gathmann Engineering Company and Gathmann Research Inc., 1937.
5. GATHMANN, EMIL, *Ingot Contour and Its Relation to Sound Steel.* Baltimore: Gathmann Engineering Company, 1925.
6. HAYWARD, C. R., *An Outline of Metallurgical Practice.* New York: D. Van Nostrand Company, 1940. 612 pp.
7. HRUSKA, J., "Ingot Molds," *Iron Age,* August 13, 1931.
8. Joint Committee of the American Iron and Steel Institute, British Iron and Steel Federation, and the Iron and Steel Industrial Research Council, "Heterogeneity of Steel Ingots—1924-1936," *Journal of the American Iron and Steel Institute.* First Report, No. 1 (1926); Second Report, No. 1 (1928); Third Report, No. 1 (1929); Fourth Report, Special Report No. 2 (1932); Fifth Report, Special Report No. 4 (1933); Sixth Report, Special Report No. 9 (1935); Supplement to Sixth Report, Special Report No. 9A (1936).
9. *Journal of the Iron and Steel Institute,* "Heterogeneity of Steel Ingots," First Report, No. 1 (1926); Second Report, No. 1 (1928); Third Report, No. 1 (1929); Fourth Report, Special Report No. 2 (1932); Fifth Report, Special Report No. 4 (1933); Sixth Report, Special Report No. 9 (1935).
10. KELLS, L. R., "Circular Ingot Heating Furnaces," *Iron and Steel Engineer,* July, 1938.
11. MORTON, W. A., "Controlled Ingot Heating," *Steel,* December 13, 1937.
12. NELSON, L. H., "Solidification of Steel in Ingot Molds," American Society of Metals, *Transactions,* 1934.
13. REAGAN, W. J., "Some Factors Affecting Life of Ingot Molds," *Metals Technology,* American Institute of Mining and Metallurgical Engineers, *Technical Paper* 745, Vol. 3 (6), September, 1937.
14. STOUGHTON, B., *Metallurgy of Iron and Steel.* New York: McGraw-Hill Book Company, 1934. 519 pp.
15. STOUGHTON, B., and A. BUTTS, *Engineering Metallurgy.* New York: McGraw-Hill Book Company, 1930. 441 pp.
16. WATSON, R. H., "The Trend in Ingot Mold Design," American Iron and Steel Institute, *Yearbook,* 1928.
17. WILLIAMS, C. E., and H. B. KINNEAR, "Copper Stools," *Metals and Alloys,* July, 1935.

CHAPTER XIII

FERROALLOYS

447. General. Ferroalloys may be defined as iron so rich in some element other than carbon that it is used as a vehicle for introducing that element, in the manufacture of iron and steel. Some of these elements are used for the peculiar properties they impart to steel when in solid solution with the iron; others because they combine either wholly or in part to form carbides; others for the beneficial effect they have on impurities in the steel; and still others to counteract harmful oxides or gases, and these latter may not remain in the steel after solidification but act as fluxes or scavengers of objectionable impurities. This discussion will be confined to those ferroalloys that are used solely in the manufacture of iron and steel. Compositions of the common ones are given in Table 65.

448. Chromium and Ferrochrome. Chromium alloys with iron in all proportions and exerts a powerful influence on steel, bringing about marked changes in its properties when subjected to heat treatment. It greatly increases hardness, owing to the retarding effect of chromium on the decomposition of certain constituents during rapid cooling, as well as its tendency to form nitrides. It increases resistance to shock by retarding the tendency toward coarse crystallization and imparts high tensile strength, combined with great ductility. On the whole it minimizes segregation and refines the grain. The use of chromium steel makes possible the satisfactory heat treatment of many important types of machined forgings and rolled products, but the scale formed is tough and closely adherent. Used with other elements, chromium possesses peculiar advantages in the production of alloy steel to meet the exacting demands of many engineering specifications. The characteristic property of chromium to resist corrosion and oxidation has accounted for the remarkable strides made in the use of stainless steel and iron during the past ten years. It is unfortunate that the chromium is so expensive, because chromium-treated carbon steels are characterized by some very attractive properties, such as:

1. Freedom from inclusions which would act as nuclei for shock and fatigue failures.

TABLE 65

COMPOSITIONS OF FERROALLOYS

Material	Per Cent														
	Fe	C	N	Si	Mn	P	S	Ca	Al	V	W	Zr	Cr	Cb	Mo
Ferrochromium, L.C.	1 to 1.5	0.06 to 2.0											67 to 72		
» » H.C.		4.5 to 7.0											66 to 70		
» » H.N.		0.2 to 5.0	0.75										60 to 70		
» » Spec. Found.		5											62 to 66		
Chromium		0.2 to 1.0											96 to 98		
Ferromanganese, Std.		6.75		1 to 7	78 to 82	0.3									
» M.C.		0.1 to 0.75			80 to 85										
» L. Phos.		1.5		1 to 2.5	80 to 85	0.1									
» L. Fe	2	7		5	85 to 90										
Spiegeleisen	25 to 30	5.5 to 6.5		3	19 to 28										
Silico—Manganese	74 to 84	1 to 3		20 to 14	65 to 70										
Silico—Spiegel	51 to 47	2 to 4		5 to 8	25 to 30										
Ferromanganese—Silicon	22 to 15	0.6 to 1		47 to 54	20 to 25										
Ferrosilicon—15%	10 to 16			14 to 20											
» 50%	9 to 2			43 to 52											
» 75%	1 to 2			70 to 82											
» 85%	3.5 to 6.0			82 to 88											
» 90%				88 to 95											
Silicon				97 to 96		0.05	0.04								
Calcium silicon				60 to 65				28 to 35							
Calcium—aluminum—silicon				50 to 53				10 to 14	8 to 12						
Calcium—Manganese—Silicon				55 to 60	8 to 10			17 to 19							
Ferrovanadium	10 to 14	3 to 0.2		8 to 1.5						35 to 40					
Ferrotungsten		0.25 to 2.0									78 to 82				
Tungsten powder		0.2									97				
Ferrozirconium 12-15	40 to 45	0.5		39 to 43								12 to 15			
» 35—40	8 to 12	0.5		47 to 52								35 to 40.0			
Ferrocolumbium				7		0.01	0.2							50 to 60	
Calcium molybdate	2.6							CaO 23.3							40.5

2. Uniformity of grain which assists in the effectiveness of heat treatments.

3. Excellent hot-working properties.

4. When suitably heat-treated, tensile properties closely approaching those of special alloy steels, ductility being especially favored by zirconium treatments.

Ferrochromium is made in low-carbon, high-carbon, and high-nitrogen grades. The high-carbon variety, containing 5 to 7 per cent of carbon, and low percentages of chromium, may be made in the blast furnace or crucible; but those higher in chromium and lower in impurities are manufactured in the electric furnace. The high-nitrogen grade, when added in the proportion of one part of nitrogen to 100 parts of chromium, tends to refine the grain and greatly increase the strength, density, and toughness of castings and ingots. The nitrogen is introduced by adding to the furnace charge this special grade of ferrochromium. All alloys are supplied either in the lump form, 1 inch up to 75 pounds, or in the crushed form, 2 inches down. Typical analyses are given in Table 65.

449. Chromium Metal. This can be supplied containing as high as 98 per cent of chromium, but lower grades are produced to meet the demands for a less expensive metal in which several per cent of iron are not detrimental. It can be supplied in maximum carbon contents of 0.2 to 0.5 per cent or, to meet requirements, as much as 9 to 11 per cent. It is used chiefly in making resistance alloys for heating appliances, non-corrosive alloys, and high-speed cutting alloys in special tools.

450. Ferromanganese. The effect of manganese on ferrous alloys in general is discussed in Articles 79 and 292.

The lower grades of ferromanganese are made in a blast furnace; alloys with higher manganese content and less objectionable impurities are made in the electric furnace. The standard grade, as its name indicates, is the one most commonly used; it is usually furnished in large lumps free from fines to entail the least oxidation loss when used as a furnace addition. The alloy should be free from sand and slag, of a uniform composition, and contain a minimum of the objectionable impurities indicated in Table 65. The low-carbon grade is used for making high-manganese additions to extremely low-carbon steel, when the carbon specifications of the steel are too low to permit the use of medium-carbon manganese. It may also be used effectively as a deoxidizer and scavenger in any grade of steel where low-carbon and low-silicon contents are necessary.

The medium-carbon grade is used for making high-manganese ad-

ditions to medium-carbon steel, when the carbon specifications of
steel are too low to permit the use of standard ferromanganese and
yet do not require the extremely low carbon ratio offered in low-carbon
ferromanganese. It may be used for making manganese additions to
low-carbon Bessemer steel, certain grades of carburizing steel, and
high-sulfur open-hearth steel, and as a deoxidizer and cleanser in the
manufacture of extremely low-carbon stainless iron and steel.

Low-phosphorus ferromanganese, containing low phosphorus and
high silicon, is used for making manganese additions to acid open-
hearth steel and other varieties of steel where phosphorus is highly
undesirable. It contains more silicon, less carbon, and less phosphorus
than the standard grade. Consumption of ferromanganese in the various grades of steel is given in Table 66.

TABLE 66
CONSUMPTION OF FERROMANGANESE BY PRODUCTS

Product	Ingot Equivalent Net Tons, 1940	Ferro-manganese Consumed, Lb.	Ferro-manganese per Ton Ingots, Lb.	Per Cent Total
Bars	10,800,000	288,700,000	26.6	29.3
Sheets and strips	19,430,000	193,700,000	10.0	19.8
Shapes and piling	6,550,000	107,000,000	16.3	11.0
Semi-finished products	5,650,000	81,200,000	14.4	8.3
Plates	5,950,000	74,400,000	12.5	7.6
Rods and wire	5,990,000	62,100,000	10.4	6.3
Tin plate	4,990,000	52,000,000	10.5	5.3
Rails	2,310,000	49,600,000	21.5	5.1
Pipe	3,730,000	43,050,000	11.5	4.4
Wheels, axles, forgings	1,530,000	28,700,000	18.8	2.9
Total	66,930,000	980,450,000		100.0

14.8 pounds of ferromanganese per ton of ingots.

Silicomanganese is a special alloy used where exacting control of
chemical and physical properties is required. The products of the
deoxidizing reactions possess more fluidity because of the lower melting points than when separate alloys are used. This feature is particularly desirable when very clean steel is demanded and higher
recoveries of manganese are obtained because of the protective action
of silicon.

Silicospiegel contains relatively small percentages of silicon and manganese and is especially suitable for making furnace additions to both acid and basic open-hearth steel. The peculiar combination of silicon and manganese thus offered in a single alloy produces a strong deoxidizing agent which forms a thin fusible slag that rises rapidly from the molten bath of steel, leaving it cleaner than if alloys of silicon and manganese were added separately. It is used principally as a deoxidizer and cleanser after "oreing down" a heat, and it is frequently used effectively for obtaining a part of the final manganese content in the steel. Silicospiegel is also suitable for making additions of manganese to cast iron in the cupola and air furnaces.*

Ferromanganese-silicon is commonly used as a softening agent for iron castings. When ferrosilicon is added to the ladle, the best results are not always obtained, owing to the low temperature of the iron. This combination of manganese and silicon lowers the melting point of the alloy, and the silicon is more readily taken into solution. Any higher-strength iron may be produced with this alloy.

451. Ferrosilicon. The effect of silicon, in general, on ferrous alloys is discussed in Article 82.

Ferrosilicon today is one of the most extensively used of all electric-furnace ferroalloys. Its popularity is very largely due to its activity in eliminating injurious oxides and gases from iron and steel. It is used in the production of a very large proportion of the open-hearth steel tonnage and also finds extensive application in practically all other steel-making processes.

The lowest grade of ferrosilicon,† containing 15 per cent silicon, is made especially for use where alloys of a higher silicon content cannot be used most effectively. It is extensively used for furnace additions of silicon in the manufacture of open-hearth steel. It is particularly suitable for acid open-hearth steel on account of its low phosphorus and sulfur content. In basic open-hearth steel it is used as a furnace deoxidizer and scavenger prior to the use of more expensive alloys. It is also used to prevent oxidation while holding the bath of steel in the furnace awaiting chemical determinations. For cupola or air furnace use in iron foundries it is preferred to pig iron of lower silicon content.

The 50 per cent grade, owing to its general adaptability, is the one extensively employed in the industry at the present time, entering primarily as a deoxidizer into the manufacture of practically all kinds of steel. Often the present exacting physical requirements imposed

* Used in melting malleable cast iron.

† A still lower grade, silvery iron, is discussed in Article 136.

by consumers of steel make it necessary for steel manufacturers to use only the purest available ferrosilicon. It must be uniform in size, conform to the chemical analysis indicated in Table 65, and be free from fines.

The 75 per cent grade is useful in the manufacture of special sheet steel for transformers, electromagnets, generators, motors, and other electric apparatus in which high magnetic permeability and electrical resistance combined with low hysteresis loss are essential. It is also used extensively in the manufacture of steels for automobile and railway springs, where a relatively high silicon content is desirable.

The 90 per cent grade is used when making large additions of silicon to steel and iron, when it is desirable to add the alloy in the most concentrated form so as to avoid the chilling effect which might occur when large masses of cold alloy are added to the molten metal. It is used in the manufacture of high-silicon sheet steel, castings or forgings for transformers, electromagnets, generators, and other electrical apparatus as well as for spring steel mentioned in the preceding paragraph.

452. **Calcium Alloys.** Calcium is exceedingly active chemically, combining readily with oxygen and other gases and reducing nearly all the metallic oxides on heating. For this reason it is a very efficient deoxidizer, degasifier, and reducing agent for metallurgical operations. It is seldom used in the pure state, being usually alloyed with other substances such as silicon, manganese, and aluminum for greater convenience and because these combinations possess many advantages over straight calcium.

Calcium-silicon alloy is used in the ladle as a deoxidizer and degasifier for both steel and cast iron because both of the elements of this alloy are active deoxidizers and form a low melting point slag which readily cleans the metal of oxides and other non-metallic inclusions. The fluidity of liquid steel is greatly improved through the use of this alloy, when added in amounts of about 2 pounds per ton. This is of particular advantage when pouring thin-section castings. The alloy is also used in basic electric furnaces to develop quickly a very fluid, reducing slag.

453. **Ferrovanadium.** Vanadium, although discovered in 1801, was not used in steel until 1896, and actually it is only within the last twenty years that its use has become common. It is a strong deoxidizer but is mainly used in steels for its alloying qualities, after deoxidation has been brought about by the use of cheaper elements. It is particularly effective in imparting a fine grain size to steels;

and castings containing small amounts of this element exhibit less marked dendritic segregations than the same castings made of vanadium-free steel. In addition, it improves the tensile strength without loss of ductility and gives a marked increase in the elastic limit, yield point, and impact strength. These combinations render vanadium steels especially adapted for service requiring high dynamic strength and fatigue and wear resistance. In high-speed tool steels vanadium imparts stability at high temperatures. While it may be used alone as an alloy in carbon steel, it is more generally used in combination with chromium, nickel, manganese, and tungsten in a wide variety of engineering and structural steels. It is also used in the production of nitriding steels. It is commonly made in four grades, ranging from the open-hearth grade containing 3 per cent carbon and 8 per cent silicon up to the high-speed steel grade containing only 0.2 per cent carbon and 1.5 silicon. All grades contain 35 to 40 per cent vanadium.

454. Tungsten Alloys. One of the principal uses of tungsten is in the manufacture of high-speed tool steels; it is also used in permanent magnets and in many tool, die, and heat-resisting steels; and in the production of non-ferrous high-speed cutting tools, such as Carboloy and various metallic carbide combinations. It is particularly effective in conferring strength and hardness on alloys operating at high temperatures.

Tungsten is furnished in two grades of ferrotungsten and as a tungsten powder. The low-carbon grade contains a maximum of 0.25 per cent carbon with 78 to 82 per cent tungsten; the high-carbon grade 1 to 2 per cent carbon with the same range of tungsten and the metallic powder about 97 per cent tungsten.

455. Molybdenum Alloys. Molybdenum is derived from the word *molybdos*, meaning leadlike, because molybdenum sulfide, in which compound it is found in nature, greatly resembles lead sulfide and graphite. Molybdenum, like vanadium, is a comparative newcomer to the ranks of alloying agents, because, although it was tested metallurgically as early as 1831 by Kote, it was not until the close of the nineteenth century that the possibilities of its use in steel were investigated. The use of molybdenum in the steel industry is now widespread. It is added to steel in three forms:

1. As calcium molybdate, containing 40 to 50 per cent molybdenum.
2. As ferromolybdenum, containing 50 to 65 per cent molybdenum.
3. As molybdenum oxide containing 47 to 50 per cent molybdenum, in briquette or canned form.

The effect of molybdenum on steel is solely that of an alloying agent because its oxides are so easily reduced that molybdenum has little cleansing action. Up to 0.25 per cent the molybdenum has no effect upon the forging and rolling properties of steel, nor does it have any effect on improving the surface of the finished metal. Added in slightly greater amounts, up to 0.3 per cent, it improves machinability. It apparently has no adverse effect on the welding characteristics of steel, but there is no evidence to show that molybdenum improves the steel from a corrosion-resisting standpoint. In low-carbon steels the effect of molybdenum is to strengthen and refine the ferrite, which effect is noticeable in hot-worked or normalized steels as an increase in toughness (that is, an increase in strength) without the corresponding decrease in the ductility that is normally associated with carbon steels. In heat treating the effect of molybdenum is to impart a certain sluggishness to transformations that may be induced by thermal treatment. Differing from nickel and manganese, molybdenum cannot stabilize austenite at room temperatures, irrespective of the proportion added. In general, higher quenching temperatures and slower cooling rates can be used for molybdenum-bearing steel than for the corresponding plain carbon stock. The element also tends to inhibit grain growth at temperatures above the critical range, increases the hardness penetration on quenching, accelerates the rate of carbon absorption in carburizing, and makes the spheroidizing treatment of carbon-molybdenum steels more difficult than for plain carbon steels. These steels also show a decreased tendency toward temper brittleness, and, at elevated temperatures, have greater creep strength and tensile strength up to 1200°F.

Molybdenum was formerly added to steels as a ferromolybdenum, but practice today is largely centered on the use of calcium molybdate or the oxide.

Calcium molybdate appears to enjoy the following advantages:

1. The method of production as well as use is relatively simple. Molybdenum sulfide is roasted to about 0.25 per cent sulfur at 1100°F. and treated with calcium hydrate. An exothermic reaction ensues, forming $CaMoO_4$ containing 48 per cent molybdenum, which is cooled, crushed, and marketed in bags containing 5 pounds of molybdenum.

2. The recoveries in the use of this addition agent, around 94 per cent, are much higher than the 89 per cent usually obtained with ferromolybdenum.

3. The contained molybdenum is about 15 cents per pound cheaper than when used in the form of ferromolybdenum.

4. No carbon is introduced into the bath.

The disadvantages connected with its use are comparatively unimportant:

1. It cannot be used for higher contents than 1.5 per cent molybdenum.
2. It cannot be used as a ladle addition because of the chilling effect it has on the metal.

Whenever possible, the best and simplest method of adding calcium molybdate is to "bury" it in the middle of the charge. In the event, however, that a preliminary analysis is required before the element can be added, it is equally satisfactory to charge the molybdate after the bath is melted down and before the slag is formed.

Molybdic oxide briquettes are a new low-cost form of molybdenum for alloying iron and steel. They are composed of a mixture of technical molybdenum trioxide and a sulfur-free pitch binder, the whole being briquetted under considerable pressure. The proportions of this molybdenum trioxide and carbon in the binder are such that the briquettes are completely self-reducing. A standard analysis of the briquettes is as follows: molybdenum trioxide, 70 to 75 per cent; carbon, maximum 12.0; iron, maximum 3.0; sulfur, maximum 0.25; insoluble residue, 10.5 per cent. The briquettes are in the form of cylinders about 3.5 inches in diameter by 4.5 inches long, and they weigh about 5 pounds; consequently, the briquettes contain exactly 2½ pounds of metallic molybdenum. The briquettes can be added with cold charges or they can be charged to the molten bath; but, if the latter procedure is followed, higher percentages of molybdenum are required. The rate of addition should be regulated to avoid possibility of excessive boil which might result in a loss of slag. The advantages claimed for this type of molybdenum-bearing material are:

1. Lower cost.
2. Less dust loss.
3. Rapid reduction.
4. High recovery, 95 to 100 per cent.
5. A minimum of slag-forming ingredients.
6. Ease of handling and compact storage.

456. Aluminum. A few ounces of stick aluminum are commonly placed in the ingot mold to complete deoxidation. Although it is a very active deoxidizing agent, it must be used with caution because of its potent effect on the grain size of the steel. It has also been found that it must be added in connection with silicon. Two explanations have been offered to account for its effect on grain size.

One of them attributes this effect to a dispersion of alumina particles of submicroscopic but critical size, which act as nuclei of crystallization and interfere with normal grain growth. Another has to do with the effect of aluminum on the solubility of carbides and nitrides.

The usual addition, to meet a fine-grained specification, varies from 12 ounces to 2 pounds per ton. Above 2 pounds per ton there appears to be little increase in the refining effect. It has been found that the manner of adding the aluminum has a very important effect, and much less is required when the metal melts below the surface of the steel.

BIBLIOGRAPHY

1. BOYLSTON, H. M., An Introduction to the Metallurgy of Iron and Steel. New York: John Wiley and Sons, 1936. 565 pp.
2. Electro Metallurgical Company, Electromet Ferro-Alloys and Metals, 1935. 61 pp.
3. FRANCIS, C. B., The Making, Shaping and Treating of Steel. Carnegie-Illinois Steel Corporation, 1940. 1440 pp.
4. STOUGHTON, B., Metallurgy of Iron and Steel. New York: McGraw-Hill Book Company, 1934. 519 pp.
5. The Titanium Alloy Manufacturing Company, Ferro-Carbon Titanium in Steel Making, Niagara Falls, 1931. 112 pp.

CHAPTER XIV

IRON AND STEEL INDUSTRY IN THE UNITED STATES

457. General. The United States is the foremost producer of iron and steel in the world, heading the list of nine major steel-producing countries. These countries—the United States, Germany, the Soviet Union, the United Kingdom, France, Japan, Belgium, Luxemburg, and Italy—account for 92 per cent of the world's production of steel. Statistics for the major steel-producing countries are given in Table 67. In terms of capital investment as well as value of product, the steel industry is second only to the automotive and in 1941 employed 633,000 workers and paid $1,301,000,000 in wages. The production of crude steel reached a peak in 1929 with the production of about 56 million tons, declined abruptly to about 14 million tons in 1932, and has since increased to a new record peak of 82,927,557 net tons in 1941.

458. Character and Location of the Industry. The capacity, production, capitalization, and other pertinent data for the leading steel producers are given in Table 68. These companies, for the most part, mine the coal and ore in their own mines and make and market the finished steel or iron; in 1941 three of them accounted for over 60 per cent of the total steel-making capacity and 10 of them for about 85 per cent. The bulk of the country's steel-making capacity is concentrated in a few areas, fortunately, under present disturbed conditions, in the interior of the country, centering in and near Pittsburgh, Youngstown, Cleveland, Chicago, and Birmingham. In addition there are large plants at Buffalo and Detroit, in eastern Pennsylvania, and on tidewater at Baltimore, Maryland. The steel-making capacity of the Pacific Coast is relatively small, but at the present time there is a movement on hand to increase the capacity of this district. The productive capacity of the United States and the tonnages and prices of common ferrous products are given in Tables 67 and 71.

459. Raw Materials. The primary raw materials for the manufacture of iron and steel are iron ore, coke, limestone, and scrap. The subject of iron ore has been quite fully discussed in Chapter II. Im-

TABLE 67

World Production and Exports of Steel and Iron

	1890	1900	1910	1918	1921	1929	1932	1939	....
Pig Iron									
United States	9,353	14,010	27,637	39,681	16,688	42,614	8,781	31,604	......
Great Britain	8,003	9,003	10,380	9,185	2,611	7,580	3,573	8,130	......
Germany		7,550	14,793	11,754	6,096	13,401	3,933	20,150	......
France		2,714	4,038	1,306	3,363	10,439	5,549	7,826	......
Belgium		1,161	1,852		862	3,970	2,783	3,019	......
Luxemburg						2,906	1,959	1,812	......
Totals	27,630	40,800	66,210		29,620	80,910	26,578	72,541	
Steel									
United States	4,346	10,382	26,512	45,178	19,783	56,433	13,681	46,768	......
Great Britain	3,637	5,130	6,477	10,434	3,625	9,655	5,257	13,559	......
Germany		6,646	13,699	13,757	8,700	16,246	5,746	24,539	......
France		1,565	3,506	1,807	3,054	9,666	5,604	8,402	......
Belgium		655	1,450		780	4,039	2,758	3,060	......
Luxemburg						2,269	1,956	1,650	......
Totals	12,450	31,030	58,656		35,942	98,308	35,002	97,979	......
Exports									
United States					2,172	2,480	596	6,076	......
Great Britain					1,076	4,379	1,889	1,750	......
Germany					2,445	5,813	2,155	1,800	......
France					1,462	4,250	2,701	1,400	......
Belgium*					911	4,400	3,217	2,950	......
Totals					8,697	21,322	10,458	13,976	......

* Figures are for combined output and exports of Belgium and Luxemburg.

ports of iron ore, largely from Chile and Cuba, coming in, by the way, free of duty, supply only a small part of the annual requirements and enter largely into the industry only along the Atlantic seaboard, where transportation costs to the plant so situated are very much less than from the domestic sources of supply.

The American iron and steel industry obtains its entire fuel requirements from domestic sources whose reserves are entirely adequate to supply domestic requirements for hundreds of years. The reserves of coking coal have never been determined; and, although they are probably not so great relative to the demand as the reserves of non-coking coal, they will probably outlast the supplies of domestic high-grade iron ore by a considerable margin. Normally, 10 to 20 per cent of the bituminous coal produced in the United States is used for the manufacture of coke; and, although a large proportion of this is used as a metallurgical fuel, there is also a demand for it by public utilities

TABLE 68*

LEADING STEEL COMPANIES

Company	Ingot Cap., Net Tons	Ingot Prod., Net Tons	Net Sales	Earnings per Ton, Ingot Cap.	Earnings per Ton, Ingot Prod.	Total Assets (000 omitted)	Total Investment (000 omitted)	Investment per Ton, Ingot Cap.	Operating Rate, Per Cent
U. S. Steel Corp.	29,720,000	22,934,000	$998,225,113	$3.44	$4.46	$1,854,586	$1,548,682	$52.11	79.2
Bethlehem Steel Corp.	11,850,000	10,704,741	602,202,618	4.11	4.55	763,724	658,990	55.61	93.3
Republic Steel Corp.	8,000,000	6,111,678	303,303,447	2.64	3.45	405,318	344,502	43.06	76.4
Jones & Laughlin Steel Corp.	3,943,750	3,338,983	153,052,249	2.61	3.08	240,478	215,368	54.61	85.0
National Steel Corp.	3,580,000	3,398,209	157,905,721	4.21	4.43	237,350	202,860	56.66	94.9
Youngstown Sheet & Tube Co.	3,494,400	2,868,902	143,054,028	3.10	3.77	251,239	229,612	65.71	82.1
Inland Steel Co.	3,300,000	3,092,100	142,173,338	4.38	4.67	173,692	151,522	45.92	93.7
American Rolling Mill Co.	3,030,180	2,093,854	112,363,529	2.52	3.65	157,022	139,863	46.16	69.1
Wheeling Steel Corp.	1,960,000	1,670,341	93,095,627	2.90	3.40	130,065	116,019	59.19	85.2
Colorado Fuel & Iron Corp.	1,131,210	815,602	31,864,811	1.54	2.14	42,937	36,563	32.32	72.1
Pittsburgh Steel Corp.	1,072,000	804,000	34,798,430	1.45	1.94	48,113	42,273	39.43	75.0
Otis Steel Co.	977,000	.....	29,072,621	0.73	.....	38,106	34,308	35.12	.....
Lukens Steel Co.	714,340	.....	18,751,175	0.99	.....	15,105	11,261	15.76	.....
Sharon Steel Corp.	560,000	532,000	21,573,295	2.39	2.51	21,013	18,416	32.89	95.0
Continental Steel Corp.	364,000	.....	18,246,391	2.14	.....	16,584	13,841	38.02	.....
Laclede Steel Co.	283,000	.....	.....	0.97	.....	8,070	6,687	23.63	.....
Keystone Steel & Wire Co.	276,500	278,535	13,279,520	5.13	5.09	12,031	10,496	37.96	100.7
.....	.....	.....	.....	.....	.....	.....	.....	.....	.....
.....	.....	.....	.....	.....	.....	.....	.....	.....	.....

Iron Age, January, 1941.

TABLE 69
PRODUCTIVE CAPACITY OF THE IRON AND STEEL INDUSTRY IN THE UNITED STATES
(JANUARY, 1942)

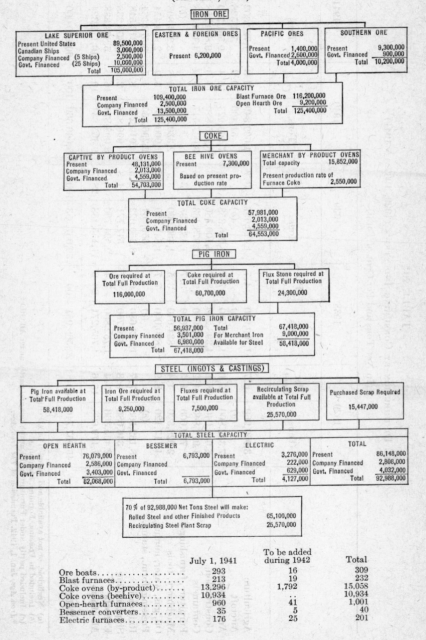

IRON ORE

LAKE SUPERIOR ORE		EASTERN & FOREIGN ORES	PACIFIC ORES		SOUTHERN ORE	
Present United States	89,500,000		Present	1,400,000	Present	9,300,000
Canadian Ships	3,000,000	Present 6,200,000	Govt. Financed	2,600,000	Govt. Financed	900,000
Company Financed (5 Ships)	2,500,000			Total 4,000,000		Total 10,200,000
Govt. Financed (25 Ships)	10,000,000					
Total	105,000,000					

TOTAL IRON ORE CAPACITY

Present	109,400,000	Blast Furnace Ore	116,200,000
Company Financed	2,500,000	Open Hearth Ore	9,200,000
Govt. Financed	13,500,000	Total	125,400,000
Total	125,400,000		

COKE

CAPTIVE BY PRODUCT OVENS		BEE HIVE OVENS	MERCHANT BY PRODUCT OVENS	
Present	48,131,000	Present 7,300,000	Total capacity	15,852,000
Company Financed	2,013,000			
Govt. Financed	4,559,000	Based on present production rate	Present production rate of Furnace Coke	2,550,000
Total	54,703,000			

TOTAL COKE CAPACITY

Present	57,981,000
Company Financed	2,013,000
Govt. Financed	4,559,000
Total	64,553,000

PIG IRON

Ore required at Total Full Production	Coke required at Total Full Production	Flux Stone required at Total Full Production
116,000,000	60,700,000	24,300,000

TOTAL PIG IRON CAPACITY

Present	56,937,000	Total	67,418,000
Company Financed	3,501,000	For Merchant Iron	9,000,000
Govt. Financed	6,980,000	Available for Steel	58,418,000
Total	67,418,000		

STEEL (INGOTS & CASTINGS)

Pig Iron available at Total Full Production	Iron Ore required at Total Full Production	Fluxes required at Total Full Production	Recirculating Scrap available at Total Full Production	Purchased Scrap Required
58,418,000	9,250,000	7,500,000	25,570,000	15,447,000

TOTAL STEEL CAPACITY

OPEN HEARTH		BESSEMER		ELECTRIC		TOTAL	
Present	76,079,000	Present	6,793,000	Present	3,276,000	Present	86,148,000
Company Financed	2,586,000	Company Financed		Company Financed	222,000	Company Financed	2,808,000
Govt. Financed	3,403,000	Govt. Financed		Govt. Financed	629,000	Govt. Financed	4,032,000
Total	82,068,000	Total	6,793,000	Total	4,127,000	Total	92,988,000

70% of 92,988,000 Net Tons Steel will make:	
Rolled Steel and other Finished Products	65,100,000
Recirculating Steel Plant Scrap	25,570,000

	July 1, 1941	To be added during 1942	Total
Ore boats....................	293	16	309
Blast furnaces................	213	19	232
Coke ovens (by-product).......	13,296	1,792	15,058
Coke ovens (beehive)..........	10,934	..	10,934
Open-hearth furnaces..........	960	41	1,001
Bessemer converters...........	35	5	40
Electric furnaces.............	176	25	201

TABLE 70*

STEEL DISTRIBUTION BY CONSUMING INDUSTRIES (1929, 1937 TO 1941)

(In Net Tons and Per Cent of Total)

	1929		1938		1939		1940		1941	
	Tons	Per Cent	Tons	Per Cent	Tons	Per Cent	Tons	Per Cent	Tons	Per Cent
Agriculture	3,060,960	6.7	1,109,920	4.7	1,420,697	3.6	1,629,849	3.3	1,722,302	2.4
Aircraft	(a)		(a)		(a)		51,400	0.2	531,528	0.9
Automotive	7,352,800	16.0	4,053,280	17.2	5,906,358	15.1	7,964,923	16.4	9,501,300	15.9
Construction	8,643,040	18.8	4,398,240	18.7	6,100,386	15.6	6,935,889	14.3	9,870,258	16.4
Containers	1,911,840	4.2	2,136,960	9.1	2,978,463	7.6	3,067,517	6.3	4,429,518	7.4
Furniture, furnishings	700,000	1.5	868,000	3.7	1,182,235	3.0	(b)		(b)	
Machinery, tools	2,028,320	4.4	831,040	3.5	1,460,000	3.7	2,330,365	4.8	3,264,898	5.4
Oil, gas, water, mining	4,117,120	8.9	1,820,000	7.7	1,841,599	4.7	1,900,286	3.9	2,814,454	4.7
Pressing, form., stamp.	(c)		(c)		659,864	1.7	2,296,355	4.7	3,572,534	5.9
Railroads	8,162,560	17.7	1,443,680	6.1	3,250,022	8.3	4,019,219	8.3	5,813,518	9.7
Shipbuilding	346,080	0.8	389,760	1.7	517,771	1.3	999,858	2.1	2,809,238	4.7
Exports	2,495,360	5.4	1,752,800	7.4	2,594,700	6.7	8,098,874	16.6	5,863,838	9.8
All other	7,179,666	15.6	4,765,271	20.2	11,155,458	28.7	9,365,834	19.1	10,119,324	16.8
Total	45,997,746	100	23,568,951	100	39,067,553	100	48,660,369	100	60,000,000	100

(a) Negligible, or not available and included in All Other.
(b) Included in Pressing, Forming, Stamping.
(c) Included partly under Furniture and Furnishings and partly under All Other.
*Iron Age, Jan. 1, 1942. Permission of The Iron Age.

TABLE 71

PRICES OF FERROUS PRODUCTS AND RAW MATERIALS

May, 1942

	Price
Cast iron, No. 2 Foundry, Chicago, per ton	$24.00
Cast iron, low-sulfur, charcoal, Chicago, per ton	31.34
Hot-rolled sheets, per pound	0.021
Galvanized sheets, per pound	0.035
Heavy rails, per ton	40.00
Forging billets, per ton	40.00
Ferromanganese, 80 per cent, N. Y. per ton	120.00
Spiegeleisen, 26–28 per cent, per ton	49.50
Silvery iron, per ton	30.75
Ferrosilicon, 25 per cent per ton	151.00
By-product coke, Chicago, per ton	12.25
Fluorspar, washed, Kentucky, per ton	25.00
Fire brick, first quality, Pa., per 1000	51.30
Silica brick, Chicago, per 1000	58.90
Chrome brick, Baltimore, per 1000	54.00
Magnesite brick, Baltimore, per 1000	76.00
Grain magnesite, Baltimore, per ton	44.00

and railroads and for domestic heating. Although the Appalachian fields in the eastern part of the United States supply 80 to 90 per cent of the domestic requirements of bituminous coal, coking coal comes mainly from western Pennsylvania, West Virginia, and Kentucky, with lesser amounts from Alabama, Virginia, Colorado, Illinois, and Utah. For the most part, because of the superior qualities of the coke produced, coking coal of western Pennsylvania, West Virginia, and Kentucky is used.

Supplies of scrap are obtained in about equal proportions from within the industry and by purchase from outside. During periods of great activity in the industry, when scrap prices are relatively high, they may be drawn from far distant points; but in recent years imports of scrap have been very small.

There are also, usually close to the steel-making industries, ample supplies of limestone for use as a flux and fire clay for the refractory brick. Some very important materials, however, are lacking in the United States, such as manganese, tin, nickel, and chromium, and these are largely imported from other countries.

460. Importance of Transportation. The steel industry is an amphibious creature, for its well-being depends on both water and land. On this basis the steel companies can be classified into three categories:

1. The lake companies; the Chicago-Gary area, for example.
2. The river companies—those located in the Pittsburgh district.
3. The land companies, such as those in the Youngstown area.

The steel man's burden is transportation, and it can be categorically said that in the past twenty years the lake companies have done very well, the river companies moderately so, and the land companies have had pretty hard sledding. From an examination of Table 10, it will be seen that rail transportation is much more expensive than water; and, since the manufacture of one ton of steel requires the assembling of about two tons of ore, two tons of coal, and one quarter ton of limestone, besides various other minor materials, the steel maker must have this matter of transportation in mind in selecting a site. Unfortunately, the steel man cannot be close to both coal and ore. Those who have visited the Calumet district know that Judge Gary's choice of Gary, Indiana, as the site of the world's largest steel plant was not governed by considerations of climate or scenery. Gary is strategically located between the cheap (being water-borne) ore of the Mesabi range and the coking coals of West Virginia and Kentucky. The land companies, however, must add 80 cents to $2.00 per ton for the transportation of this ore; and the river companies are in no better shape, for the Ohio River flows southwest. In the matter of coal, however, the river companies do have a slight advantage because river freight is of the order of 30 cents per ton as against $1.90 to Cleveland or $2.60 to Chicago. It is obvious, then, that land companies are confronted with inescapably high costs.

When we come to consider the marketing of the product, we find that geography is again a very important factor. In recent years there has been a tremendous expansion of manufacturing facilities in the Middle West, notably in the Calumet district and around Detroit and Milwaukee. Lake companies are, therefore, nearer the new markets and have water transportation, and it is a significant fact that the center of the steel industry is slowly moving west and north toward Chicago (see Figure 14). So far as transportation of the finished product is concerned, the river companies do have cheap transportation, but unfortunately they have a saturated market. Pittsburgh, for example, consumes only 25 per cent of its own steel. From this point of view the land companies again find themselves in an unfortunate position, for they must ship by rail and into markets already supplied with productive capacity.

461. Export Trade in Iron and Steel. Save for scrap, the United States has never been much of an exporter of iron and steel. Japan has been by far the largest market for scrap, taking 37 per cent of our total tonnage in 1929 and 55 per cent in the interval of 1934 to 1936. The United Kingdom and Italy have been next in importance. Japan and Italy, both deficient in ferrous materials for steel manufacture, have found attractive surplus supplies available in the United States; and, of course, so far as Japan is concerned, there is no important foreign source of scrap nearer than the United States. Canada and Japan have taken most of the relatively small exports of United States pig iron. The South American countries take the bulk of the United States exports of semi-finished and finished iron and steel, although in recent years Japan has taken an increasing amount. Canada ordinarily is the most important single market, although exports to Canada have been falling off in recent years from a high of 45 per cent in 1929 to 17 per cent in 1937 (World War II has brought with it a great and sudden increase).

462. **Import Trade.*** The imports of finished and semi-finished iron and steel products into the United States, not including iron ore, are of still less importance than the exports—only 289,157 gross tons of finished and semi-finished in 1937. In 1937 India and the Netherlands supplied the bulk of the total imports of pig iron (111,697 gross tons), largely of foundry grades and largely for the Pacific coast. Up to World War II both these countries not only had large surpluses available for export since they have no important steel works, but also enjoy the advantage of very cheap labor. Belgium, Luxemburg, Germany, France, and Sweden were the principal exporters of finished and semi-finished products. On the whole, Belgium, Luxemburg, Germany, and France were the principal suppliers of rail and structural steels, whereas Sweden, the United Kingdom, and Germany specialized in tool and special steels.

THE BASING POINT SYSTEM IN THE STEEL INDUSTRY

463. **General.** This system of disposing of goods is as peculiar to the steel industry as the Lake Erie price for iron ore (Chapter II), and the price of steel rails, which remained constant for some twelve years. Although this basing point system has been under attack for a number of years, there are certain conditions peculiar to the steel industry which appear to make some such system necessary. For example, the vendor of drugs, flour, lumber, or soap knows fairly closely what his cost of operations are so far as payroll, rent, utility costs, and fixed charges are concerned. His customers either come to the store for their

* United States Tariff Commission, Iron and Steel, *Report* 128.

purchases or they have the articles delivered at a nominal cost. He knows exactly what he pays for the goods he sells in his store. This is not so in the steel industry. The sale of steel is very flexible. It is frequently difficult to determine what fixed charges should be added to steel. The enormous amount of capital, as well as the complicated capital structure of the steel industry, makes it difficult to arrive at any just distribution. The necessity of locating mills in very limited districts, determined more by the sources of raw materials than by sale of finished product, is another serious handicap involved in the operation of a steel mill. Wheat and lumber are obtainable all over the United States, as are potatoes, apples, and cement, but adequate supplies of ore are available only in the Mesabi district, and coking coal in Kentucky, West Virginia, and Pennsylvania. Last, and probably most important, is the fact that the cost of transportation of steel products to the consumer is so great that these customers are not interested in prices at the factory. They are concerned more with the delivered costs at the point of consumption. Out of all of these difficulties has grown what is known as the "basing point system."

In 1750, when the steel industry was in its infancy, the center of production was in the Allegheny district, and prices were quoted free on board at Philadelphia. This point was chosen because Philadelphia was the most important port for the receipt of foreign iron. With the discovery of ore deposits in the Lake Superior district and the coking coals already referred to, the industry moved westward, with the result that by 1884 nearly all prices were quoted free on board Pittsburgh. In the year 1901 the United States Steel Corporation was formed; and, since it produced more than half the country's steel, the delivered price system came into general use in the shape of the infamous "Pittsburgh plus" system in which all prices were quoted delivered to their destination from Pittsburgh regardless of the point of production. By 1908 this system was broken up, at least for the time being, by the rapid growth of the Illinois Steel Corporation in the Chicago district, and again during the first World War when there was a strict government control of prices. After the conflict the Pittsburgh system was again renewed and continued until 1923, when, as a result of a price war, Chicago won its fight to become permanently a basing point. In 1924 the Federal Trade Commission entered the fight by ordering certain subsidiaries of the United States Steel Corporation to "cease and desist" from selling at prices based on any point except the one at which production actually occurred. In the following years the Federal Trade Commission continually denounced the delivered price methods, but ironically the NRA Steel Code recognized the basing point system, when it was investigated in 1932, and claimed that it was not a price-fixing system but a competitive method of selling. Further revisions have since been made, until at the present time there are about eighty basing point systems in this country.

464. Pittsburgh Plus System. To clarify the working of the "Pittsburgh plus" system, or, for that matter, any basing point system,

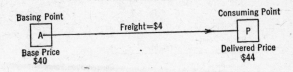

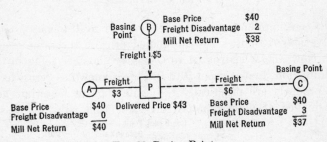

Fig. 99. Basing Point.

let us refer to Figure 99. Under the former system, if a certain base price, say $40.00, prevailed at Pittsburgh and the rail freight to the consuming point was $4.00, the price of the steel to the consumer at the point of consumption was $44.00. Now let us assume that three plants for three different basing points are selling steel to the same consuming point. If the transportation costs from A, B, and C, the three producing points, to the consuming point, P, are $3.00, $5.00, and $6.00, respectively, the price of steel at the destination will be $43.00, or the base price plus transportation charges from the nearest basing point. Now, the plants at B and C have to pay part of the freight charges out of their own pockets. The handicap of selling from a plant farther from a consuming point than some other producer gives the former plant a "freight disadvantage," and the payment for part of the freight charges by the plant having a freight disadvantage is known as "freight absorption." Since companies B and C have to pay these charges, the actual amount of money they receive from the sale is lower, and this amount of money received is known as "mill net return." Also, the act of shipping to a consuming point by plants such as B and C, which are farther from this usage point than producing plant A, is known as "market penetration."

Let us again assume a situation as shown in Figure 100. A consuming point Q, which is closer to plant B, buys steel from plant A. In

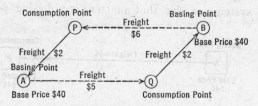

FIG. 100. Cross Hauling.

turn the consumption point, P, which is closer to A, buys its steel from B for various reasons, since the quoted price is the same from both plants. Now, the steel from A to Q passes the steel going in the opposite direction; that is, from B to P. This is known as "cross hauling," if the products are practically the same type of materials and are being shipped at approximately the same time.

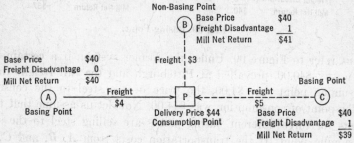

FIG. 101. Phantom Freight.

Still another peculiarity has to do with "phantom freight," shown in Figure 101, which results when all plants are not situated on the same basing points. It has been more or less a rule that a plant should not become a basing point unless it produces more steel than the territory in which it is situated can consume. Point B in the diagram is just such a plant. As stated before, the delivered price at P is equal to the base price plus the transportation from the nearest basing point. Now A is the nearest basing point, but B is closer to P with respect to railroad miles. Since B is not a basing point, it must add to the base price the freight charge of $4.00, which is the cost of shipping from plant *A* to the purchasing point. However, the actual cost of shipping the steel from plant *B* to buying point *P* is only $3.00. On the surface it would seem that the purchaser was being forced to pay transportation charges which he did not justifiably owe. This is not actually the case, for the cost at the destination is supposed to be the only factor that interests the buyer of the steel, and he should not be concerned with just how the $44 is divided.

In summarizing it can be said that the basing point system as it now functions has many imperfections; and, although a change for the better is as much desired by the steel corporations as by the consumers and others interested in the industry, the present system will continue to operate until something that is better, not just different, is worked out.

BIBLIOGRAPHY

1. American Iron and Steel Institute, *Annual Statistical Numbers,* New York.
2. *Iron Age,* Annual Statistical Numbers. New York: Chilton Company.
3. Iron and Steel, United States Tariff Commission, *Report* 128, 1938. 527 pp.
4. *Steel,* Annual Statistical Numbers, Cleveland, Penton Publishing Company.
5. *Steel Facts,* American Iron and Steel Institute, New York, 1937 to date.

INDEX